Mathematics

A* Study Guide for INTERNATIONAL GCSE

Jim Newall

www.galorepark.co.uk

Orders: please contact Bookpoint Ltd, 130 Milton Park, Abingdon, Oxon OX14 4SB. Telephone: +44 (0)1235 827827. Lines are open 9.00a.m.–5.00p.m., Monday to Saturday, with a 24-hour message answering service. Visit our website at www.galorepark.co.uk for details of other revision guides for Common Entrance, examination papers and Galore Park publications.

Published by Galore Park Publishing Ltd
An Hachette UK company
338 Euston Road, London, NW1 3BH
www.galorepark.co.uk

Impression number 10 9 8 7 6 5 4 3 2 1
2018 2017 2016 2015 2014

Design and typesetting by DTP Media, Maidstone, Kent
Technical illustrations by DTP Media, Maidstone, Kent
Printed in Spain

A catalogue record for this title is available from the British Library

ISBN 978 1 905735 464

Contents

Page

Section 4

Introduction

A good grounding in mathematics is essential to further study in many disciplines including science, engineering, medicine, social sciences, economics and finance. It is, of course, needed for higher level study in mathematics itself and the related areas of statistics and game theory. Good basic mathematics is also essential for everyday life. For example, you use ratio to compare the prices of goods in different size packs, and you use mathematics to interpret statistical diagrams which are widely used in the media and on the internet.

This revision guide presents the facts and mathematical techniques you need to know as clearly and logically as possible to help you gain both knowledge and understanding. You will learn best if you use this book interactively: make your own notes on paper as you go along, or highlight key facts and mathematical techniques you struggle with. You may like to make spider diagrams to help you link ideas together or summarise sections. Find out which study methods work best for you – and good luck with your studies and exams!

How is this book organised?

This book follows the structure laid out in the Edexcel Level 1/Level 2 Certificate in Mathematics (KMAO), Edexcel International GCSE in Mathematics (Specification A) (4MAO) (Higher tier) and the Cambridge International Examinations IGCSE® Mathematics (0580) specification (Extended curriculum).

Material that is only applicable to Edexcel students is indicated by this symbol. 

Material that is only applicable to Cambridge students is indicated by this symbol. 

Each section begins with a list of what you are expected to know for that particular topic, followed by the material that you need to learn and worked examples to show how to do the calculations. The Test yourself exercises can then be used to practise answering questions on that topic. You should work through this material in the way that suits you best. You may choose to work through the exercises by yourself or with a friend. The answers to the Test yourself exercises are given at the back of the book. If you have not got the correct answer, try to do the question again to see if you have just made a careless error in the calculation. If not, go back to the worked example to see if that helps you to see where you have gone wrong.

Throughout the book you will find tip boxes that will help you to achieve the A* grade. Some of these apply to all topics: others highlight mistakes that often cause candidates to trip up with certain calculations.

Towards the end of each section is a review box that acts as a checklist. Once you have worked through the section, check that you can do everything listed in the box. If not, use the page references to refer back to the text and practise that part again.

Each section concludes with a set of Practice questions. These are written in the style you will encounter in your exam paper and should help you achieve your A*. Practice makes perfect, so once you have completed the questions in this book, get hold of some actual past papers.

How will I be assessed?

Edexcel 

Two written papers are taken at the end of the course.

There are separate papers for Foundation (1F and 2F) and Higher (3H and 4H) tier candidates. For all candidates each paper lasts 2 hours and is worth 50% of the marks.

Successful candidates must meet all three assessment objectives:
AO1 Number and algebra
AO2 Geometry
AO3 Data handling

A formula sheet (like the one at the back of this book) will be provided.

Cambridge candidates take **two** papers from the following:

Paper 1 (Core): short-answer questions based on the core curriculum, lasting 1 hour and worth 35% of the overall mark

or

Paper 2 (Extended): short-answer questions based on the extended curriculum, lasting 1 hour and 30 minutes and worth 35% of the overall mark

and

Paper 3 (Core): structured questions based on the core curriculum, lasting 2 hours and worth 65% of the overall mark

or

Paper 4 (Extended): structured questions based on the extended curriculum, lasting 2 hours and 30 minutes and worth 65% of the overall mark.

Successful candidates must meet both assessment objectives:
AO1: Mathematical techniques
AO2: Applying mathematical techniques to solve problems

A formula sheet will not be provided so you will need to learn all the formulae.

Some help with revision

The most common error is to think you have revised well just because you have spent a long time on it. The following advice should help you revise effectively.

- Never work for more than 30 minutes at a stretch. Take a break.
- Don't revise all day. Divide the day into thirds (you will have to get up at a sensible time) and work two-thirds of the day at most.
- Always start your revision where you finished your last session and briefly review what you covered before. You absorb facts better if you always meet them in more or less the same order.
- Don't revise what you already know. That's like practising a complete piano piece when there is only a short part of it that is causing you problems.
- Annotate your revision notes and make use of coloured highlighting to indicate areas of particular difficulty.
- Do some of your revision with other students. The knowledge that others find parts of the syllabus tricky can be comforting and other students may well have found an effective way to cope, which they can pass on to you.
- Finally, remember that International GCSE mathematics has no hidden pitfalls. If you learn the facts and understand the principles, you will secure the high grade you deserve.

Also available in the A* range

English A Study Guide for GCSE and IGCSE* by Susan Elkin, ISBN 978 1 905735 426
Chemistry A Study Guide for International GCSE* by Frank Benfield, ISBN 978 1 905735 440
Biology A Study Guide for International GCSE* by Pamela Maitland, ISBN 978 1 905735 457
Physics A Study Guide for International GCSE* by Penny Johnson, ISBN 978 1 905735 563

Section One

1 Number

You will be expected to:

- ☆ recognise and use different kinds of numbers such as primes and irrational numbers
- ☆ work with fractions, decimals and percentages
- ☆ understand and use powers, roots and indices
- ☆ use set notation and work with sets and Venn diagrams
- ☆ use ratio and proportion
- ☆ determine the accuracy of numbers
- ☆ apply number in a range of situations
- ☆ use an electronic calculator.

1.1 Basic number

Numbers

Natural numbers are positive whole numbers and zero.

Integers are natural numbers and negative whole numbers. They can be represented on a number line.

A prime number is a number with only two factors: 1 and itself. 1 is not a prime number.

A factor of a number is a number that divides exactly into a whole number.

A prime factor is a factor that is also a prime number.

A square number is a number multiplied by itself.

Rational numbers are integers and fractions and can be written in exact form.

Irrational numbers cannot be written as fractions.

Real numbers are integers and decimals. Rational and irrational numbers are real numbers.

Worked example

1. State whether each of these numbers is rational or irrational.

   (a) -2 (b) $\frac{3}{7}$ (c) $\sqrt{7}$ (d) π

2. Write 60 in prime factor form.

Answer

1. (a) rational because -2 is an integer

   (b) rational because $\frac{3}{7}$ is a fraction

   (c) irrational because $\sqrt{7}$ cannot be written as a fraction

   (d) irrational because π is not an exact number – the decimal places carry on forever.

2. Divide the number by prime numbers until the answer is a prime number.

$$\begin{array}{r|l} 2 & 60 \\ 2 & 30 \\ 3 & 15 \\ & 5 \end{array}$$

So $60 = 2 \times 2 \times 3 \times 5$

Write the product of prime factors in index form: $60 = 2^2 \times 3 \times 5$

Test yourself

1. State whether each of these numbers is rational or irrational.

(a) 5.6^2 (b) $\frac{22}{7}$ (c) $\sqrt{121}$ (d) $\sqrt{1000}$ (e) $\pi \div 3$ (f) $3.1\dot{6}$

2. Write the following numbers in prime factor form.

(a) 28 (b) 40 (c) 81 (d) 144 (e) 125 (f) 180

Order of operations

The order of operations is:

- **B**rackets
- **I**ndices (or p**O**wers)
- **D**ivision
- **M**ultiplication
- **A**ddition
- **S**ubtraction

Test yourself

1. Here are some lists of numbers, signs and a pair of brackets. In each case use **all** of them to make a correct calculation.

(a) 2, 5, 6, 8, –, ×, =, ( )

(b) 2, 3, 4, 10, +, ÷, =, ( )

(c) 3, 10, 15, 15, –, ×, =, ( )

Directed numbers

You can show positive and negative numbers on vertical and horizontal number lines.

Directed numbers can be used in practical situations.

Test yourself

1. The temperatures at midday on a certain day in five places were:

Moscow: –6 °C; Yellowknife: –21 °C; Helsinki: –4.5 °C; Cairo: 15 °C; Rio de Janeiro: 27.5 °C.

(a) What is the difference in temperature between:

(i) Moscow and Yellowknife

(ii) Cairo and Helsinki

(iii) Helsinki and Yellowknife?

(b) (i) Between which two paces is the temperature difference the greatest?

(ii) What is the greatest temperature difference?

2. The heights above and below sea level of five places are:

Almere, Netherlands: –2 m; Berlin, Germany: 34 m; Death Valley, USA: –86 m; Lake Assal, Djibouti: –155 m; Parliament Hill, London: 98 m.

What is the difference in height between:

(a) Almere and Parliament Hill

(b) Death Valley and Lake Assal

(c) Berlin and Lake Assal?

1.2 Fractions

Fraction problems

To order fractions, convert them all to equivalent fractions with a common denominator.

To express a number as a fraction of another number, divide the first number by the second number.

Test yourself

1. Put the following sets of fractions in ascending order.

   (a) $\frac{1}{2}, \frac{2}{5}, \frac{3}{10}, \frac{7}{10}, \frac{11}{20}$ (b) $\frac{2}{3}, \frac{3}{4}, \frac{5}{6}, \frac{7}{8}, \frac{7}{12}$ (c) $\frac{3}{5}, \frac{1}{7}, \frac{7}{10}, \frac{5}{14}, \frac{9}{14}$

2. Calculate the following.

   (a) $\frac{1}{7}$ of £28 (b) $\frac{4}{5}$ of 45 kg (c) $\frac{3}{10}$ of 70 cm (d) $\frac{11}{12}$ of 108 litres

Adding and subtracting fractions

When adding and subtracting fractions:

- change all fractions to an equivalent fraction so that they have a common denominator
- add or subtract the numerators
- cancel common factors from the numerator and denominator
- change the fraction to a mixed number if it is top heavy.

When adding and subtracting mixed numbers, split the calculation into whole numbers and fractions.

Test yourself

1. Calculate the following.

   (a) $\frac{3}{5}+\frac{2}{3}+\frac{7}{10}$ (b) $\frac{1}{4}+\frac{5}{8}+\frac{7}{12}$ (c) $1\frac{1}{2}+2\frac{3}{5}+3\frac{3}{10}$

   (d) $\frac{3}{4}-\frac{5}{8}+\frac{1}{2}$ (e) $5\frac{11}{16}-1\frac{1}{2}-2\frac{3}{8}$ (f) $8\frac{4}{5}-2\frac{5}{6}-1\frac{3}{10}$

Multiplying and dividing fractions

When multiplying fractions:

- convert any mixed numbers to top-heavy fractions
- multiply the numerators together and multiply the denominators together
- cancel any common factors from the numerator and denominator
- change to a mixed number if the answer is a top-heavy fraction.

When dividing by a fraction:

- change any mixed numbers to top-heavy fractions
- multiply by the reciprocal of the fraction (turn it upside down)
- change to a mixed number if the answer is a top-heavy fraction.

Test yourself

1. Calculate the following.

   (a) $\frac{7}{10}\times\frac{5}{14}$ (b) $\frac{3}{5}\times\frac{10}{21}$ (c) $1\frac{3}{7}\times2\frac{3}{8}$ (d) $3\frac{1}{3}\times2\frac{7}{10}$

   (e) $\frac{6}{7}\div\frac{2}{3}$ (f) $\frac{11}{12}\div\frac{5}{6}$ (g) $2\frac{1}{4}\div1\frac{4}{5}$ (h) $3\frac{4}{7}\div1\frac{7}{8}$

Converting fractions to decimals and percentages

To convert a fraction to a decimal, divide the numerator by the denominator.

To convert a fraction to a percentage, divide the numerator by the denominator and multiply by 100%.

Test yourself

1. Convert each of the following fractions
(i) to a decimal (ii) to a percentage.

(a) $\frac{2}{5}$ (b) $\frac{3}{10}$ (c) $\frac{9}{10}$

(d) $\frac{7}{20}$ (e) $\frac{5}{8}$ (f) $\frac{11}{16}$

TIP

Many exam questions use simple values of fractions, decimals and percentages. It is worth learning some of these equivalents.
For example, $\frac{3}{4}=0.75=75\%$.

1.3 Decimals

Decimals, fractions and percentages

To convert a decimal to a fraction, make the denominator 10, 100 or 1000 and then cancel common factors if possible.

To convert a decimal to a percentage, multiply by 100%.

Test yourself

1. Convert each of the following decimals
(i) to a fraction (ii) to a percentage.
(a) 0.8 (b) 0.15 (c) 0.28 (d) 0.86 (e) 0.425 (f) 0.784

2. Put the following groups of decimals in ascending order.
(a) 0.2, 0.02, 0.22, 0.022, 0.0022 (b) 0.35, 0.38, 0.036, 0.035, 0.0036

Recurring decimals

You can convert a **recurring decimal** to a fraction. Let the recurring decimal equal x, multiply both sides by a power of 10 and then subtract the second equation from the first one.

If there is one recurring digit, multiply by 10.

If there are two recurring digits, multiply by 100, etc.

Recurring decimals can be shown by a dot above each digit that recurs or by three dots after the last digit.

Worked example

Write 0.3939... as a fraction.

Answer

Let: $x = 0.3939...$

Multiply by 100: $100x = 39.39...$

Subtract first equation from second equation: $99x = 39$

So: $x = \frac{39}{99} = \frac{13}{33}$ and $0.3939... = \frac{13}{33}$

> **TIP** Remember to give your answer in its simplest form. In this case, check that there are no factors common to both the numerator and denominator.

Test yourself

1. Convert the following recurring decimals to fractions.

(a) 0.55... (b) 0.7272... (c) $0.\dot{4}\dot{5}$ (d) 0.702 702... (e) $0.5\dot{3}$ (f) 0.233 33...

1.4 Percentages

Percentages

To convert a percentage to a decimal, divide by 100%.

To convert a percentage to a fraction, put the number as the numerator and 100 as the denominator in the fraction. Cancel any common factors.

You can use the percentage multiplier to solve percentage problems. It is the percentage expressed as a decimal.

The multiplier for a percentage increase is the multiplier added to 1. To calculate a new value after this percentage increase, multiply the original number by this new multiplier.

The multiplier for a percentage decrease is the multiplier subtracted from 1. To calculate a new value after this percentage decrease, multiply the original number by this new multiplier.

To calculate one quantity as a percentage of another, divide the first number by the second number and then multiply by 100%.

Worked example

1. The price of a pair of training shoes is £65. Calculate the new price after an increase of 8%.
2. The number of people going to see a film in a cinema is 495 one day and 465 the next day.

   Calculate the percentage decrease in the number of people.

Answer

1. The percentage multiplier for an 8% increase is $1 + 0.08 = 1.08$.

   New price $= £65 \times 1.08 = £70.20$

2. Decrease $= 495 - 465 = 30$

   Percentage decrease $= 30 \div 495 \times 100\% = 0.0606 \times 100\% = 6\%$

> **TIP** When dealing with money, always give two decimal places, even though the second decimal place is not shown on your calculator.

Test yourself

1. Convert each of the following percentages
   (i) to a decimal (ii) to a fraction.
   (a) 60% (b) 25% (c) 65% (d) 76% (e) 87.5% (f) 93.75%

2. Increase the following quantities by the percentage given.
   (a) £26 by 15% (b) 55 kg by 11% (c) 35 litres by 22%
   (d) 150 g by 35% (e) 145 cm by 42% (f) £99 by 18%

3. Decrease the following quantities by the percentage given.
   (a) £35 by 15% (b) 48 litres by 25% (c) 80 g by 18%
   (d) 125 kg by 38% (e) 225 m by 56% (f) £49 by 45%

4. Express the second quantity as a percentage of the first quantity.
   (a) 45 litres, 38 litres (b) 78 kg, 60 kg (c) 56 cm, 48 cm
   (d) 125 m, 42 m (e) £64, £12.50 (f) 220 kg, 10 kg

5. Calculate the value for each of the following percentage changes.
   (a) 250 with a 15% increase followed by a 12% increase
   (b) 780 with a 25% increase followed by a 16% decrease
   (c) 424 with a 10% decrease followed by a 15% increase
   (d) 620 with a 20% decrease followed by a 14% decrease
   (e) 36 with a 20% increase followed by a 20% decrease
   (f) 175 with a 28% decrease followed by a 28% increase

Reverse percentages

You use the reverse percentage to find the original amount when you know that a quantity has been increased or decreased by a certain percentage. You can use the multiplier method.

Worked example

1. The number of people going into a cafe each day increased by 12% to 280.

   Calculate the original number of people going into the cafe each day.

2. A shop decreases its prices by 40% in a sale. A shirt costs £15 in the sale.

   Calculate the original price of the shirt.

Answer

1. The multiplier for a 12% increase is $1+0.12=1.12$

   Divide the number by the multiplier.

   Original number of people $=280\div1.12=250$.

2. The multiplier for a 40% decrease is $1-0.4=0.6$

   Divide the number by the multiplier.

   Original price of the shirt $=£15\div0.6=£25$

TIP

When finding the original number, divide the current number by the percentage (multiplier) of the original number that the current number is. For example, if a quantity has decreased by 25%, it is 75% of the original number, so divide by 0.75 to work out the original number.

Test yourself

1. Calculate the original quantity given the final quantity and the percentage increase.

(a) 180 g, 20% (b) £74.35, 35% (c) 98.6 litres, 45%

(d) 41.5 cm, 66% (e) 201.5 mm, 55% (f) £189.60, 58%

2. Calculate the original quantity given the final quantity and the percentage decrease.

(a) 48 cm, 25% (b) 80 mm, 37.5% (c) £132, 12%

(d) 171 g, 24% (e) 217.6 litres, 32% (f) £213.12, 52%

Interest

When you take out a loan you pay interest on the amount of money you borrow. You get interest on money you have in a savings account.

Simple interest is when the interest is calculated on the amount of money you have invested or borrowed.

In many savings accounts, the interest is added to the account at least once a year. The interest for the next year is then calculated on the original amount (the principal) and the interest that has been paid so far. This is known as compound interest.

Use a multiplier to calculate compound interest. Use the following formula:

$$\text{total amount} = P\left(1 + \frac{r}{100}\right)^n$$

where P is the amount invested, r is the percentage interest rate and n is the number of years of compound interest.

Worked example

1. Sayeed has £800 on his credit card. The interest rate is 26% per year.

   Calculate how much interest he pays in a year.

2. Jemma has £500 in a savings account. The interest rate is 2.5% per year compound interest.

   How much money will Jemma have after 4 years?

Answer

1. Interest paid $= £800 \times 0.26 = £208$

2. Total amount $= £500\left(1 + \frac{2.5}{100}\right)^4$

   $= £500 \times 1.025^4$

   $= £500 \times 1.103813$

   $= £551.91$

TIP

Do not round your answer part way through the calculation. Keep all of the decimal places and round the answer at the end. In this case round to 2 decimal places, which is to the nearest penny.

Test yourself

1. Sasha borrows £400 at 1.6% per month simple interest. What is the total amount he has to pay back after 3 months?

2. Sarah invests £1500 at 3% interest for 4 years. Calculate the value of the investment after this time when the interest is

   (a) simple (b) compound.

3. Alex borrows £1200 at a simple interest rate of 6% per year. He repays the loan and the total amount he has to pay is £1488. How many years has he borrowed the money for?

4. Ellen borrows £750 at 1.8% per month compound interest. She repays the loan after 5 months How much interest does she pay?

5. The table shows the total value of an investment of £2500 over several years.

Number of years	1	2	3	4
Value	£2587.50	£2678.06	£2771.79	£2868.81

   (a) Is the interest simple or compound?

   (b) What is the rate of interest per year?

6. Harry invests £1800. He has a choice of two accounts, one paying 2.7% per year simple interest and one paying 2.5% per year compound interest.
   Which account should he invest the money in when he invests for

   (a) 3 years (b) 8 years?

Compound interest problems

You can use the compound interest formula to solve practical problems.

Worked example

A car depreciates (goes down in value) by 20% per year. Sean bought a car for £9000. Calculate the value of the car after 3 years.

Answer

Value of car $= £9000\left(1-\frac{20}{100}\right)^3 = £9000(1-0.2)^3 = £9000(0.8)^3$

$= £9000 \times 0.512 = £4608$

Test yourself

1. Megan buys a car for £11 000. It depreciates by 18% per year. Calculate the value of the car after 4 years. Give your answer to the nearest whole number.

2. House prices have been increasing in one area at a compound rate of 8% per year. Ben bought a house in this area 8 years ago for £78 000. What is the value of his house now, to the nearest thousand pounds?

3. Samina's salary has been increasing at an average compound rate of 4% per year. Her salary is now £22 508. What was her salary 5 years ago?

4. The population of Tanzania according to the 2012 census is 44 928 923. The population has been growing at a compound rate of 2.9%.
   (a) Calculate the population in
   (i) 2008 (ii) 2000.
   (b) In what year will the population exceed 60 million? Assume that the growth continues at the same rate.

5. A scientist finds that the population of a certain type of bird on an island was 60 000 in 2008 and 40 000 in 2012. Calculate the percentage rate of decline in the population.

6. A researcher find that the bacteria population in an agar culture is 10 000, to the nearest thousand. The population doubles every 20 minutes.
   (a) What multiplier would you use in the formula to calculate the population after a certain time?
   (b) Calculate the population after 3 hours.

1.5 Powers, roots and indices

Square numbers and cube numbers

A square number is a number multiplied by itself.

When the square root of a number is multiplied by itself, you get the original number. A number has two square roots – one positive and one negative.

A cube number is a number multiplied by itself twice.

A cube root is the inverse of a cube number. When the cube root of a number is multiplied by itself twice, you get the original number.

You can use your calculator to find square and cube numbers and square and cube roots.

Test yourself

1. Find the following numbers.
   (a) 1.6^2 (b) 2.5^3 (c) $\sqrt{0.81}$ (d) $\sqrt{1.44}$ (e) $\sqrt[3]{0.512}$ (f) $\sqrt[3]{3.375}$

Indices

You can write a number that is multiplied by itself several times more simply using indices. For example, $3 \times 3 \times 3 \times 3$ can be written as 3^4. This is said as '3 to the power 4'.

Any number to the power 1 is the number itself.

Any number to the power zero is 1.

When you multiply powers of the same number or variable, you add the indices:

$x^a \times x^b = x^{(a+b)}$

When you divide one power of a number or variable by another power of the same number or variable, you subtract the second power from the first power:

$x^a \div x^b = x^{(a-b)}$

When you raise a power to a second power, you multiply the indices:

$(x^a)^b = x^{ab}$

When the variable or number has a negative index, this means that it is the reciprocal of the variable or number:

$x^{-a} = \frac{1}{x^a}$

When the variable or number has a fractional index in the form $\frac{1}{n}$, it is the nth root of the variable:

$x^{\frac{1}{n}} = \sqrt[n]{x}$

When you have an expression in the form $\left(\frac{a}{b}\right)^{-\frac{n}{m}}$ you can invert it to calculate it as a fraction:

$\left(\frac{b}{a}\right)^{\frac{n}{m}}$

Worked example

Evaluate (a) $27^{\frac{2}{3}}$ (b) $121^{-\frac{1}{2}}$ (c) $2^{\frac{1}{2}} \times 2^{-\frac{5}{2}}$

Answer

(a) $27^{\frac{2}{3}} = \left(\sqrt[3]{27}\right)^2 = 3^2 = 9$

(b) $121^{-\frac{1}{2}} = \frac{1}{121^{\frac{1}{2}}} = \frac{1}{\sqrt{121}} = \frac{1}{11}$

(c) $2^{\frac{1}{2}} \times 2^{-\frac{5}{2}} = 2^{\frac{1}{2} + -\frac{5}{2}} = 2^{-\frac{4}{2}} = 2^{-2} = \frac{1}{2^2} = \frac{1}{4}$

TIP Remember that when a questions says 'evaluate', it means 'work out'.

TIP Don't use your calculator on questions like this. Simplify the calculation as much as possible first using your knowledge of indices. Then work out the answer.

Test yourself

1. Evaluate the following.
   Give your answer as a fraction, where appropriate.

   (a) $8^{\frac{5}{3}}$ (b) 6^{-3} (c) $144^{-\frac{1}{2}}$ (d) $81^{-\frac{3}{4}}$ (e) $\frac{1}{27^{-\frac{2}{3}}}$ (f) $\frac{1}{36^{-\frac{3}{2}}}$

2. Work out the following.

   (a) $3^{-4} \times 3^5$ (b) $4^{-\frac{3}{2}} \times 4^2$ (c) $5^{-\frac{3}{2}} \times 5^{-\frac{1}{2}}$ (d) $8^{-\frac{2}{3}} \times 8^{\frac{4}{3}}$ (e) $2^{\frac{5}{2}} \times 8^{-\frac{5}{3}}$ (f) $6^{\frac{3}{2}} \times 16^{-\frac{1}{2}}$

HCF and LCM

The highest common factor of two or more numbers is the largest number that divides exactly into them.

The lowest common multiple of two or more numbers is the smallest number that is an exact multiple of both numbers.

Worked example

(a) Find the HCF of 24 and 80.

(b) Find the LCM of 24 and 80.

A question will often ask you to write the numbers as products of prime factors. You should then use the prime factors to find the HCF and LCM.

Answer

(a) Write the two numbers as products of prime factors. If you need help with working out the prime factors, go back to section 1.1.

$24 = 2^3 \times 3$, $80 = 2^4 \times 5$

The HCF is the product of all the prime factors that are common to both numbers. This is $2^3 = 8$.

The HCF of 24 and 80 is 8.

(b) The LCM is the product of prime factors that are not common to both numbers and the prime factors that are common to both numbers.

The product of the prime factors that are common to both numbers is 2^3.

The product of the prime factors that are not common to both numbers is $2 \times 3 \times 5$.

Multiply out the product of the prime factors: $2^3 \times 2 \times 3 \times 5 = 240$

The LCM of 24 and 80 is 240.

Test yourself

1. What is the HCF of:

(a) 84 and 126 (b) 72 and 192 (c) 66 and 154
(d) 90 and 162 (e) 75 and 120 (f) 84 and 231?

2. What is the LCM of each pair of numbers in Q1?

Standard form

Very large and very small numbers can be given in standard form.

A number in standard form is given in the following way: $A \times 10^n$ where $1 \leqslant A < 10$ and n is an integer.

Worked example

1. Write 2 590 000 in standard form.
2. Work out $3(4.6 \times 10^9 - 4 \times 10^7)$.

   Give your answer in standard form.

TIP Remember that the number must be greater than or equal to 1 and less than 10 for the number to be in standard form. If the number is greater than or equal to 10, or less than 1, it is not in standard form.

Answer

1. 2.59×10^6
2. $3(4.6 \times 10^9 - 4 \times 10^7) = 3(4.6 \times 10^9 - 0.04 \times 10^9) = 3(4.56 \times 10^9) = 13.68 \times 10^9 = 1.368 \times 10^{10}$

Test yourself

1. Write the following numbers in standard form.

(a) 365 000 (b) 46 000 000 (c) 7 820 000
(d) 0.000 34 (e) 0.0056 (f) 0.000 001 94

2. Work out the following. Give your answers in standard form.

(a) $5(3 \times 10^7 - 5 \times 10^6)$ (b) $2(3 \times 10^6 - 8 \times 10^4)$ (c) $5(5 \times 10^8 - 4 \times 10^6)$
(d) $3(9.5 \times 10^9 - 5 \times 10^8)$ (e) $2(8.6 \times 10^8 - 5 \times 10^6)$
(f) $3(7.9 \times 10^7 - 3 \times 10^5)$

3. The table shows the areas of five different countries and the area of the country that is covered by water.

Country	Area of country (km^2)	Area covered by water (km^2)
Canada	9.98×10^6	8.91×10^5
Finland	3.38×10^5	3.38×10^4
Kenya	5.81×10^5	1.33×10^4
New Zealand	2.68×10^5	4.29×10^3
Vietnam	3.31×10^5	2.12×10^4

(a) Which country has the largest area covered by water?
(b) Which country has the smallest area?
(c) Which country has the smallest percentage of area covered by water?
(d) Which country has the largest percentage of area covered by water?

Surds

A **surd** is a whole number that is written as a root.

You need to remember the four general rules for simplifying surds:

$\sqrt{p}\times\sqrt{q}=\sqrt{pq}$

$\sqrt{p}\div\sqrt{q}=\sqrt{\frac{p}{q}}$

$\sqrt[r]{p}\times\sqrt[s]{q}=\sqrt[rs]{pq}$

$\sqrt[r]{p}\div\sqrt[s]{q}=\sqrt[\frac{r}{s}]{\frac{p}{q}}$

You can use surds in calculations. Simplify the surd by taking square numbers outside the square root sign.

When surds appear as fractions in answers, the denominator is usually a whole number. **Rationalising** the denominator means you multiply by another surd to give a whole number.

Worked example

1. Simplify $(1+2\sqrt{3})(2-3\sqrt{3})$
2. Rationalise the denominator of $\frac{2\sqrt{5}}{\sqrt{8}}$.

Answer

1. Multiply out the brackets:

$$(1+2\sqrt{3})(2-3\sqrt{3})=(1\times2)+(1\times-3\sqrt{3})+(2\sqrt{3}\times2)+(2\sqrt{3}\times-3\sqrt{3})$$
$$=2-3\sqrt{3}+4\sqrt{3}+(2\times-3\times\sqrt{3}\times\sqrt{3})$$
$$=2-3\sqrt{3}+4\sqrt{3}-18$$

Collect like terms: $=\sqrt{3}-16$

The numbers in surds are always whole numbers. Like terms have the same number in the surd.

2. Multiply the numerator and denominator by $\sqrt{8}$: $\frac{2\sqrt{5}\times\sqrt{8}}{\sqrt{8}\times\sqrt{8}}=\frac{2\sqrt{40}}{8}$

Simplify the surd: $\frac{2\sqrt{40}}{8}=\frac{2\sqrt{4\times10}}{8}=\frac{2\sqrt{4}\sqrt{10}}{8}=\frac{2\times2\sqrt{10}}{8}=\frac{4\sqrt{10}}{8}=\frac{\sqrt{10}}{2}$

TIP

Rationalise means turn the number into a rational number, that is remove the surd from the denominator.

Test yourself

1. Simplify the following surds into the form $p\sqrt{q}$.

   (a) $\sqrt{32}$ (b) $\sqrt{75}$ (c) $\sqrt{63}$ (d) $\sqrt{125}$ (e) $\sqrt{600}$ (f) $\sqrt{48}$

2. Simplify the following.

   (a) $3\sqrt{5}\times2\sqrt{3}$ (b) $2\sqrt{3}\times5\sqrt{3}$ (c) $3\sqrt{8}\times2\sqrt{2}$

   (d) $28\sqrt{12}\div4\sqrt{3}$ (e) $24\sqrt{15}\div6\sqrt{5}$ (f) $6\sqrt{18}\div2\sqrt{2}$

3. Simplify the following.

   (a) $(2+\sqrt{5})(3+\sqrt{5})$ (b) $(3+\sqrt{6})(4+\sqrt{6})$ (c) $(3+\sqrt{2})^2$

   (d) $(2-\sqrt{3})^2$ (e) $(1-\sqrt{3})(1+2\sqrt{3})$ (f) $(3+2\sqrt{2})(2-\sqrt{2})$

4. Rationalise the denominator of:

   (a) $\frac{1}{\sqrt{2}}$ (b) $\frac{1}{\sqrt{6}}$ (c) $\frac{6}{\sqrt{3}}$ (d) $\frac{4\sqrt{2}}{\sqrt{3}}$ (e) $\frac{\sqrt{3}}{\sqrt{7}}$ (f) $\frac{6-3\sqrt{2}}{\sqrt{3}}$

1.6 Sets

Set notation

A collection of items such as numbers, objects or symbols is called a set.

A set is named by a capital letter. The numbers, objects or symbols in a set are called elements.

The elements are listed in curly brackets and separated by commas.

When you cannot list all the elements, you can use dots, e.g. $A=\{x: x \text{ is a multiple of } 3\}=\{3, 6, 9, 12, 15, ...\}$

When every element in A is also in B, A is a subset of B. A is a proper subset of B when $A \neq B$.

You can describe sets using the following inequality symbols:

$<$ less than
$>$ greater than
$\leqslant$ less than or equal to
$\geqslant$ greater than or equal to

For example, $B=\{x: a\leqslant x\leqslant b\}$.

Sets can also be defined using equations, e.g. $C=\{(x, y)\ y=mx+c\}$.

You should know the following set notation:

$n(A)$ number of elements in set A
$\in$ is an element of
$\notin$ is not an element of
A' complement of set A or not a member of A

$\varnothing$	empty set
$\mathscr{E}$	universal set
$A \subseteq B$	A is a subset of B
$A \subset B$	A is a proper subset of B
$A \nsubseteq B$	A is not a subset of B
$A \not\subset B$	A is not a proper subset of B
$A \cup B$	union of A and B
$A \cap B$	intersection of A and B

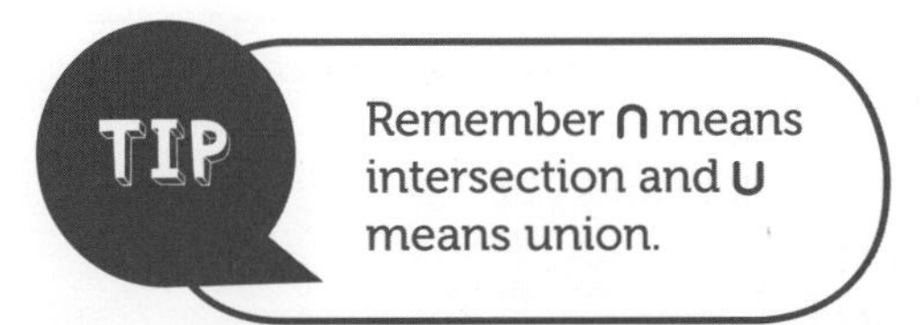

Worked example

$A = \{\text{factors of } 9\}$

(a) List the elements of A.

(b) List all the subsets of A.

(c) Which one of the subsets is not a proper subset?

(d) Write down $n(A)$.

Answer

(a) $A = \{1, 3, 9\}$

(b) $\{1\}, \{3\}, \{9\}, \{1, 3\}, \{1, 9\}, \{3, 9\}, \{1, 3, 9\}, \varnothing$

(c) $\{1, 3, 9\}$

(d) $n(A) = 3$

Test yourself

1. $B = \{\text{factors of } 10\}$
(a) List the elements. (b) List all the subsets. (c) Write down $n(B)$.

2. $C = \{\text{letters in the word ball}\}$
(a) List the elements. (b) List all the subsets. (c) Write down $n(C)$.

3. $D = \{x: x^2 = 25\}$
(a) List the elements. (b) List all the subsets. (c) Write down $n(D)$.

4. $\mathscr{E} = \{\text{integer } x: 20 \leqslant x \leqslant 30\}$
$E = \{\text{multiples of } 5\}$, $F = \{\text{factors of } 75\}$
List the elements of: (a) $E \cap F$ (b) $E \cup F$ (c) $E' \cap F$

5. $\mathscr{E} = \{\text{prime numbers} < 15\}$
$H = \{\text{factors of } 30\}$, $I = \{\text{factors of } 33\}$
List the elements of: (a) $H \cap I$ (b) $H' \cap I$ (c) $H' \cap I'$

6. $\mathscr{E} = \{\text{days of the week}\}$
$J = \{\text{days containing letter a}\}$, $K = \{\text{days containing letter t}\}$, $L = \{\text{days containing letter o}\}$
(a) List the elements of: (i) $J \cap L$ (ii) $J' \cap K$ (iii) $K \cap L$
(b) Is J a proper subset of $\mathscr{E}$? Explain your answer.

Venn diagrams

You can show sets on a Venn diagram.

Worked example

$\mathscr{E}$ = {positive whole numbers $\leqslant$ 20}
A = {multiples of 3}
B = {multiples of 5}

(a) Draw a Venn diagram to show these sets.

(b) List the elements of: (i) A' (ii) $A \cap B$ (iii) $A' \cap B$ (iv) $A \cup B$

(c) Show $A \cap B'$ by shading a copy of the diagram.

Answer

(a) First list the elements of each set.

$\mathscr{E}$ = {1, 2, 3, 4, 5, 6, 7, 8, 9, 10, 11, 12, 13, 14, 15, 16, 17, 18, 19, 20}

A = {3, 6, 9, 12, 15, 18}

B = {5, 10, 15, 20}

Now draw a Venn diagram with two overlapping circles and label them A and B.

Put all the elements in the correct place on the diagram. There is one element, 15, that is in both A and B. It goes in the space where the two circles overlap.

All the elements that are not in A or B go in the area outside the circles.

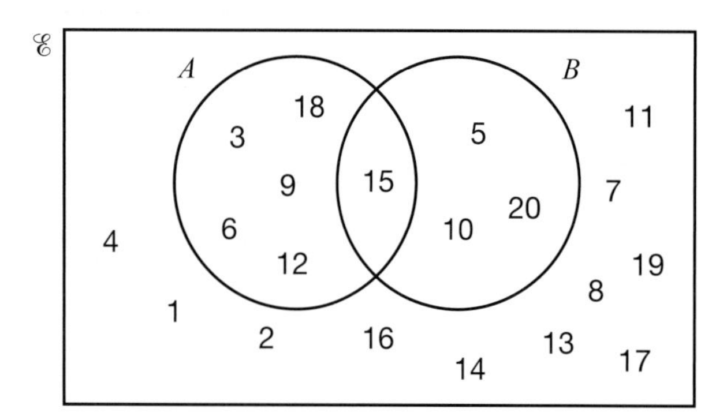

(b) (i) {1, 2, 4, 5, 7, 8, 10, 11, 13, 14, 16, 17, 19, 20}

(ii) {15} (iii) {5, 10, 20} (iv) {3, 5, 6, 9, 10, 12, 15, 18, 20}

(c) Shade A with one type of hatching and B' with another type of hatching. The area with both hatchings is the area you need.

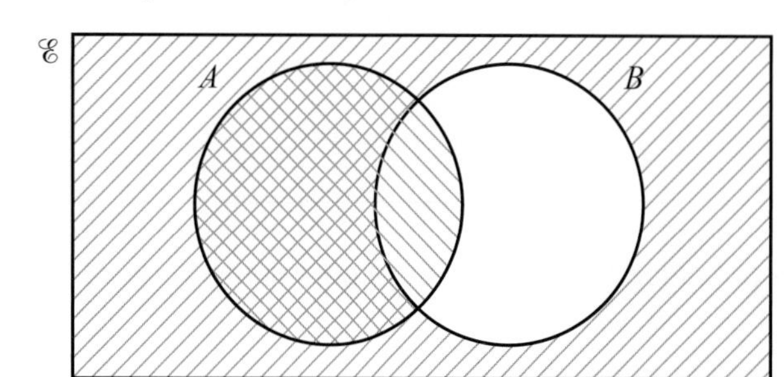

Test yourself

1. $\mathscr{E}=\{\text{integer } x\text{: } 19<x<31\}$

$C=\{\text{multiples of 2}\}$, $D=\{\text{multiples of 5}\}$

(a) Copy the Venn diagram and show the sets on it.

(b) List the elements of:

(i) $C\cap D$

(ii) $C\cup D$

(iii) $C'\cap D$

2. $\mathscr{E}=\{\text{c, d, e, h, o, r, s, t}\}$

$E=\{\text{c, h, o, r, e}\}$, $F=\{\text{c, h, e, s, t}\}$

(a) Show these sets on a Venn diagram.

(b) List the elements of: (i) $E'\cup F$ (ii) $E\cap F'$ (iii) $(E\cup F)'$

3. $\mathscr{E}=\{\text{integer } x\text{: } 0<x\leqslant 15\}$

$G=\{\text{multiples of 2}\}$, $H=\{\text{multiples of 3}\}$, $I=\{\text{multiples of 5}\}$

(a) Show these sets on a Venn diagram.

(b) List the elements of: (i) $(G\cup H)\cap I$ (ii) $G\cup(H\cap I)$ (iii) $G'\cap(H\cap I')$

4. $\mathscr{E}=\{\text{e, g, i, m, n, o, p, r, t, u}\}$

$J=\{\text{p, r, i, m, e}\}$, $K=\{\text{m, u, t, e}\}$, $L=\{\text{m, i, n, t}\}$

(a) Show these sets on a Venn diagram.

(b) List the elements of: (i) $J\cap(K\cap L)$ (ii) $(J'\cap K)\cup L$ (iii) $((J\cup K)\cup L)'$

5. On copies of this Venn diagram shade:

(a) $M\cap N'$

(b) $(M\cup N)'$

(c) $M'\cup N'$

(d) $M'\cap N'$

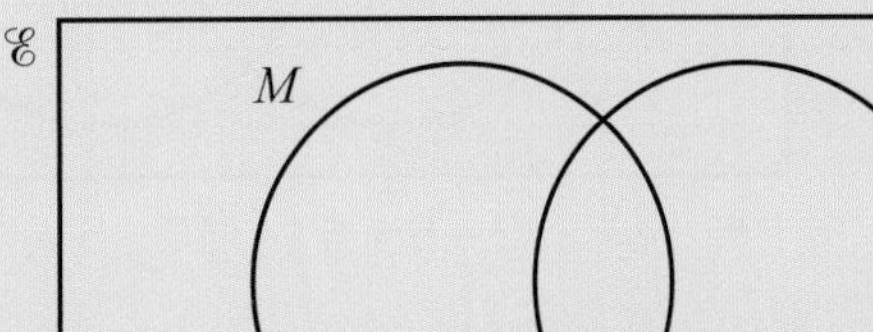

6. On copies of this Venn diagram shade:

(a) $(O\cap P)\cup Q$ (b) $O'\cap(P\cup Q)$ (c) $O'\cap(P'\cap Q')$ (d) $(O\cup P)'\cap Q$

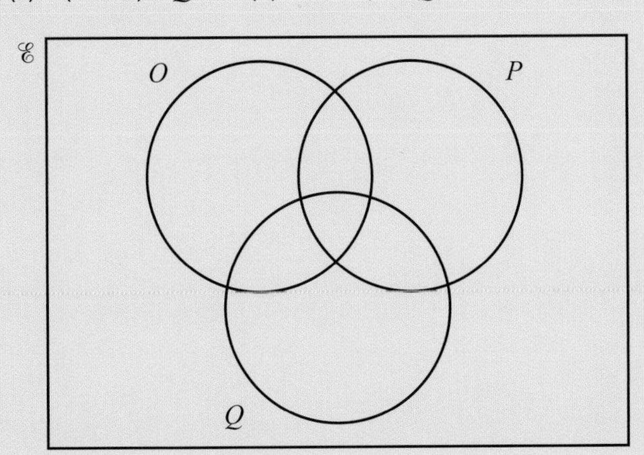

EDE

Solving problems with sets

You can use Venn diagrams to help solve practical problems.

Worked example

20 people order drinks are in a cafe. 12 order coffee (C). 10 order food (F). 6 order both.

(a) Draw a Venn diagram to show this information.

(b) How many people do not order coffee or food?

Answer

(a) You know the following information:

$n(\mathscr{E})=20$
$n(C)=12$
$n(F)=10$
$n(C \cap F)=6$

Use this information to fill in the Venn diagram, starting with the number of people who order both coffee and food.

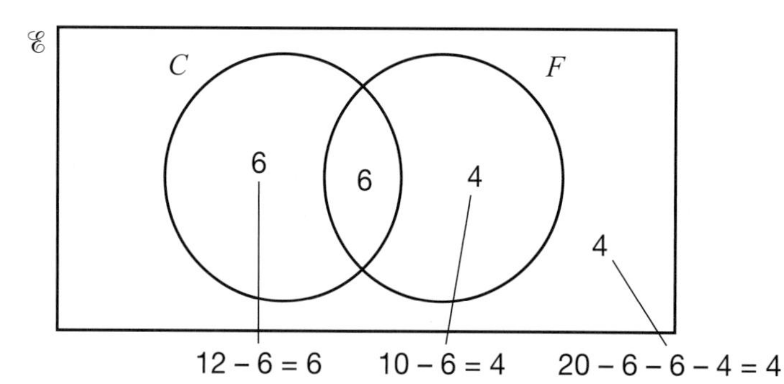

(b) 4 people do not order coffee or food.

Test yourself

1. A group of people were asked if they had downloaded films (F) or music (M) in the last month. The numbers of people are shown in the Venn diagram.

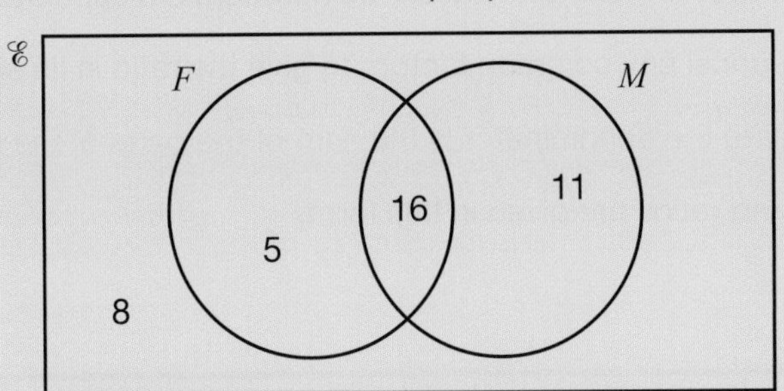

(a) How many had downloaded music?

(b) How many had downloaded films but not music?

(c) How many people had downloaded both?

(d) How many people were there in the survey?

2. A group of 70 people were asked if they had ever been to Greece (G), Spain (S) and Turkey (T). The numbers of people are shown in the Venn diagram.

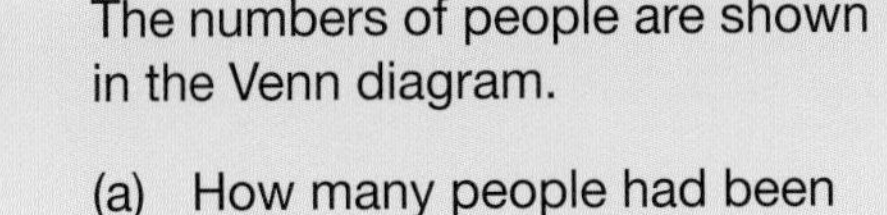

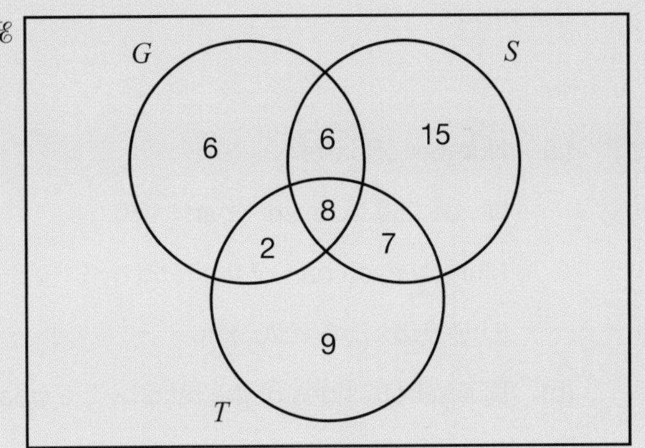

(a) How many people had been to all three countries?

(b) How many people had been to at least two countries?

(c) How many had been to Spain?

(d) The number of people who had not gone to any of the countries is missing. Calculate the number.

3. A group of 30 people were asked if they watched two TV programmes, C and D. 13 people watched C and 18 watched D. 11 watched both.

(a) Show this information on a Venn diagram.

(b) How many people did not watch either programme?

4. A class of students are all studying at least one subject from Geography (G), History (H) and Spanish (S).

17 are studying Geography.

13 are studying History.

23 are studying Spanish.

3 are studying all three subjects.

7 are studying Geography and History.

11 are studying Geography and Spanish.

8 are studying History and Spanish.

(a) Show this information on a Venn diagram.

(b) How many are studying only one of the subjects?

1.7 Ratio and proportion

Ratio

You can use a ratio to compare the sizes of two or more quantities. The numbers are separated by a colon (:).

The quantities must be in the same units. Cancel any common factors to give the ratio in its simplest form.

You can also express ratios as fractions where the denominator is the sum of the parts of the ratio.

Ratios can also be given in the form $1:n$. Map ratios are given in this form.

You can use a ratio to calculate other values.

Worked example

1. (a) Share £50 in the ratio 2:3.

   (b) Give the ratio in the form $1:n$.

2. The ratio of boys to girls in a class is 4:5. There are 24 boys in the class. How many girls are in the class?

Answer

1. (a) Number of parts $=2+3=5$

   Divide £50 by 5, so 1 part = £10.

   Multiply each part of the ratio by £10. So £50 shared in the ratio 2:3 is

   $2\times£10:3\times£10=£20:£30$.

   (b) Divide both sides of the ratio by the smallest number, 2: $\frac{2}{2}:\frac{3}{2}$

   Simplify the ratio: $1:1.5$

2. 4 parts is 24 students.

   Divide by 4, so 1 part is 6 students.

   Number of girls $=5$ parts $=5\times6=30$

Test yourself

1. Give these ratios: (i) in their simplest form (ii) in the form $1:n$.
   (a) 9:15 (b) 8:30 (c) 28:49
   (d) 60 cm:4 m (e) 3 hours:20 minutes (f) 80 cents:$5

2. Share £330 in the ratio 4:7.

3. The ratio of adults to children at a showing of a film is 5:9. There are 350 people at the showing. How many adults and how many children were at the showing?

4. A fruit syrup is diluted with water in the ratio 1:9. There is 1.5 litres of drink. How much syrup and water is used?

5. A recipe for biscuits uses butter, flour and sugar in the ratio 5:9:6. There is 500 g of biscuit dough. How much of each ingredient was used?

6. The ratio of tea, coffee and other drinks sold in a cafe is 2:3:5. One day 450 drinks were sold. How many of each type of drink was sold?

7. A cocktail uses apple juice, raspberry puree and boysenberry juice in the ratio 7:1:2. There is 500 ml of the cocktail. How much of each ingredient was used?

8. The ratio of adults to children at a fairground is 7:5. There are 95 children at the fairground. How many adults are there?

9. The ratio of full price tickets to concessionary tickets sold at an attraction is in the ratio 9:4. One day 450 full price tickets are sold. How many concessionary tickets were sold?

10. The profits of a business are split between the two owners Rebecca and Shami in the ratio 5:4. Rebecca gets £30 000 profit one year. How much does Shami get?

11. Simon is making a cocktail using orange juice, lime juice and mango puree in the ratio 5:2:3. He has 750 ml of orange juice. How much lime juice and mango puree does he need?

12. Three sisters share sweets in the ratio of their ages. Rachel is 8, Megan is 9 and Sadie is 11. Sadie has 44 sweets. How many do Rachel and Megan get each?

13. A recipe for biscuits uses flour, butter and sugar in the ratio 8:4:5. Harry uses 140 g of butter. How much flour and sugar does he need?

Increasing and decreasing quantities by a ratio

You can increase and decrease quantities using ratios.

Worked example

A photo measures 8 cm by 10 cm.

(a) It is enlarged in the ratio 4 : 5. Calculate the new dimensions of the photo.

(b) It is reduced in the ratio 3 : 5. Calculate the new dimensions of the photo.

Answer

(a) 4 : 5 is the same as 1 : 1.25

Multiply the dimensions by 1.25

The dimensions of the enlargement are $8\,\text{cm} \times 1.25$ by $10\,\text{cm} \times 1.25 = 10\,\text{cm}$ by 12.5 cm

(b) 3 : 5 can be expressed as a fraction, $\frac{3}{5}$.

Multiply the dimensions by this fraction.

The dimensions of the photo are $8\,\text{cm} \times \frac{3}{5}$ by $10\,\text{cm} \times \frac{3}{5} = 4.8\,\text{cm}$ by 6 cm

Test yourself

1. Increase 250 in the following ratios.
(a) 4 : 1 (b) 3 : 2 (c) 6 : 5 (d) 9 : 4 (e) 14 : 5 (f) 19 : 10

2. Decrease 200 in the following ratios.
(a) 1 : 2 (b) 2 : 5 (c) 7 : 10 (d) 3 : 8 (e) 4 : 25 (f) 11 : 16

3. A recipe for potato pancakes uses the following ingredients for 4 people.

500 g potatoes
20 g butter
2 teaspoons chopped fresh parsley
30 g grated cheese
50 g flour
50 ml vegetable oil

Increase the ingredients to serve 10 people.

4. A recipe for risotto uses the following ingredients for 8 people.

80 g butter
440 g risotto rice
900 ml boiling water
200 g cooked peas
100 g grated cheese
60 ml lemon juice

Decrease the ingredients to serve 3 people.

Rates

The rate at which a quantity changes is a measure of how quickly it changes.

You can use rates to solve problems.

Worked example

A decorator can paint walls at the rate of $6\,m^2$ per hour.

How long will it take the decorator to paint

(a) a wall with an area of $15\,m^2$

(b) $1\,m^2$?

Answer

(a) Time taken $= \frac{\text{area of wall}}{\text{area painted per hour}} = \frac{15}{6} = 2.5$ hours

(b) Time taken $= \frac{60 \text{ minutes}}{6} = 10$ minutes

Test yourself

1. A bamboo plant grows at the rate of 6 cm/day.
  (a) How tall will the bamboo be after 8 days? Assume that the initial height of the bamboo is 0 cm.
  (b) How long will it take for the bamboo to reach its maximum height of 11 m?

2. Water flows out of a tap at the rate of 1 litre every 10 seconds.
  (a) What is the rate of flow in litres per minute?
  (b) How long would it take to fill a 90 litre bath?

3. Water flows out of a shower head at the rate of 2.5 litres/minute.
  (a) How many litres of water would a person use when taking a 5 minute shower?
  (b) A new shower head is fitted which reduces the flow rate to 1.9 litres/minute. How much less water would be used in a 5 minute shower?

4. A consumer organisation tests the fuel consumption of a car and finds that it is 8.9 litres/100 km.
  (a) How much fuel will the car use to travel 250 km?
  (b) How far can the car travel on 50 litres of fuel?
  (c) What is the fuel consumption in km/litre?

5. A consumer organisation measures the carbon dioxide output of a particular car as 105 g/km.
  (a) How many kilograms of carbon dioxide is emitted by the car on a journey of 75 km?
  (b) How far does the car travel when it emits 12 kg of carbon dioxide?

6. The carbon dioxide level in the atmosphere measured at Mauna Loa in Hawaii increased from 318 p.p.m. in 1960 to 400 p.p.m. in 2013.
Calculate the average rate of increase of carbon dioxide per year over this period.

Average speed

Average speed can be worked out using the formula speed $= \frac{\text{distance}}{\text{time}}$.

The formula can be rearranged to work out distance or time.

Worked example

A car travels 140 km in 1 hour and 45 minutes. What is its average speed?

Answer

First put the time in decimal form:

1 hour and 45 minutes $= 1\frac{45}{60}$ hours $= 1\frac{3}{4}$ hours $= 1.75$ hours

speed $= \frac{140 \text{ km}}{1.75 \text{ hours}} = 80$ km/h

Remember that 0.45 of an hour is NOT 45 minutes – it is 0.45×60 minutes $= 27$ minutes.

Test yourself

1. A train travels 250 km in 2 hours and 30 minutes. What is its average speed?
2. A sprinter runs 400 m in 50 seconds. What is the sprinter's average speed?
3. A marathon runner runs 42.195 km in 3 hours. What is the runner's average speed?
4. A snail moves 30 cm in 10 minutes. What is its average speed in cm/min?
5. An aeroplane travels 6300 km in 8 hours and 15 minutes. Calculate its average speed.
6. A person walks 2 km in 25 minutes. What is the person's average speed?
7. A cyclist is cycling at an average speed of 18 km/h. How long will it take to cycle 45 km?
8. A train travels at an average speed of 250 km/h. How long will it take to travel 600 km?
9. A runner runs at an average speed of 6.5 m/s. How long will it take to run 3000 m?
10. An aeroplane travels at an average speed of 770 km/h. The flight takes 6 hours and 45 minutes. What is the distance of the flight?
11. Samira walks at 5 km/h. It takes her 36 minutes to walk to school from home. How far is it to school?
12. Ben drives a car at an average speed of 80 km/h. He starts his journey at 08.45 and arrives at his destination at 11.30. How far does he travel?
13. Change the following speeds to kilometres per hour.
    (a) 12 m/s (b) 20 m/s (c) 0.5 m/s
    (d) 32 m/s (e) 75 m/s (f) 175 m/s
14. Change the following speeds to metres per second.
    (a) 18 km/h (b) 24 km/h (c) 50 km/h
    (d) 90 km/h (e) 160 km/h (f) 750 km/h

Direct proportion

When two quantities vary in direct proportion, as one quantity increases, the second quantity also increases.

You can use the unitary method to solve problems. Work out the value of one item first.

Worked example

Seven pens cost £3.92. How much do 12 pens cost?

Answer

Find the cost of one pen: £3.92 ÷ 7 = £0.56

Multiply this cost by 12 to find the cost of 12 pens: 12 × £0.56 = £6.72

Test yourself

1. Three bags of flour have a mass of 2.25 kg. What is the mass of 7 bags of flour?
2. A car can travel 126 km on 9 litres of fuel. How far can the car travel on 16 litres of fuel?
3. Six books cost $39. How much do 25 books cost?
4. Four litres of milk cost £1.48. How much do 17 litres cost?
5. A printer takes 14 seconds to print out a 5 page document. How long would the printer take to print a 22 page document?
6. A recipe for 12 biscuits uses 150 g of butter, 250 g of flour and 100 g of sugar. How much of each ingredient is needed to make 25 biscuits? Give your answers to the nearest 10 g.

Inverse proportion

When two quantities vary in inverse proportion, as one quantity increases, the second quantity decreases.

You can solve problems using inverse proportion.

Worked example

A car travels at an average speed of 60 km/h for 2 hours. How long does it take when the car travels at 80 km/h?

Answer

First find the total distance = average speed × time
= 60 km/h × 2 hours = 120 km

Divide the distance by the new speed to find the time: time = distance ÷ average speed
= 120 km ÷ 80 km/h
= 1.5 hours (or 1 hour and 30 minutes)

Test yourself

1. Five friends share a taxi to the airport. The taxi costs £12 each. How much will it cost per person when there are only four people sharing the cost?
2. A cyclist takes 4.5 hours to complete a journey at an average speed of 16 km/h. What speed would the cyclist need to cycle at to complete the journey in 3.5 hours?
3. A car travels for 6 hours at an average speed of 70 km/h. How long will the journey take when the average speed is 50 km/h?
4. It takes 3 painters 8 days to paint a house. How long would it take 4 painters?
5. Harry can print 25 20-page documents using one ream of paper. How many complete 6-page documents can he print?

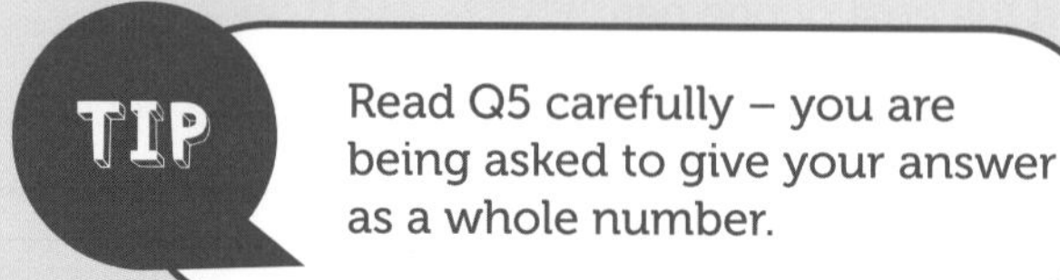

6. Sam is buying wallpaper. He is looking at three types, costing \$0.75/m, \$1.05/m and \$1.30/m. He has enough money to buy 60 m of the wallpaper that costs \$1.30/m.
   How many metres of the other two wallpapers can he buy?

1.8 Accuracy

Decimal places and significant figures

The digits to the right of the decimal point are decimal places.

The first significant figure is the first non-zero digit.

Zeroes are significant when there are non-zero digits around them.

Use the rules of rounding when you are asked to round to a specified number of decimal places or significant figures.

Test yourself

1. Round each of the following numbers to:

(i) 1 significant figure	(ii) 2 significant figures	(iii) 3 significant figures
(iv) 1 decimal place	(v) 2 decimal places	(vi) 3 decimal places.
(a) 346.2576	(b) 67.3857	(c) 3.621 56
(d) 0.529 431	(e) 0.091 842	(f) 0.005 376 51

Upper and lower bounds

All measured values have been rounded – some more than others depending on how accurately they can be measured. For example, if you measure the length of an object with a ruler that is marked in millimetres, you can only measure the length to the nearest millimetre.

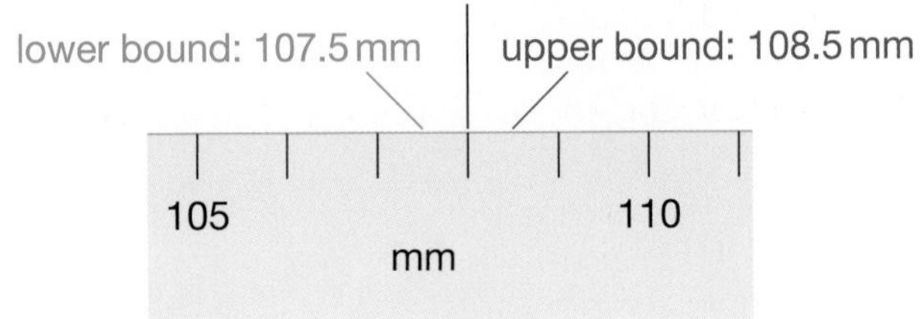

The upper bound is the maximum possible value.

The lower bound is the minimum possible value.

The upper and lower bounds are usually given as a range using inequality signs.

TIP Giving the upper bound as less than 1000.5 cm^3 is the same as saying that it is $1000.49999999....\text{ cm}^3$.

Worked example

The volume of a bottle is 1000 cm^3 to the nearest cm^3.

What are the upper and lower bounds for the volume of the bottle?

Answer

The upper bound is the highest value that rounds down to 1000 cm^3, that is $1000.499...\text{ cm}^3$.

The lower bound is the lowest value that rounds up to 1000 cm^3, that is 999.5 cm^3.

Give the lower and upper bounds as a range: $999.5\text{ cm}^3 \leqslant \text{volume} < 1000.5\text{ cm}^3$.

Test yourself

TIP Remember that you can't have part of an apple or part of a person.

1. Find the upper and lower bounds for each of the following.

(a) The number of apples in a box is 100 to 1 significant figure.

(b) The population of Mexico City is 9 million to the nearest million.

(c) The length of a table is 1.7 m to 1 decimal place.

(d) The mass of a book is 250 g to 2 significant figures.

(e) The length of a book is 21 cm to the nearest centimetre.

(f) The distance between two towns is 58 km to 2 significant figures

Calculations with upper and lower bounds

When you do calculations with quantities that have upper and lower bounds, the value you calculate also has upper and lower bounds.

You can find them as follows:

Operation	Upper bound	Lower bound
addition	$x_{\text{upper}}+y_{\text{upper}}$	$x_{\text{lower}}+y_{\text{lower}}$
subtraction	$x_{\text{upper}}-y_{\text{lower}}$	$x_{\text{lower}}-y_{\text{upper}}$
multiplication	$x_{\text{upper}}\times y_{\text{upper}}$	$x_{\text{lower}}\times y_{\text{lower}}$
division	$x_{\text{upper}}\div y_{\text{lower}}$	$x_{\text{lower}}\div y_{\text{upper}}$

Worked example

1. A rectangle has dimensions 8 cm by 5 cm to the nearest centimetre.

   Find the upper and lower bounds for: (a) the perimeter (b) the area.

2. Simon travels 150 km to the nearest kilometre in 2 hours to the nearest 5 minutes.

   What are the upper and lower bounds for the average speed of his journey?

   Give your answer in km/h.

Answer

1. Upper and lower bounds for the length and width are:

   $7.5\text{ cm} \leqslant \text{length} < 8.5\text{ cm}$; $4.5\text{ cm} \leqslant \text{width} < 5.5\text{ cm}$

   (a) Upper bound for perimeter $= 2\times$ maximum possible length $+ 2\times$ maximum possible width
   $= 2\times 8.5\text{ cm} + 2\times 5.5\text{ cm} = 28\text{ cm}$

   Lower bound for perimeter $= 2\times$ minimum possible length $+ 2\times$ minimum possible width
   $= 2\times 7.5\text{ cm} + 2\times 4.5\text{ cm} = 24\text{ cm}$

   So $24\text{ cm} \leqslant \text{perimeter} < 28\text{ cm}$

   (b) Upper bound for area $=$ maximum possible length $\times$ maximum possible width
   $= 8.5\text{ cm}\times 5.5\text{ cm} = 46.75\text{ cm}^2$

   Lower bound for area $=$ minimum possible length $\times$ minimum possible width
   $= 7.5\text{ cm}\times 4.5\text{ cm} = 33.75\text{ cm}^2$

   So $33.75\text{ cm}^2 \leqslant \text{area} < 46.75\text{ cm}^2$

2. First work out the upper and lower bounds for distance and time:

$149.5\,\text{km} \leqslant \text{distance} < 150.5\,\text{km}$

The time is to the nearest 5 minutes, so the minimum possible time will be 2.5 minutes less and the maximum possible time will be 2.5 minutes more.

TIP Remember that 20 minutes is not 0.2 hours. It is 0.333... hours.

Give the time as a decimal:

minimum possible time $= 1\frac{57.5}{60}$ hours $= 1.958$ hours

maximum possible time $= 2\frac{2.5}{60}$ hours $= 2.042$ hours

So $1.958 \text{ hours} \leqslant \text{time} < 2.042 \text{ hours}$

$$\text{Upper bound for average speed} = \frac{\text{maximum possible (largest) distance}}{\text{minimum possible (smallest) time}}$$

$$= \frac{150.5 \text{ km}}{1.958 \text{ hours}} = 76.86\,\text{km/h}$$

$$\text{Lower bound for average speed} = \frac{\text{minimum possible (smallest) distance}}{\text{maximum possible (largest) time}}$$

$$= \frac{149.5\,\text{km}}{2.042\,\text{hours}} = 73.21\,\text{km/h}$$

So $73.2\,\text{km/h} \leqslant \text{average speed} < 76.9\,\text{km/h}$

TIP When finding the lowest bound for a division, you need the smallest number, so you need the smallest number in the numerator (top line) and the largest number in the denominator (bottom line).

Test yourself

1. A box has dimensions $5.0\,\text{cm} \times 10.0\,\text{cm} \times 6.0\,\text{cm}$ to the nearest millimetre.
   What are the upper and lower bounds for the volume?

2. A machine fills 0.33 litre bottles to the nearest hundredth of a litre. The machine has 30 litres of liquid to the nearest tenth of a litre.
   What are the upper and lower bounds for:
   (a) the total volume of liquid and volume of liquid in a bottle
   (b) the number of bottles that can be filled completely?

3. A large lift can safely carry 1750 kg to the nearest ten kilograms. The average person has a mass of 65 kg to the nearest kilogram.
   What are the upper and lower bounds for:
   (a) the mass of an average person and the mass that can be carried by the lift
   (b) the number of people with average mass that the lift can safely carry?

4. The population of the Netherlands is 16.8 million to the nearest hundred thousand. The land area of the Netherlands is 41 500 km^2 to the nearest hundred square kilometres.
   (a) What are the upper and lower bounds for the country's population and area?
   (b) Population density is the population divided by the land area. What are the upper and lower bounds for its population density?

5. An athlete runs 200 m to the nearest half metre in 22.5 seconds to the nearest tenth of a second.
   What are the upper and lower bounds for:
   (a) distance and time
   (b) the athlete's average speed in m/s?

6. A car can go 600 km to the nearest kilometre on a tank of petrol. The tank contains 45 litres to the nearest half litre.
   Calculate the upper and lower bounds for the distance the car can travel on a litre of petrol.

1.9 Applying number

Estimating quantities

You can use known quantities to make estimates of other quantities:

20 centimetres: the length of an average person's foot

1 metre: a long stride for an average person, or the distance from an average person's waist to the ground

1 kilometre: two and a half times around an athletics track

10 grams: approximately the mass of a UK 50 pence coin

1 kilogram: mass of a bag of sugar

1 tonne: mass of a small car

5 millilitres: volume of liquid on a teaspoon

1 centilitre: volume of a small glass

1 litre: volume of a full carton of fruit juice

Test yourself

1. Estimate the values of the following.
   (a) the length and mass of your pen
   (b) the length, width, thickness and mass of this book
   (c) the size of the desk you are sitting at
   (d) the dimensions of the room you are in
   (e) your own height
   (f) the length and mass of a mobile phone

Time

Times can be given and calculated using the 12-hour and 24-hour clocks.

Timetables usually use the 24-hour clock (except in the USA).

Worked example

Here is an extract of a train timetable.

Ragby Central	1503	1518	1533	1548	1603	1618
Anytown	1506	–	1536	–	1606	–
Badgerville	1511	1525	1541	1555	1611	1625
Crummytown	1515	1531	1545	1551	1615	1631
Dawton	1522	1538	1552	1608	1622	1638
Eastville	1537	1551	1607	1621	1637	1651

(a) I catch the 1536 from Anytown and go to Eastville. How long does the journey take?

(b) I need to be in Eastville by 4pm. Which train should I catch from Badgerville?

Answer

(a) Train arrives in Eastville at 1607.

As the journey starts at 1536 and finishes at 1607, to work out how long the journey takes, split it into two parts:

$1600 - 1536 = 24$ minutes
$1607 - 1600 = 7$ minutes

So the journey takes $24 + 7 = 31$ minutes

(b) The latest train I can get arrives at 1551. This train leaves Badgerville at 1525.

Test yourself

1. Write down the times shown on the following clocks:
(i) in 12-hour format (ii) in 24-hour format.

(a)

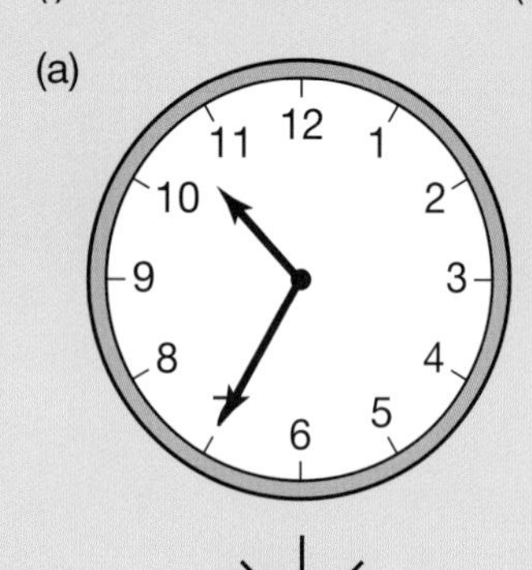

(b)

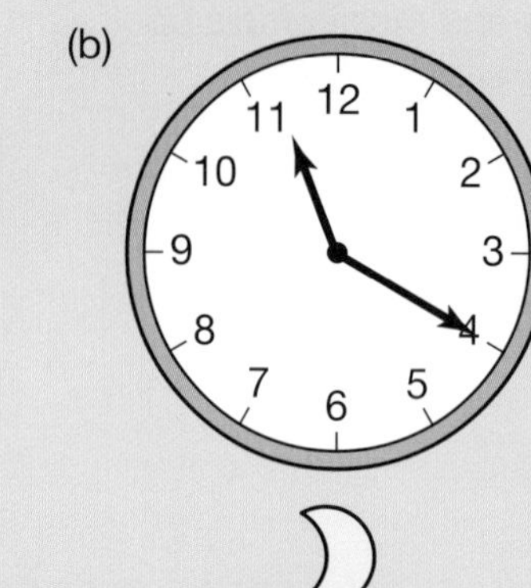

(c)

(d)

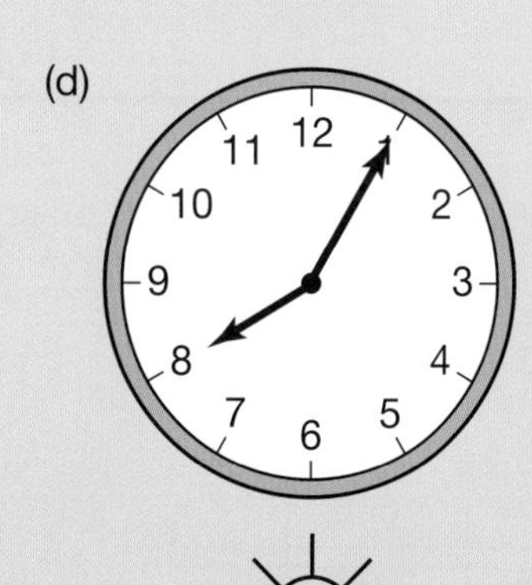

(e)

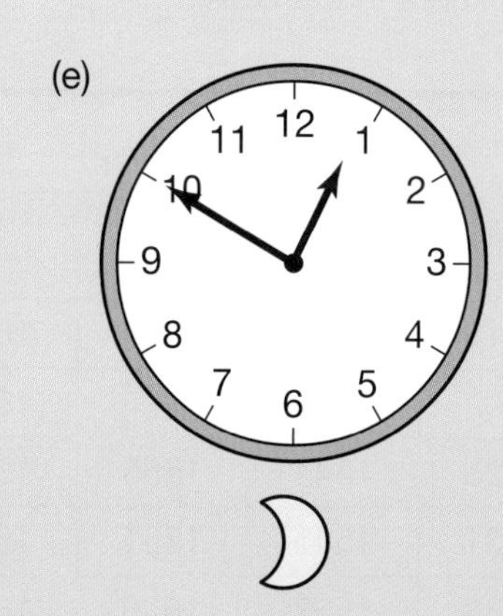

(f)

2. Sam leaves home at 0735. He arrives at work at 0825. How long does his journey take?

3. Rachel flies from Paris to Split. The flight leaves at 2020 and arrives at 2255. How long is the flight?

4. A film starts at 7.40 pm and finishes at 9.25 pm. How long is the film?

5. A train departs at 2130 and arrives at 0822. How long did the journey take?

6. A TV channel starts at 6.30 pm and finishes at 2.55 am. How long is the channel on air?

7. Look at the timetable in the worked example.
(a) How long does it take to get to Eastville from Ragby Central on the 1603 departure from Ragby Central?
(b) How much quicker is the train that leaves Ragby Central at 1548?
(c) How long is the journey from Anytown to Dawton?

Money and currency conversions

You can convert between currencies using exchange rates.

Exchange rates change and are usually published every working day.

Worked example

The exchange rate on one day between euros and Danish krone is €1 = 7.45 kr.

(a) Convert €24 to Danish krone.

(b) Convert 168 kr to euros.

Answer

(a) Multiply by the exchange rate: €24 = 24 × 7.45 = 178.80 kr

(b) Divide by the exchange rate: 168 kr = 168 ÷ 7.45 = €22.55

Test yourself

1. The exchange rate on one day between the US dollar and the Mexican peso is US$1 = MXN$12.82.

(a) Convert US$45 to Mexican pesos.

(b) Convert MXN$300 to US dollars.

2. The exchange rate on one day between pounds sterling and Brazilian reals is £1 = R$3.42.

(a) Convert £55 to Brazilian reals.

(b) Convert R$500 to pounds.

3. The exchange rate on one day between the Australian dollar and the Singapore dollar is A$1 = S$1.14.

(a) Convert A$75 to Singapore dollars.

(b) Convert S$350 to Australian dollars.

4. The exchange rate on one day between the Malaysian ringgit and the Sri Lankan rupee is MYR1 = Lkr41.20.

(a) A flight costs MYR235.99. What is this in Sri Lankan rupees?

(b) A meal costs Lkr525. What is this in Malaysian ringgits?

5. The exchange rate on one day between the Hong Kong dollar and the Indian rupee is HK$1 = ₹7.72.

(a) A pair of trainers cost HK$599.99. What is this in Indian rupees?

(b) A train ticket costs ₹245. What is this in Hong Kong dollars?

6. The exchange rate on one day between the Chinese renminbi and the South African rand is RMB1 = R1.63.

(a) A bill in a restaurant is RMB156. What is this in South African rand?

(b) A flight costs R765.40. What is this in Chinese renminbi?

1.10 Electronic calculators

You should know how to use your calculator correctly so that you can do calculations efficiently and correctly. You should be able to use the brackets functions.

Use an appropriate number of decimal places. For example, if an answer is to be given to three decimal places, you should work to at least four decimal places during the calculation.

You can check that your answer is reasonable by rounding the numbers in the calculation and then working out the answer.

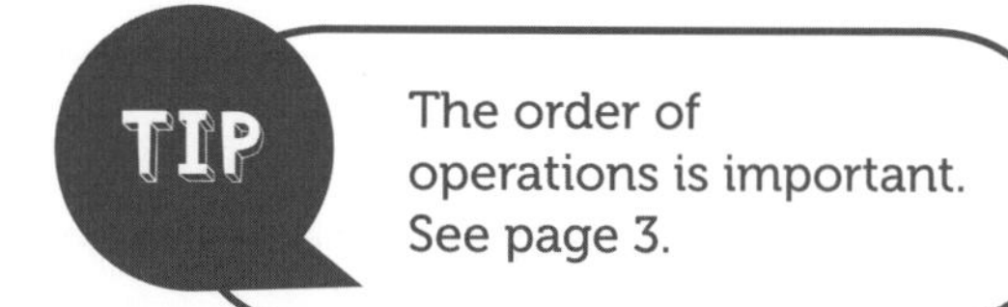

Worked example

Work out $\frac{\sqrt{13.2^2 - 5.6^2}}{0.563 \times 1.8}$. Check that your answer is sensible.

In questions like this you must write down each stage in the calculation to show that you have worked out each stage correctly, otherwise you may not get all of the marks available. Remember that there are usually marks available for showing your working.

Answer

Write down each stage in the working:

$$\frac{\sqrt{13.2^2 - 5.6^2}}{0.563 \times 1.8} = \frac{\sqrt{174.24 - 31.36}}{0.563 \times 1.8} = \frac{\sqrt{142.88}}{0.563 \times 1.8} = \frac{11.9532}{0.563 \times 1.8} = \frac{11.9532}{1.0134} = 11.80$$

Round all of the numbers: $\frac{\sqrt{13^2 - 6^2}}{0.6 \times 2} = \frac{\sqrt{169 - 36}}{1.2} = \frac{\sqrt{133}}{1.2} \approx \frac{11.5}{1.2} \approx 10$

So the answer is sensible.

Test yourself

1. Work out the following. Check that your answers are sensible.

(a) $6.2^2 + 3.7 \times 8.2$ (b) $11.5 \times 8.3 - 9.2^2$ (c) $\frac{5.4 \times 10.2 - 25.5^2}{3.68 \times 5.1}$

(d) $\frac{0.53^2 \times 14.2^2}{7.4^2 - 32.3}$ (e) $\frac{\sqrt{15.25 + 3.85 \times 6.91}}{18.23 \times 0.46}$ (f) $\frac{\sqrt{0.85^2 - 0.23^2}}{0.93 \times 0.61}$

You should now be able to:

- ★ understand, use and order integers (see page 2)
- ★ add, subtract, multiply, divide and use brackets (see page 3)
- ★ calculate with fractions (see page 4)
- ★ calculate with decimals (see page 6)
- ★ convert recurring decimals into fractions (see page 6)
- ★ calculate with percentages (see page 7)
- ★ use reverse percentages and repeated percentage change (see page 8)
- ★ solve problems involving compound interest (see page 9)
- ★ use exponential growth and decay (see page 10)
- ★ use index laws to evaluate numerical expressions (see page 12)
- ★ evaluate highest common factors and lowest common multiples (see page 13)
- ★ use standard form (see page 14)
- EDE ★ know what surds are and be able to manipulate them (see page 15)
- ★ understand and use sets and set notation (see page 16)
- EDE ★ use sets in practical situations (see page 20)
- ★ use ratio and proportion to solve problems (see page 22)
- ★ calculate upper and lower bounds (see page 29)
- ★ carry out calculations for everyday situations (see page 33)
- ★ carry out calculations involving mass, length, area, volume, capacity, time and money (see page 33)
- ★ use a scientific calculator effectively (see page 36).

Practice questions

1. Use your calculator to find:

(a) $\dfrac{\sqrt{3.75}}{25.3-8.2}$ **(2)**

(b) $\sqrt{\dfrac{18.2+5.6}{2.3\times4.7}}$ **(2)**

2. Work out $5(6\times10^9-8\times10^7)$ giving your answer in standard form. **(2)**

3. Write down all the working to show that $\dfrac{\frac{2}{7}\times\frac{2}{5}}{\frac{2}{7}+\frac{2}{5}}=\dfrac{1}{6}$ **(3)**

4. A train leaves a station every 10 minutes starting at 0700. The last train leaves at 2100.
How many times does a train leave the station during one day? **(2)**

5. Use your calculator to find the value of the following. Give your answer to three significant figures.

(a) $5.1^1 \times 2^0$ **(1)**

(b) 5.6^{-2} **(1)**

(c) 2.7^{-3} **(1)**

When answers are not exact, remember to give your answers to the accuracy specified in the question or on the front of the exam paper.

6. The cost of making a tablet is £48 to the nearest pound. Calculate the lower and upper bounds for the cost of making 780 tablets. **(2)**

7. Hassan incorrectly wrote $1+\frac{2}{3}+\frac{1}{6}+\frac{3}{8}=1\frac{6}{17}$. Show the correct working and write down the answer as a mixed number. **(3)**

8. An aeroplane travels at 560 m.p.h. Convert this speed into metres per second.

(1 mile = 1.609 km) **(3)**

9. Find the values of p, q and r.

(a) $4^p = 0.0625$ **(2)**

(b) $2^q \times 2^{2q} = 512$ **(2)**

(c) $8^r = 0.5$ **(2)**

10. Sean spends money on rent and travel to work in the ratio 8:3. He spends $600 per month on rent. How much does he spend on travel? **(2)**

11. From the list of numbers below find:

(a) a prime number **(1)**

(b) a cube number. **(1)**

121 122 123 124 125 126 127

12. Find the value of $\left(\frac{216}{125}\right)^{-\frac{4}{3}}$. Give your answer as an exact fraction. **(2)**

13. The population of a city is 1 358 000 to the nearest thousand.

(a) Write 1 358 000 in standard form. **(1)**

(b) Write down the lower and upper bounds of the population in standard form. **(2)**

14. Tanya paid interest on a loan of £1200 at a rate of 14% compound interest per year. Calculate the total amount she has to pay back after 2 years. **(2)**

15. Show that $3^{-2}+2^{-3}=\frac{17}{72}$. Show all your working. **(3)**

16. The lowest overnight temperature in a town is recorded every day during a week in November. The temperatures, in °C, are shown below.

1 –4 –2 0 –3 0 1

Calculate the difference between the lowest and highest temperatures. **(1)**

17. Jamie works 9 hours a week in a shop. His hours are increased by 20%.
Calculate how long Jamie now works. Give your answer in hours and minutes. **(3)**

18. Sonia changes £400 into euros when the rate is £1 = €1.167. She spends €300 and changes the remaining euros back into pounds when the rate is £1 = €1.243.

Calculate the amount Sonia now has in pounds. **(3)**

19. A person loses 6% of their mass on a diet. The person's mass is now 79.9 kg.
Calculate the mass of the person before the diet. **(2)**

20. In the Venn diagram, $\mathscr{E}$ = {students in a class}, F = {students studying French}, G = {students studying German}.

$n(\mathscr{E}) = 25$, $n(F \cap G) = 8$, $n(F) = 12$, $n(G) = 14$

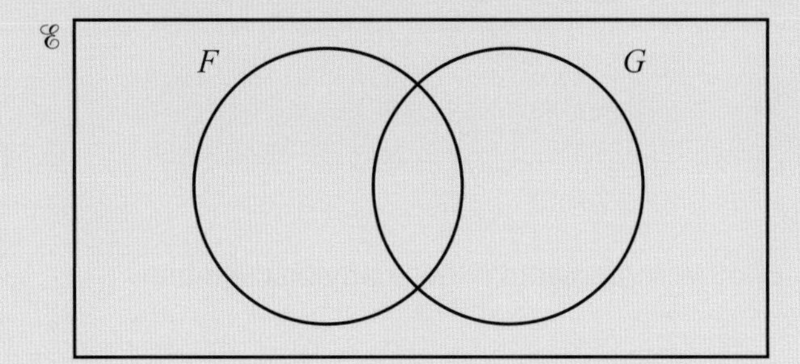

Find:

(a) $n(F \cup G)$ **(1)**

(b) $n(F \cap G)$ **(1)**

(c) $n(F \cap G)'$ **(1)**

21. Farid and Ryan bought a van for their business for £11 000. Ryan paid 35% and Farid paid the rest.

(a) (i) How much did Farid pay towards the cost of the van? **(2)**

(ii) Write down the ratio of payments Farid : Ryan in its simplest form. **(1)**

(b) In the first year it cost £2450 to run the van. Farid, Ryan and Sunni shared the cost in the ratio 7 : 5 : 2. Calculate the amount each person paid to run the van. **(3)**

(c) (i) The van loses 21% of its value each year. Calculate the value of the van after three years. **(2)**

(ii) Calculate the overall percentage loss of the van's value after three years. **(2)**

(iii) What is Farid's share in the van now worth? **(1)**

22. $48 = 2 \times 2 \times 2 \times 2 \times 3$ as a product of prime factors.

(a) Write the number 208 as a product of prime factors. **(2)**

(b) Find the value of the highest common factor of 48 and 208. **(1)**

(c) Find the value of the lowest common multiple of 48 and 208. **(1)**

23. A group of students go on a school trip by train.

(a) Jess buys tickets for adults and students.
Student tickets cost £7.50. Jess buys 44 student tickets and receives a discount of 15%.
How much does she spend on student tickets? **(2)**

(b) Jess spends £59.28 on adult tickets after a discount of 22%. Calculate the original price of the adult tickets. **(2)**

(c) The ratio of students : adults is 11 : 2. Calculate the number of adults. **(2)**

(d) The train travels a distance of 150 km, leaving at 0838 and arriving at 1008.
Calculate the average speed of the train in km/h. **(3)**

24. Nia has a recipe which makes 20 biscuits. The ingredients are:

140 g flour
100 g sugar
140 g ground almonds
200 g butter

(a) She only has 250 g of butter but plenty of other ingredients. How many biscuits can she make? **(2)**

(b) How many grams of ground almonds does she need to make this number of biscuits? **(2)**

25. (a) Use your calculator to work out the value of $\frac{36.9}{54.2-28.3}+1.8^2$. Write down all the figures on your calculator display. **(2)**

(b) Give your answer correct to three significant figures. **(1)**

26. Show that $\frac{8}{9}-\frac{5}{6}=\frac{1}{18}$. Show all stages in your working. **(2)**

27. The perimeter of a triangle is 110 cm.
The lengths of the sides of the triangle are in the ratio 6 : 3 : 2. Work out the length of the longest side of the triangle. **(2)**

28. $\mathscr{E}=\{5, 6, 7, 8, 9, 10, 11, 12, 13, 14, 15\}$
$A=\{\text{multiples of 3}\}$, $B=\{\text{multiples of 5}\}$
List the members of the set:

(a) $A \cap B$ **(1)**

(b) $A \cup B$ **(1)**

29. Ellen invested £7000 for 4 years at 3% per annum compound interest. Calculate the value of the investment at the end of 4 years. **(3)**

30. In 2012, the population of Ethiopia was 86 613 986. The number of people who spoke Amharic as their first language was 28 322 773.

(a) Express the proportion of people who spoke Amharic as their first language as a percentage of the population of Ethiopia. Give your answer correct to 1 decimal place. **(2)**

(b) Between 2010 and 2012 the population increased by 5.5%. What was the population in 2010? Give your answer to the nearest thousand. **(3)**

31. $A = \{3, 5, 7, 9, 11\}$

$A \cap B = \{7, 9\}$, $A \cup B = \{3, 5, 7, 8, 9, 10, 11\}$

List the members of set B. **(2)**

32. Show that the recurring decimal $0.5\dot{7}$ is $\frac{26}{45}$. **(2)**

33. The wingspan of an aeroplane is 64.8 m. The ratio of the wingspan to the length is 7 : 8.

(a) Work out the length of the aeroplane **(2)**

(b) A model is made of the aeroplane. The model is 37 cm long. Find the ratio of the length of the model to the length of the aeroplane. Give your ratio in the form $1 : n$. **(3)**

34. The population of Tanzania increased by 33.5% between 1990 and 2000 and by 31.7% between 2000 and 2010. Calculate the percentage increase between 1990 and 2010. **(3)**

35. In a sale, normal prices are reduced by 35%. The normal price of a shirt was £19.99. Work out the sale price. **(2)**

36. The length of Megan's journey home from a friend's house is 90 km. The journey takes 1 hour and 15 minutes. What is her average speed in km/h? **(3)**

37. Sasha borrows £120 from a short-term moneylender for 15 days. There is a £5 fee for transferring the money and the interest rate is 1% simple interest per day.

(a) How much does Sasha have to repay at the end of 15 days? **(2)**

(b) Express the cost as a percentage of the amount Sasha borrowed. **(2)**

38. Express $\sqrt{140} + \sqrt{35}$ in the form $k\sqrt{5}$ where k is a surd. **(3)**

Section Two

2 Algebra

You will be expected to:

- work with algebraic expressions and fractions
- solve linear, simultaneous and quadratic equations and inequalities
- draw linear, quadratic, cubic and reciprocal functions, distance–time, speed–time and conversion graphs
- know the equation of a straight line and how to calculate gradient, midpoint and length of a line segment
- be able find the nth term of a sequence
- use function notation.

2.1 Use of symbols and indices

Using letters

You can use a letter to represent variables in formulae, equations and expressions.

A variable is a quantity that can take any value.

An expression is a combination of letters and numbers.

An equation is an expression that also has an equals sign.

A formula is a special kind of equation that is used to work out quantities such as the area of a rectangle.

Test yourself

1. For each of the following questions, write down an algebraic expression.

(a) Milly has 4 bags of marbles. Each bag contains n marbles. How many marbles does she have altogether?

(b) She gets 5 more marbles. How many does she have now?

(c) She takes 3 marbles out of each bag. How many marbles are in each bag?

2. Sadie goes shopping with $\$M$ and spends $\$N$. How much money does she have left?

3. Michelle is x years old. Josie is 3 years older than Michelle. Maria is twice Michelle's age. Alice is 5 years younger than Michelle.
Write down expressions for Josie's, Maria's and Alice's ages.

4. Five pens cost £P. What is the cost of one pen?

5. Tom is t years old. Owen is half Tom's age.

(a) Write down an expression for Owen's age.

(b) Write down an expression for Owen's age in 4 years' time.

6. A square has side length $3a$. Write down an expression for the perimeter of the square.

Using indices

You should know the index laws given in section 1.5, page 11.

Any number to the power 1 is the number itself.

Any number to the power 0 is 1.

Worked example

1. (a) Write $\frac{5}{x^4}$ in index form. (b) Write $3x^{-2}$ in fraction form.

2. Simplify these expressions.

   (a) $5p^3 \times 3p^{-2}$ (b) $6q^3 \div 2q^{-2}$ (c) $(2r^2)^3$

Answer

1. (a) $5x^{-4}$ (b) $\frac{3}{x^2}$

2. (a) The terms are being multiplied so multiply the coefficients and add the indices.

   $5 \times 3 \times p^{3+-2} = 15p$

   (b) The first term is being divided by the second one, so divide the first coefficient by the second coefficient, and subtract the index in the second term from the index in the first term.

   $(6 \div 2) \times q^{3--2} = 3q^5$

   (c) The term inside the brackets is being cubed, so cube the coefficient and multiply the indices together.

   $2^3 \times r^{2 \times 3} = 8r^6$

Test yourself

1. Write the following in fraction form.

(a) $4x^{-2}$ (b) $7p^{-5}$ (c) $8y^{-3}$

2. Write the following in index form.

(a) $\frac{5}{m^6}$ (b) $\frac{2}{y^4}$ (c) $\frac{9}{x}$

3. Simplify these expressions.

(a) $4a^5 \times 5a^2$ (b) $(3a^3)^2$ (c) $-3a^4 \times -2a^{-7}$

(d) $6a^6 \div 3a^2$ (e) $30a^5 \div 5a^{-2}$ (f) $15a^{-2} \div 5a^{-3}$

(g) $2a^3b^4 \times 5a^2b^5$ (h) $4a^2b^3 \times 3a^{-1}b^{-2}$ (i) $5a^{-5}b^3 \times 6a^5b^{-5}$

(j) $9a^2b^7 \div 3ab^5$ (k) $12a^5b^{-3} \div 3a^{-2}b^{-5}$ (l) $18a^{-7}b^{-2} \div 6a^2b^{-3}$

(m) $\frac{2a^2b^3c \times 6abc^2}{4a^2bc}$ (n) $\frac{3a^3b^2c^5 \times 6a^{-2}b^3c^{-1}}{2abc^3}$ (o) $\frac{3a^3b^5 \times 4a^3c^2 \times 2b^3c^4}{2a^2b^{-2}c^{-2} \times 5a^3b^5c^4}$

Fractional indices

An expression with an index of the form $\frac{1}{n}$ is the same as the nth root of the term, $\sqrt[n]{}$.

An expression of the form $\left(\frac{a}{b}\right)^{-n}$ is the same as an expression of the form $\left(\frac{b}{a}\right)^{n}$, that is invert the expression and change the sign of the index.

Worked example

1. Solve $32^x=\frac{1}{2}$
2. Simplify $\frac{2}{5}x^{\frac{1}{2}}\div 2x^{-2}$

Answer

1. $32=2^5$, so $32^{\frac{1}{5}}=2$, $32^{-\frac{1}{5}}=\frac{1}{2}$ and $x=-\frac{1}{5}$
2. Subtract the second index from the first index: $\frac{1}{2}--2=\frac{5}{2}$

   Divide the first coefficient by the second coefficient: $\frac{2}{5}\div 2=\frac{1}{5}$

   So $\frac{2}{5}x^{\frac{1}{2}}\div 2x^{-2}=\frac{1}{5}x^{\frac{5}{2}}$

Test yourself

1. Solve:

(a) $216^x=\frac{1}{6}$ (b) $25^x=\frac{1}{125}$ (c) $144^x=\frac{1}{12}$

(d) $4^x=\frac{1}{32}$ (e) $81^x=\frac{1}{27}$ (f) $121^x=\frac{1}{11}$

2. Simplify the following.

(a) $3x^{-5}\times\frac{2}{3}x^{\frac{3}{2}}$ (b) $\left(\frac{5d^{\frac{5}{2}}}{2}\right)^2$ (c) $2x^{\frac{5}{2}}\times 3x^{-2}$

(d) $\left(2y^{\frac{1}{2}}\right)^4$ (e) $5x^{\frac{3}{2}}\times 2x^{-3}$ (f) $4y^{\frac{5}{2}}\times 3y^{-\frac{7}{2}}\times 2y^{\frac{9}{2}}$

2.2 Algebraic manipulation

Simplifying expressions

You can simplify expressions by multiplying them out and then collecting like terms.

Worked example

Simplify the following.

(a) $3mt \times 6t$ (b) $3m \times 2n + 4m \times m + 3m \times 2m - 5m \times 2n$

Answer

(a) Multiply the coefficients.
Add the indices of the letters together.

$3 \times 6 \times m \times t \times t = 18mt^2$

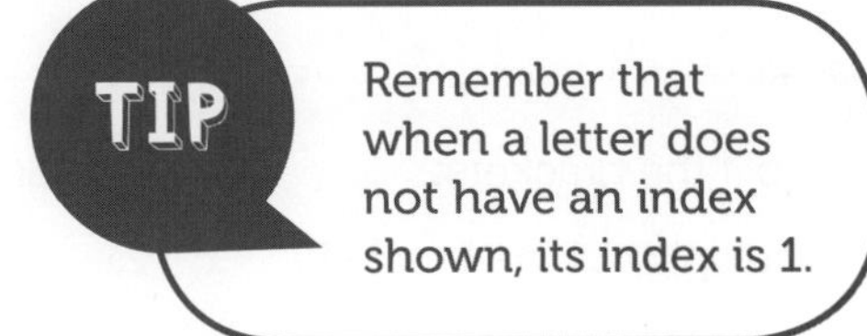

(b) $3 \times 2 \times m \times n + 4 \times m \times m + 3 \times 2 \times m \times m - 5 \times 2 \times m \times n$

$= 6mn + 4m^2 + 6m^2 - 10mn$

$6mn$ and $-10mn$ are like terms in mn.

$4m^2$ and $6m^2$ are like terms in m^2.

So the simplified expression is $-4mn + 10m^2$

Test yourself

1. Simplify the following.

(a) $6xy \times 3y$

(b) $4pq \times 2p^2q$

(c) $-2qr \times 3q^2r$

(d) $-3x^2y \times -3xy^2$

(e) $3m^2t \times 4mt$

(f) $2x^2 \times 3xy \times 2y$

(g) $2y \times 3x + 4y^2 \times 3x + 5x \times 4y$

(h) $2p^2q^2 \times 5p - 3pq^2 \times 6p + 2p^2 \times 2q^2$

(i) $-2qr^2 \times 3q + 6q^2r \times 3qr + 5r \times 2q^2r$

(j) $3xy \times 2x + 4xy \times y + 4y \times 2xy - 5xy \times 3x$

(k) $4pq^2 \times 2 + 3p \times 2q^2 + 2pq \times 4q + 6p^2 \times 2q$

Brackets

When expanding an expression with single brackets, multiply each term inside the brackets by the term outside the brackets.

When there are two brackets (one group of terms in brackets is multiplied by another group of terms in brackets), there are three methods of expanding the brackets:

- split the brackets – split the terms in the first brackets and multiply each term by the terms in the second brackets
- use FOIL – this is the order that you multiply the terms in (first terms, outer terms, inner terms, last terms)
- use the box method, which is similar to the box method used for long multiplication.

You should choose the method which suits you best.

When squaring terms in brackets, write down the terms in brackets twice and expand the brackets.

An expression where the highest power of any term is 2 is called a quadratic expression.

Worked example

1. Expand $(x-3)(x+2)$
2. Expand $(x+5)(x+4)$
3. Expand $(2x-3)^2$

Answer

1. Split the brackets: $x(x+2)-3(x+2)$

   Multiply out the brackets: $x^2+2x-3x-6$

   Collect like terms x^2-x-6

2. Using FOIL:

   Multiply the first terms: $x \times x = x^2$

   Multiply the outer terms: $x \times 4 = 4x$

   Multiply the inner terms: $5 \times x = 5x$

   Multiply the last terms: $5 \times 4 = 20$

   So $(x+5)(x+4) = x^2+4x+5x+20$

   Collect like terms: $= x^2+9x+20$

3. Write down the terms in brackets twice: $(2x-3)(2x-3)$

   Using the box method:

$\times$	$2x$	-3
$2x$	$4x^2$	$-6x$
-3	$-6x$	$+9$

   So $(2x-3)^2 = 4x^2-6x-6x+9$

   Collect like terms: $= 4x^2-12x+9$

Test yourself

TIP Remember that a minus sign outside brackets applies to all terms inside the brackets.

1. Expand the brackets and simplify:

(a) $3(2+4h)+3(5+2h)$ (b) $x(3+y)+y(5-x)$
(c) $5(3k-2)-4(2k+3)$ (d) $4(5k-2)-3(3-3k)$
(e) $4p(n+3m)+5n(2p+3m)$ (f) $3x(x+5)-2x(4-2x)$

2. Expand the brackets.

(a) $(x+2)(x+7)$ (b) $(x+5)(x-3)$ (c) $(y-3)(y-7)$
(d) $(y-4)(y+3)$ (e) $(m+2)(m-2)$ (f) $(x-5)(x+5)$
(g) $(2x+1)(3x+1)$ (h) $(2x+5)(5x+3)$ (i) $(3m-2)(4m+3)$
(j) $(5n+4)(3n-5)$ (k) $(7+4x)(6-5x)$ (l) $(4-2x)(3+6x)$
(m) $(x-6)^2$ (n) $(2x+4)^2$ (o) $(5-3x)^2$

Factorisation

When factorising an expression containing two or more terms, look for the highest common factor. Expressions that do not have a common factor cannot be factorised.

Worked example

Factorise: (a) $6x-10y$ (b) $2k^2+8k$ (c) $3xy^2-3x^2y$

Answer

(a) The highest common factor is 2.

So $6x-10y=2\times3x-2\times5y=2(3x-5y)$

(b) The highest common factor is $2k$.

So $2k^2+8k=2k\times k+2k\times4=2k(k+4)$

(c) The highest common factor is $3xy$.

So $3xy^2-3x^2y=3xy\times y+3xy\times -x=3xy(y-x)$

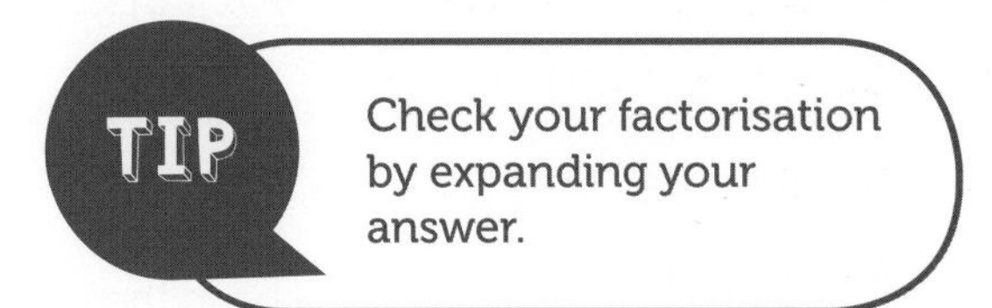

Test yourself

1. Factorise the following expressions.

(a) $xy+2x$ (b) $8p-8pq$ (c) $5mn+10n^2$

(d) $6xy-12x^2z$ (e) $3ab^2+6a^2b-9ab$ (f) $4pqr-8p^2q+16pq^2r$

Factorising quadratic expressions

Factorising a quadratic expression is the reverse of expanding the brackets.

There are patterns to look for when factorising a quadratic expression:

$x^2+ax+b=(x+p)(x+q)$ where $p+q=a$ and $pq=b$

$x^2-ax+b=(x-p)(x-q)$

x^2+ax-b or $x^2-ax-b=(x-p)(x+q)$

Where the term in x^2 has a coefficient:

$ax^2+bx+c=(mx+p)(nx+q)$ where $mn=a$ and $pq=c$.

Worked example

Factorise: (a) $x^2 - x - 12$ (b) $8x^2 - 34x + 21$

Answer

(a) The factorised expression will be in the form $(x-p)(x+q)$

So $pq = -12$ and $p+q = -1$

Look for values of p and q that give a product of –12 and a sum of –1.

Factor pairs of 12 are 1 and 12, 2 and 6, and 3 and 4.

+3 and –4 have a sum of –1 and a product of –12

So $x^2 - x - 12 = (x-4)(x+3)$

(b) The factorised expression will be in the form $(mx-p)(nx-q)$.

Look for products of m and n that will give 8.

The possible factor pairs are 1 and 8, and 2 and 4.

Look for products of p and q that will give 21. Remember that from the form of the equation, both p and q will be negative.

The possible factor pairs are –1 and –21, and –3 and –7.

Now look for combinations of these factors that add up to –34.

1	2	–1	–3
8	4	–21	–7

The combination of 2×–3 (=–6) and 4×–7 (=–28) gives –34.

So $8x^2 - 34x + 21 = (2x-7)(4x-3)$

Test yourself

1. Factorise the following.

(a) $x^2 + 11x + 24$ (b) $x^2 + 9x + 20$ (c) $x^2 + 2x - 15$

(d) $x^2 - x - 42$ (e) $x^2 - 10x + 16$ (f) $x^2 - 12x + 27$

(g) $6x^2 + 12x + 6$ (h) $10x^2 + 29x + 10$ (i) $12x^2 + 3x - 15$

(j) $10x^2 - 24x - 18$ (k) $4x^2 - 20x + 24$ (l) $15x^2 - 41x + 14$

Algebraic fractions

You can simplify and combine fractions that contain algebra using the same rules that you use to add, subtract, multiply and divide fractions.

Addition: $\frac{a}{b} + \frac{c}{d} = \frac{ad+bc}{bd}$

Subtraction: $\frac{a}{b} - \frac{c}{d} = \frac{ad-bc}{bd}$

Multiplication: $\frac{a}{b} \times \frac{c}{d} = \frac{ac}{bd}$

Division: $\frac{a}{b} \div \frac{c}{d} = \frac{a}{b} \times \frac{d}{c} = \frac{ad}{bc}$

Worked example

1. Simplify: (a) $\frac{2}{x}+\frac{2x}{3y}$ (b) $\frac{1}{x-3}\div\frac{7}{3x-9}$

2. Write $\frac{1}{x-1}-\frac{x+2}{2x+1}$ as a single fraction as simply as possible.

Answer

1. (a) $\frac{2}{x}+\frac{2x}{3y}=\frac{2\times 3y+2x\times x}{x\times 3y}=\frac{6y+2x^2}{3xy}$

(b) $\frac{1}{x-3}\div\frac{7}{3x-9}=\frac{1}{x-3}\times\frac{3x-9}{7}=\frac{3x-9}{7(x-3)}=\frac{3(x-3)}{7(x-3)}=\frac{3}{7}$

TIP Remember that you find the common denominator by multiplying the denominator of each fraction together.

2. Using the subtraction rule:

$\frac{1}{x-1}-\frac{x+2}{2x+1}=\frac{1(2x+1)-(x-1)(x+2)}{(x-1)(2x+1)}$

TIP You don't need to expand the brackets in the denominator.

Simplify: $=\frac{2x+1-(x^2-x+2x-2)}{(x-1)(2x+1)}=\frac{2x+1-x^2+x-2x+2}{(x-1)(2x+1)}=\frac{-x^2+x+3}{(x-1)(2x+1)}$

Test yourself

1. Simplify each of these.

(a) $\frac{2x-3}{3}-\frac{x}{7}$ (b) $\frac{2x}{3}-\frac{3(x-5)}{2}$ (c) $\frac{2(3x-3)}{5}-\frac{10(x+2)}{3}$

(d) $\frac{5x}{3}+\frac{5}{3x+1}$ (e) $\frac{4}{x+1}+\frac{5}{x-1}$ (f) $\frac{x+3}{x+1}-\frac{x+2}{x-1}$

(g) $\frac{x-1}{x+1}\times\frac{2}{x-1}$ (h) $\frac{2}{y+3}\times\frac{y}{3}$ (i) $\frac{5y+2}{3}\times\frac{9}{5y-3}$

(j) $\frac{3x}{5}\div\frac{2x}{15}$ (k) $\frac{x+3}{x+1}\div\frac{3x}{x+1}$ (l) $\frac{3x}{x-2}\div\frac{x-2}{5x}$

2. Write each of the following as a single fraction as simply as possible.

(a) $\frac{1}{x-2}+\frac{2}{x+3}$ (b) $\frac{x+1}{x-1}+\frac{x+1}{x-2}$ (c) $\frac{x}{3x+4}-\frac{1}{2x+1}$

2.3 Expressions and formulae

Substituting numbers into expressions and formulae

You can create formulae in letters and symbols when they have been given in words.

You can evaluate expressions and formulae by substituting values into them.

Worked example

The area A of a rectangle is found by multiplying the length l by the height h.

(a) Write a formula for calculating the area of a rectangle.

(b) Use your formula to calculate the area of a rectangle where the length is 15 cm and the height is 3 cm.

Answer

(a) $A = lh$

(b) $A = 15\,\text{cm} \times 3\,\text{cm} = 45\,\text{cm}^2$

Test yourself

1. The area A of a square is found from the square of the length of one side.
(a) Write a formula for the area of a square.
(b) Use your formula to work out the area of a square of side:
(i) 12 cm (ii) 5.1 cm (iii) 3.7 m

2. The area of a circle A is the square of its radius multiplied by 3.14.
(a) Write a formula for the area of a circle.
(b) Use your formulae to work out the area of a circle of:
(i) radius 5 cm (ii) radius 8 mm (iii) diameter 2 m

3. Evaluate the expression $b^2 - 4ac$ when:
(a) $a=1, b=2, c=3$ (b) $a=-3, b=3, c=4$ (c) $a=5, b=-4, c=6$

4. Evaluate $2a(a - b^2 + 3c)$ when:
(a) $a=2, b=3, c=1$ (b) $a=3, b=5, c=3$ (c) $a=4, b=4, c=7$

5. Evaluate $x^2 + 3y^2$ when:
(a) $x=2, y=3$ (b) $x=3, y=-2$ (c) $x=-5, y=4$

6. Evaluate $3p(q^2 + r^2)$ when:
(a) $p=2, q=3, r=5$ (b) $p=4, q=6, r=2$ (c) $p=-3, q=-4, r=-3$

TIP When evaluating expressions, substitute the values in first before multiplying out the brackets.

Rearranging formulae

The subject of a formula is the variable (letter) that only appears once, on its own, in the formula. It is usually on the left-hand side of the equals sign.

You can make another variable in the formula the subject by rearranging the formula so that this variable is on its own on the left-hand side of the equals sign.

Do the same operation on both sides of the equals sign when rearranging the formula.

Worked example

$p=3q-2$. Make q the subject of the formula.

Make sure that you get all terms with the new subject in them on the same side of the equals sign.

Answer

Add 2 to both sides: $p+2=3q-2+2$

$p+2=3q$

Divide both sides by 3: $\frac{p+2}{3}=q$

Reverse the formula so that q is on the left-hand side:

$$q=\frac{p+2}{3}$$

Test yourself

1. Rearrange the following formulae to make p the subject.

(a) $T=\frac{p}{3}+4$ (b) $A=\frac{p}{v}$ (c) $C=4p+5q$

(d) $m=p^2+4$ (e) $C=5p+q^2$ (f) $k=4p^2$

Rearranging more complex formulae

Sometimes the variable that you want to make the subject appears more than once in the formula.

Collect the terms with this variable on one side of the equals sign, factorise this side of the formula (take out the variable as a common factor) and divide both sides by the terms in the brackets.

Worked example

Make m the subject of the formula $mn=np-mp$.

Answer

First get both of the terms containing m on one side of the equals sign.

Add mp to both sides of the formula: $mn+mp=np$

Factorise the left-hand side: $m(n+p)=np$

Divide both sides by $n+p$: $\frac{m(n+p)}{n+p}=\frac{np}{n+p}$

So $m=\frac{np}{n+p}$

Test yourself

1. Rearrange the following formulae to make m the subject.

(a) $T-mt=mR^2$ (b) $B=mpq-2+4ms$ (c) $2m^2=m^2p+2p$

(d) $Rm+1=\sqrt{\frac{m^2}{c}}$ (e) $c=\sqrt{\frac{m}{m+3}}$ (f) $mA^2=mC-mt+1$

Make sure you show all stages in the rearrangement of the formula to make it clear to the examiners what you are doing. When squaring a formula to remove a square root sign, remember to square everything outside the square root sign.

2.4 Linear equations

Linear equations

A linear equation has only one variable and the index of the variable is 1.

You can solve a linear equation to find the value of the variable that satisfies the equation, that is makes it true.

To solve an equation, get all the terms with the variable in it on one side of the equals sign and all of the terms that are just numbers on the other side of the equals sign. When doing this, do the same operation to both sides of the equation.

Worked example

1. Solve $3(x-3)=x+11$
2. Solve $\frac{7-x}{3}=4$
3. Solve $\frac{3}{4}x+2=11$

Answer

1. Multiply out the brackets: $3x-9=x+11$
   Subtract x from both sides: $3x-x-9=x-x+11$
   $2x-9=11$
   Add 9 to both sides: $2x-9+9=11+9$
   $2x=20$
   Divide both sides by 2: $x=10$
2. Multiply both sides by 3: $7-x=12$
   Subtract 7 from both sides: $-x=5$
   Multiply both sides by –1: $x=-5$
3. Subtract 2 from both sides: $\frac{3}{4}x=9$
   Multiply both sides by 4: $3x=36$
   Divide both sides by 3: $x=12$

Test yourself

1. Solve:

(a) $4x+5=29$ (b) $2x-3=15$ (c) $7x+25=4$

(d) $\frac{2}{5}x=24$ (e) $\frac{2x+3}{5}=5$ (f) $\frac{25-3x}{8}=2$

(g) $2x-7=x+5$ (h) $2(2x-5)=3(x-4)$ (i) $3(2x+7)=2(3+4x)-3x$

(j) $\frac{x+8}{3}=2x+1$ (k) $\frac{3(x+1)}{9}=\frac{x-1}{2}$ (l) $\frac{2}{3}x+5=\frac{3}{4}x+4$

Solving problems with equations

You can set up equations to solve problems.

Worked example

The length of a rectangle is 4 cm longer than its width. The perimeter of the rectangle is 30 cm. Set up an equation for the perimeter of the rectangle and solve it to find the dimensions of the rectangle.

Answer

Let width of rectangle $= x$ cm

So length of rectangle $= (x+4)$ cm

Perimeter $= 2\times$ length $+ 2\times$ width

$$30=2\times x+2\times(x+4)$$
$$30=2x+2x+8$$
$$30=4x+8$$

Solve the equation for x:

$$30-8=4x+8-8$$
$$22=4x$$
$$x=22\div4=5.5\text{ cm}$$

So the dimensions of the rectangle are: width 5.5 cm and length $5.5+4=9.5$ cm

TIP You may find it helpful to draw a diagram showing the rectangle and label the sides.

Test yourself

1. Sam bought six garden chairs and a table. The total cost was £185.
   The table cost £45 more than a chair.
   What is the cost of a chair and the cost of a table?

2. The angles in a triangle are $x°$, $(2x+15)°$ and $(3x-45)°$. What are the sizes of the three angles?

3. A girl is y years old. Her mother is twice her age plus 11 years. Her grandmother is 6 times her age less 10 years. Their combined age is 109 years. What are the ages of the three people?

4. The side of a square is $(5x-4)$ cm long. The perimeter of the square is $(16x+4)$ cm.
   Find the length of the side of the square and its perimeter.

5. Jan buys six bottles of water and a bottle of fruit cordial. The fruit cordial cost £1.75. The total cost was £4.09. What was the cost of a bottle of water?

6. A type of carpet costs £14.99 per square metre and £50 for fitting it. The total cost was £259.86. How many square metres of carpet were used?

2.5 Proportion and variation

Direct variation and direct proportion

Direct variation and direct proportion mean the same thing.

There is direct variation between two variables when the ratio of the two variables is constant.

When two variables are proportional to each other, they are linked by an equation with a constant of proportionality, k.

The ratio can be linear (a multiple of the variable, x), or proportional to the square of the variable (x^2), the square root of the variable $\left(\sqrt{x}\right)$, or the cube of the variable (x^3).

The symbol for variation or proportion is $\propto$.

When solving problems involving proportionality:

- set up a statement using the proportionality symbol
- set up an equation using a constant of proportionality
- use the information given to find the value of the constant of proportionality
- put the constant of proportionality into the equation and use it to find other values.

Worked example

1. V is directly proportional to I. When $V=10$, $I=2$.

   (a) Find the formula connecting the variables.

   (b) Find: (i) I when $V=25$ (ii) V when $I=9$.

2. T is proportional to $\sqrt{M}$. When $M=4$, $T=20$.

   (a) Find the formula connecting the variables.

   (b) Find: (i) T when $M=64$ (ii) M when $T=5$.

Answer

1. (a) Set up the statement: $V \propto I$

   Set up the equation: $V=kI$

   Put values of V and I into the equation: $10=2k$

   Solve for k: $k=10\div 2=5$

   So $V=5I$

   (b) (i) Put $V=25$ into the equation: $25=5I$

   Solve for I: $I=25\div 5=5$

   (ii) Put $I=9$ into the equation: $V=5\times 9=45$

2. (a) Set up the statement: $T \propto \sqrt{M}$

   Set up the equation: $T=k\sqrt{M}$

   Put values of T and M into the equation: $20=k\sqrt{4}=2k$

   Solve for k: $k=20\div 2=10$

   So $T=10\sqrt{M}$

   (b) (i) Put $M=64$ into the equation: $T=10\sqrt{64}=10\times 8=80$

   (ii) Put $T=5$ into the equation: $5=10\sqrt{M}$

   $\sqrt{M}=0.5$

   Square both sides: $M=0.25$

Test yourself

1. The distance travelled by an aeroplane is directly proportional to the time taken for the journey. The aeroplane travels 1800 km in 3 hours.

(a) How long will the aeroplane take to travel 6000 km?

(b) How far will the aeroplane travel in 5.5 hours?

2. The cost of petrol for a journey is directly proportional to the distance travelled. The cost for a journey of 50 km is £4.50.

(a) What is the cost of a 375 km journey?

(b) How far can you travel for £54?

3. The change in gravitational potential energy of a box in joules is directly proportional to the change in height of the box in metres. When the change in height is 3 m, the change in gravitational potential energy is 75 J.

(a) What is the gain in energy when the box is moved 9 m upwards?

(b) What is the change in height when the change in energy is –160 J?

4. The mass in grams of a circular plate is proportional to the square of the diameter in centimetres. A 20 cm diameter plate has a mass of 150 g.

(a) What is the mass of a 28 cm plate?

(b) What is the diameter of a plate that has a mass of 200 g?

5. P is proportional to the square of Q. When $P=48$, $Q=4$.

(a) Find Q when $P=243$. (b) Find P when $Q=5$.

6. The energy of an object in joules varies directly with the square of the object's speed in m/s. The object has 2000 J of energy when moving at 20 m/s.

(a) Find the energy of the object when it is moving at 45 m/s.

(b) Find the speed of the object when it has 720 J of energy.

7. The volume of a ball V is proportional to the cube of its radius r. When $V=288\text{ cm}^3$, $r=4\text{ cm}$.

(a) Find r when $V=972\text{ cm}^3$. (b) Find V when $r=5\text{ cm}$.

8. y is proportional to the cube of x. When $x=3$, $y=270$.

(a) Find x when $y=17280$. (b) Find y when $x=6$.

9. The mass in g of a solid rubber ball varies directly with the cube of its radius in cm. A ball of radius 3 cm has a mass of 135 g.

(a) Find the mass of a ball of radius 2.5 cm.

(b) Find the radius of a ball of mass 320 g.

10. The time period of a pendulum (time taken to complete one swing), in seconds, is proportional to the square root of the length of the pendulum in cm.
A pendulum of length 25 cm has a period of 1 second.

(a) Calculate the time period of a pendulum that is 16 cm long.

(b) Calculate the length of a pendulum that has a time period of 2 seconds.

11. v is proportional to the square root of w. When $w=25$, $v=7.5$

(a) Find v when $w=49$. (b) Find w when $v=9$.

12. g is proportional to the square root of h. When $h=64$, $g=2.4$.

(a) Find g when $h=121$. (b) Find h when $g=1.8$.

Inverse variation and inverse proportion

Inverse variation and inverse proportion mean the same thing.

There is inverse variation between two variables when one variable decreases as the other variable increases. The first variable changes as the reciprocal of the second variable. The product of the two variables is a constant, the constant of proportionality, k.

The variation can be proportional to the reciprocal of the variable $\left(\frac{1}{x}\right)$ or the reciprocal of the square of the variable $\left(\frac{1}{x^2}\right)$.

The variation can also be proportional to the reciprocal of the square root of the variable $\left(\frac{1}{\sqrt{x}}\right)$.

You can solve problems involving inverse variation in the same way as solving problems involving direct variation.

Worked example

F is proportional to $\frac{1}{x^2}$. When $x=3$, $F=4$.

(a) Find the formula connecting the variables.

(b) Find (i) F when $x=5$ (ii) x when $F=0.36$.

Answer

(a) Set up the statement: $F \propto \frac{1}{x^2}$

Set up the equation: $F=\frac{k}{x^2}$

Put values of F and x into the equation: $4=\frac{k}{9}$

Solve for k: $k=4\times9=36$

So $F=\frac{36}{x^2}$

(b) (i) Put $x=5$ into the equation: $F=\frac{36}{5^2}=\frac{36}{25}=1\frac{11}{25}$ or 1.44

(ii) Put $F=0.36$ into the equation: $0.36=\frac{36}{x^2}$

Solve for x: $x^2=\frac{36}{0.36}=100$

So $x=\sqrt{100}=\pm10$

Test yourself

1. y is inversely proportional to x. When $y=0.5$, $x=8$.
   (a) Calculate y when $x=10$.
   (b) Calculate x when $y=\frac{1}{3}$.

2. p is inversely proportional to q. When $p=5$, $q=5$.
   (a) Calculate p when $q=4$.
   (b) Calculate q when $p=2.5$.

3. n is inversely proportional to m. When $n=0.01$, $m=10$.
   (a) Calculate n when $m=0.2$.
   (b) Calculate m when $n=0.25$.

4. p is inversely proportional to the square of q. When $q=2$, $p=3.75$.
   (a) Calculate p when $q=8$.
   (b) Calculate q when $p=0.9375$.

5. y is inversely proportional to the square of x. When $y=4$, $x=5$.
   (a) Calculate x when $y=1$.
   (b) Calculate y when $x=12$.

6. n is inversely proportional to the square of m. When $m=5$, $n=0.01$.
   (a) Calculate m when $n=0.0025$.
   (b) Calculate n when $m=8$.

2.6 Quadratic equations

Solving quadratic equations by factorisation

A quadratic equation is in the form $ax^2+bx+c=0$ where a, b and c are integers.

You can solve a quadratic equation by factorising it:

- first rearrange the equation so that it is in the form given above, if it is not already in this form
- factorise the equation (see section 2.2)
- when you have factorised it, the value of one of the brackets must be zero, so set the terms in each pair of brackets equal to zero in turn to find the two values of x.

When $a=0$, the equation is no longer a quadratic equation.

When $b=0$, to solve the equation, rearrange it in the form $ax^2=-c$ and take square roots on both sides.

Worked example

Solve the equations: (a) $3x^2-4x=4$ (b) $9x^2-16=0$

Answer

(a) First, rearrange the equation so that it is in the general form: $3x^2-4x-4=0$

Factorise the equation: $(3x+2)(x-2)=0$

Set the terms in each pair of brackets to zero and solve:

$3x+2=0$ $x-2=0$
$3x=-2$ $x=2$
$x=-\frac{2}{3}$

(b) Rearrange the equation in the form $ax^2=-c$: $9x^2=16$

Divide both sides by 9: $x^2=\frac{16}{9}$

Take square roots on both sides: $x=\sqrt{\frac{16}{9}}=\pm\frac{4}{3}$

TIP

Leave any solutions that are not integers as fractions.

Test yourself

1. Solve the following equations by factorisation.
(a) $4x^2=3x$ (b) $x^2+6x+8=0$ (c) $x^2+x-30=0$
(d) $3x^2+2x-5=0$ (e) $6x^2-3x=30$ (f) $8x^2-6x=9$

Solving quadratic equations using the formula

Sometimes you cannot solve quadratic equations by factorisation. In these cases, you can use the quadratic formula to solve quadratic equations in the form $ax^2+bx+c=0$ that have solutions that are real numbers.

The solutions to the equation are given by $x=\frac{-b\pm\sqrt{b^2-4ac}}{2a}$.

Worked example

Solve the quadratic equation $3x^2-3x=5$. Give your answers correct to 2 decimal places.

Answer

First rearrange the equation in the form $ax^2+bx+c=0$: $3x^2-3x-5=0$

Use the quadratic formula: $a=3$, $b=-3$, $c=-5$

$$x=\frac{--3\pm\sqrt{(-3)^2-4\times3\times-5}}{2\times3}$$

$$x=\frac{3\pm\sqrt{9+60}}{6}$$

$$x=\frac{3\pm\sqrt{69}}{6}==\frac{3\pm8.307}{6}=\frac{11.307}{6}\text{or}-\frac{5.307}{6}=1.88\text{ or }-0.88$$

Test yourself

1. Solve the following equations using the quadratic formula. Give your answers correct to 2 decimal places.
   (a) $3x^2+6x+2=0$ (b) $4x^2-7x+1=0$
   (c) $4x^2+5x-6=0$ (d) $3x^2-6x=8$
   (e) $6x^2-9x=-2$ (f) $4x^2=8+6x$

TIP

Often the factorisation in an exam question will be simple and not require you to use the formula. Try factorising the equation before using the formula.

If the question asks you to give your answer correct to 2 decimal places, this is a hint that you will need to use the quadratic formula.

Solving quadratic equations by completing the square

You can also solve quadratic equations by completing the square.

The expansion $(x+p)^2=x^2+2px+p^2$

This can be rearranged to give $(x+p)^2-p^2=x^2+2px$ and you can use this to solve quadratic equations.

To solve quadratic equations this way:

- look at the coefficients a and b: divide the whole equation by a and rewrite $x^2+\frac{b}{a}x$ as $\left(x+\frac{b}{2a}\right)^2-\left(\frac{b}{2a}\right)^2$
- substitute for $x^2+\frac{b}{a}x$ in the equation
- set $\left(x+\frac{b}{2a}\right)^2=c-\left(\frac{b}{2a}\right)^2$
- take square roots and work out the values of x.

Worked example

Solve the equation $2x^2+8x+3=0$ by completing the square. Give your answer to 2 decimal places.

EDE Give your answer as a surd.

Answer

Divide by a (= 2): $x^2+4x+\frac{3}{2}$

Rewrite in the form $\left(x+\frac{b}{2a}\right)^2-\left(\frac{b}{2a}\right)^2$: $x^2+4x=(x+2)^2-4$

Substitute into the original equation: $(x+2)^2-4+\frac{3}{2}=0$

$$(x+2)^2=4-\frac{3}{2}$$

$$(x+2)^2=\frac{5}{2}$$

Take square roots: $x+2=\pm\sqrt{\frac{5}{2}}$

So $x=-0.42$ or -3.58

EDE $x=-2+\sqrt{\frac{5}{2}}$ or $-2-\sqrt{\frac{5}{2}}$

TIP

Remember to give your answer in the form asked for in the question.

Test yourself

1. Solve the following equations by completing the square, giving your answers to 2 d.p.
   (a) $x^2-8x+2=0$ (b) $x^2+10x+8=0$ (c) $2x^2-14x+9=0$

EDE

2. Solve the following equations by completing the square, giving your answers as surds.
   (a) $x^2+6x+3=0$ (b) $x^2-12x+7=0$ (c) $2x^2+9x-4=0$

   The area of a rectangle is $45\,cm^2$. One side is 4 cm longer than the other side. Set up and solve a quadratic equation to find the dimensions of the rectangle.

2.7 Simultaneous linear equations

Solving simultaneous equations

Simultaneous equations are two or more equations that have a unique solution. Simultaneous equations normally have two variables.

There are two methods of solving simultaneous equations – the elimination method and the substitution method.

In the substitution method, make one of the variables in one of the equations the subject of the equation. Then substitute this equation into the other equation and solve for the remaining variable.

In the elimination method:

- make the coefficients of one of the variables in both equations the same by multiplying the whole equation by an integer
- add the two equations together or subtract one equation from the other to eliminate this variable. Solve this equation for the remaining variable.

In both methods, once you have found the value of one of the variables, substitute this value into one of the original equations to find the value of the other variable.

Then substitute both values into the other equation to check your answer.

You can use the method you find easiest.

Worked example

Solve the following pairs of simultaneous equations.

(a) $3x+2y=20$; $4x-y=23$ (b) $5x+2y=20$, $4x-3y=-7$

TIP

Number the equations and write down what you are doing to make it clear to the examiner.

Answer

(a) Using the substitution method:

Number the equations:

$$3x+2y=20 \quad (1)$$
$$4x-y=23 \quad (2)$$

Use (2). Make y the subject of the equation: $-y=23-4x$

So $y=4x-23$

Substitute into (1): $3x+2(4x-23)=20$

Solve for x: $3x+8x-46=20$

$11x=66$

$x=6$

Substitute the value of x into (1): $3\times6+2y=20$

$18+2y=20$

$2y=2$

$y=1$

Check the answers by substituting both values into (2): $4\times6-1=24-1=23$ ✓

(b) Using the elimination method:

Number the equations:

$$5x+2y=20 \quad (1)$$
$$4x-3y=-7 \quad (2)$$

Multiply (1) by 3 and (2) by 2:

$$15x+6y=60 \quad (3)$$
$$8x-6y=-14 \quad (4)$$

Add (3) and (4) to eliminate y: $15x+8x+6y-6y=60+-14$

Solve for x: $23x=46$

$x=2$

Substitute the value of x into (1): $5\times2+2y=20$

$2y=20-10$

Solve for y: $2y=10$

$y=5$

Check the answers by substituting both values into (2): $4\times2-3\times5=8-15=-7$ ✓

Test yourself

1. Solve the following pairs of simultaneous equations using the substitution method.

(a) $3x-y=10$, $2x+y=5$ (b) $4x-5y=-22$, $2x+6y=40$

2. Solve the following pairs of simultaneous equations using the elimination method.

(a) $3x+2y=8$, $3y-2x=25$ (b) $2x-4y=38$, $3x+5y=-31$

(c) $5x+3y=47$, $2x+4y=30$ (d) $6y-3x=-21$, $4x-4y=8$

Simultaneous equations and graphs

Simultaneous equations can also be shown as lines on a graph. The solution of two simultaneous equations is the point where the two lines intercept (cross each other).

If the lines do not intercept, they are not simultaneous equations as there is no solution.

Worked example

Solve these simultaneous equations by drawing their graphs for $-2 \leqslant x \leqslant 4$.

$y=x^2$ and $y-x=4$

Answer

Find the coordinates of some points on each graph:

x	−2	0	2	4
$y=x^2$	4	0	4	16
$y=x+\mathbf{4}$	2	4	6	8

Draw the graphs on the same axes, $-2 \leqslant x \leqslant 4$, and $0 \leqslant y \leqslant 16$.

The graphs intercept twice, so there are two solutions: when $x=-1.6$ and $x=2.6$.
The solutions are (−1.6, 2.5) and (2.6, 6.7).

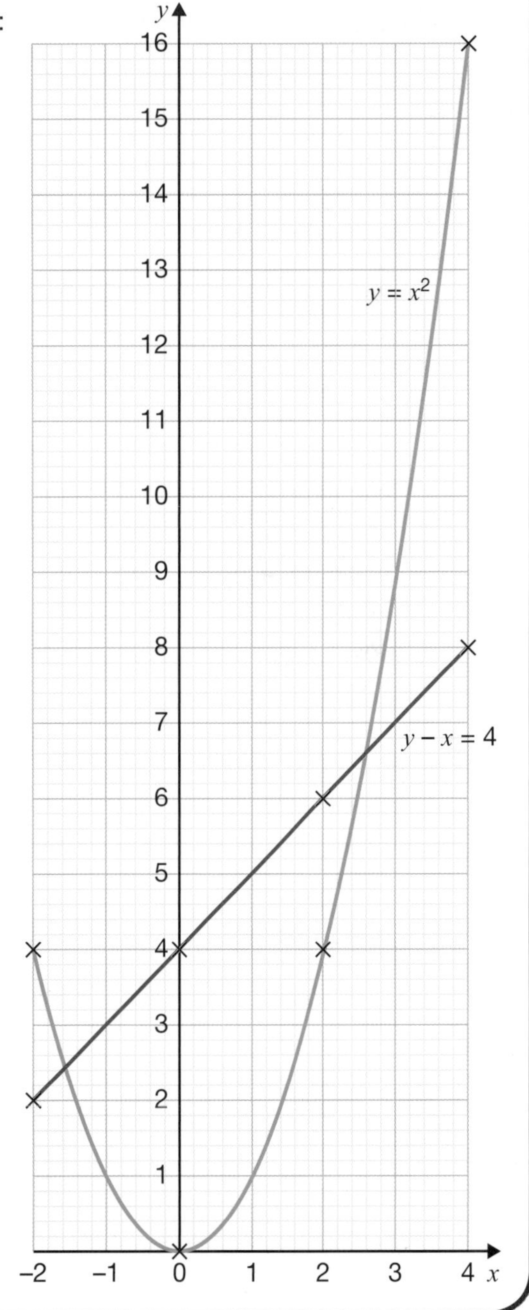

Test yourself

1. Solve the following simultaneous equations by drawing graphs.

   (Hint: one of the pairs of equations does not have a solution.)

   (a) $y=3x+3$, $y=2x+1$, $-4 \leqslant x \leqslant 0$
   (b) $y=4-x$, $y=3x-2$, $0 \leqslant x \leqslant 4$
   (c) $x+2y=6$, $2x-y=-4$, $-2 \leqslant x \leqslant 6$
   (d) $4y-2x=6$, $2y-4x=6$, $-4 \leqslant x \leqslant 0$
   (e) $y=x^2-4$, $2y-x=2$, $-3 \leqslant x \leqslant 3$
   (f) $y=-x^2$, $y=2-x$, $-4 \leqslant x \leqslant 4$

EDE

Simultaneous non-linear and linear equations

You can also solve simultaneous equations when one equation is non-linear and the other is linear.

Use the substitution method – substitute the linear equation into the non-linear equation and solve for x.

Worked example

Solve this pair of simultaneous equations: $y=1-3x-x^2$, $y+2x=-5$.

Answer

Number the equations: $y=1-3x-x^2$ (1)

$y+2x=-5$ (2)

Rearrange (2) to make y the subject: $y=-5-2x$

Substitute the rearranged equation into (1): $-5-2x=1-3x-x^2$

Rearrange in the form $ax^2+bx+c=0$: $x^2+x-6=0$

Factorise: $(x+3)(x-2)=0$

So $x=-3$ or 2

Substitute for x in (2): $y+2\times-3=-5$, so $y=-5+6=1$

$y+2\times2=-5$, so $y=-5-4=-9$

So the solutions are $(-3, 1)$ and $(2, -9)$.

Test yourself

1. Solve these pairs of simultaneous equations.

   (a) $y=x^2-1$, $y=2x-1$
   (b) $y=x^2-3x+3$, $y=x+8$
   (c) $x^2+y^2=25$, $2y+x=5$
   (d) $y=x^2-4x$, $y+2x=3$
   (e) $y=3x-x^2$, $2x-y=2$
   (f) $y=4+2x-x^2$, $2x+y=4$

2. The perimeter of a rectangle is 60 cm. The area of the rectangle is 200 cm^2. Set up a pair of simultaneous equations and solve them to find the dimensions of the rectangle.

TIP

Check your answers by putting the values you have found into the original equations and checking that they are true.

2.8 Graphs

Coordinates and gradients

The coordinates of a point are given in the form (x, y) where x is the distance along the x or horizontal axis, and y is the distance up or down the y or vertical axis.

You can plot points in all four quadrants and join them up to form straight lines. A straight line between two points is called a line segment.

The slope of a straight line is called its gradient. You can work out the gradient of a straight line using gradient = change in $y \div$ change in x. Gradients can be positive or negative.

Worked example

Calculate the gradient of the line segment joining the two points (–3, 7) and (5, 3).

Answer

$$\text{Gradient} = \frac{\text{change in } y}{\text{change in } x} = \frac{3-7}{5--3} = \frac{-4}{8} = -\frac{1}{2}$$

Test yourself

1. Plot the following pairs of coordinates on the same axes and join the pairs with straight lines.

(a) (2, 1) and (6, 9)
(b) (1, 3) and (7, 6)
(c) (4, –7) and (7, 2)
(d) (3, –9) and (8, –7)
(e) (–5, 1) and (–3, 9)
(f) (–9, –2) and (–7, 8)
(g) (–10, –3) and (–2, –1)
(h) (–9, –10) and (1, –8)
(i) (4, 4) and (10, 1)
(j) (2, 4) and (0, 10)
(k) (4, –1) and (9, –6)
(l) (–2, –2) and (7, –5)
(m) (–8, 9) and (0, 7)
(n) (–6, 8) and (–4, 0)
(o) (–7, –2) and (–4, –8)
(p) (–9, 3) and (–7, –7)

2. Calculate the gradient of each line segment you drew in Q1.

Length and midpoint of a line segment

The midpoint of a line segment connecting two points is the point that is halfway along the line segment or halfway between the two points.

You can find the midpoint by adding the x-coordinates and dividing by 2, and adding the y-coordinates and dividing by 2.

You can find the length of a line segment using Pythagoras' theorem. The line segment is the hypotenuse of a right-angled triangle. The other two sides are parallel to the x- and y-axes.

To find the length of a line segment, find the difference in the x-coordinates and the difference in the y-coordinates, square the differences, add them together and then take the square root.

Worked example

Find: (a) the midpoint

(b) the length of the line segment joining the points (–3, 7) and (5, 3).

Answer

(a) $\text{Midpoint} = \left(\frac{\text{sum of } x\text{-coordinates}}{2}, \frac{\text{sum of } y\text{-coordinates}}{2}\right) = \left(\frac{-3+5}{2}, \frac{7+3}{2}\right)$

$= \left(\frac{2}{2}, \frac{10}{2}\right) = (1, 5)$

(b) $\text{Length of line segment} = \sqrt{(\text{difference in } x\text{-coordinates})^2 + (\text{difference in } y\text{-coordinates})^2}$

$= \sqrt{(5--3)^2 + (3-7)^2} = \sqrt{8^2 + (-4)^2} = \sqrt{64+16} = \sqrt{80}$

$= 8.94$ units

Test yourself

1. Find the midpoints and the lengths of the line segments you drew in the preceding exercise.

$y=mx+c$

The equation of a straight line can be given in the form $y=mx+c$, where m is the gradient of the line and c is the point where the line crosses the y-axis, that is at $(0, c)$.

A vertical line has the equation $x=a$ and a horizontal line has the equation $y=b$.

When you know the gradient of a line and the point where it crosses the y-axis you can write down the equation of the line.

You can draw graphs of a straight line from its equation. The easiest way is by drawing a line with gradient m that goes through the point $(0, c)$.

You can also plot the graph as follows:

- select three values of x
- substitute these values of x into the equation to work out the corresponding y-values
- plot these points
- join the points with a straight line
- label the graph with its equation.

It helps to create a table of values, and to use $x=0$ as one of the values of x.

TIP

Remember that vertical lines have the equation $x=$ a number and horizontal lines have the equation $y=$ a number.

Worked example

1. Draw the graph of $y=\frac{x+4}{2}$ for $-6 \leqslant x \leqslant 6$.

2. Look at the graph opposite. Write down its equation.

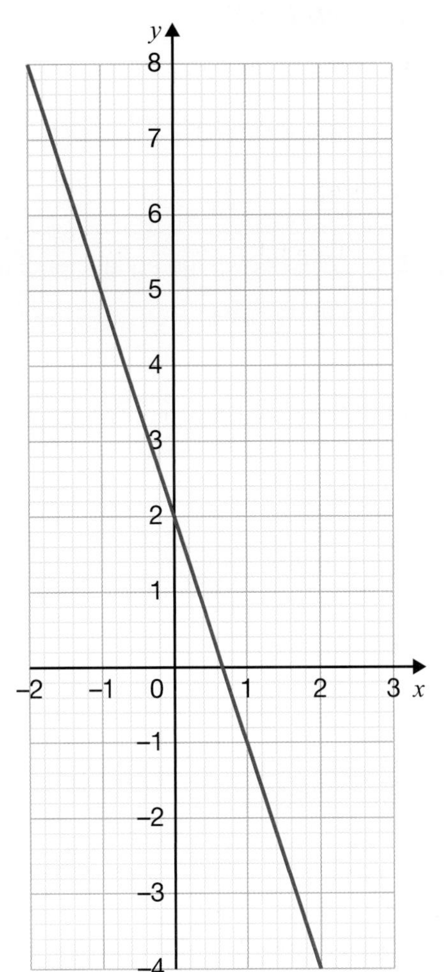

Answer

1. Pick three values of x: –6, 0 and 6.

   Draw up a table of values:

x	–6	0	6
y	–1	2	5

Draw suitable axes. Use the range for x you are given and $-1 \leqslant y \leqslant 5$ (from the values of y calculated).

Plot the points and join the points with a straight line.

Label the graph.

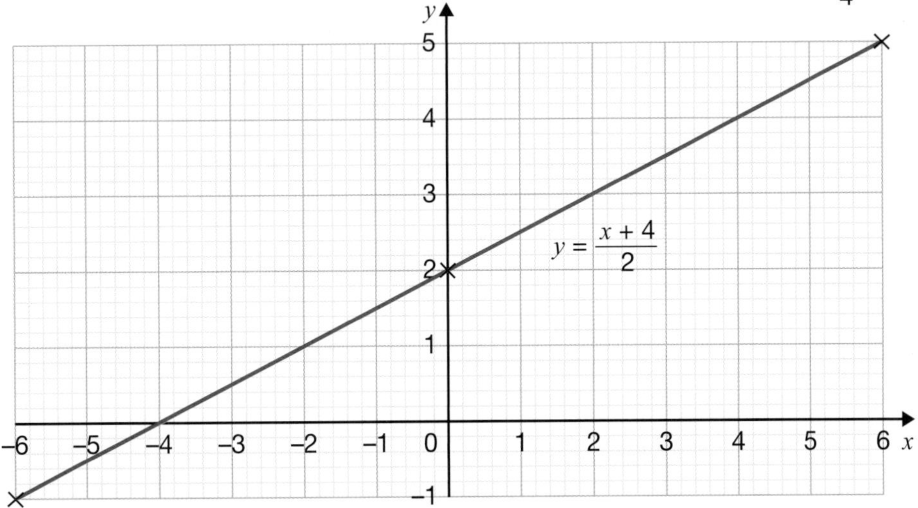

2. The equation will have the form $y=mx+c$ as the graph is a straight line.

   Pick two points on the line and find the gradient:

   $$\text{Gradient}=\frac{\text{difference in } y}{\text{difference in } x}=\frac{-4-2}{2-0}=\frac{-6}{2}=-3$$

   The graph crosses the y-axis at the point (0, 2), so $c=+2$.

   The equation of the line is $y=-3x+2$.

Test yourself

1. Draw the graphs of the following equations.

(a) $y=2x-3$, $-3 \leqslant x \leqslant 3$ (b) $y=\frac{x}{3}+4$, $-12 \leqslant x \leqslant 3$ (c) $y=4-2x$, $-3 \leqslant x \leqslant 3$

(d) $y=\frac{-x-4}{4}$, $-4 \leqslant x \leqslant 4$ (e) $x-2y=6$, $-4 \leqslant x \leqslant 6$ (f) $3x+4y=12$, $-4 \leqslant x \leqslant 4$

2. Write down the equations of the following graphs.

(a)

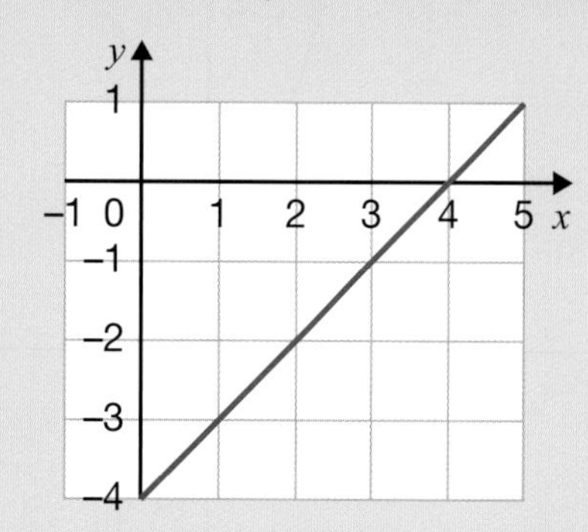

(b)

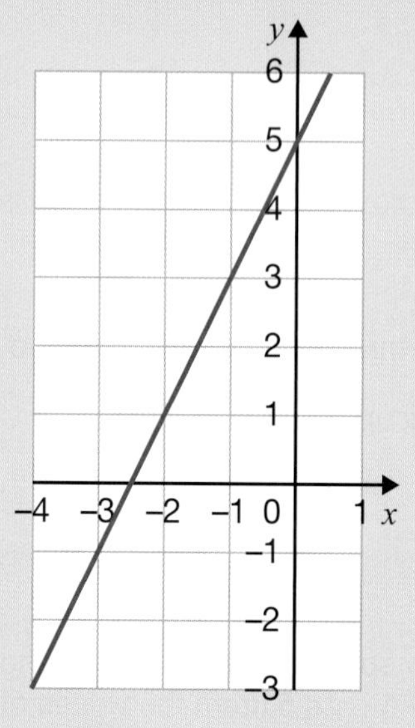

(c)

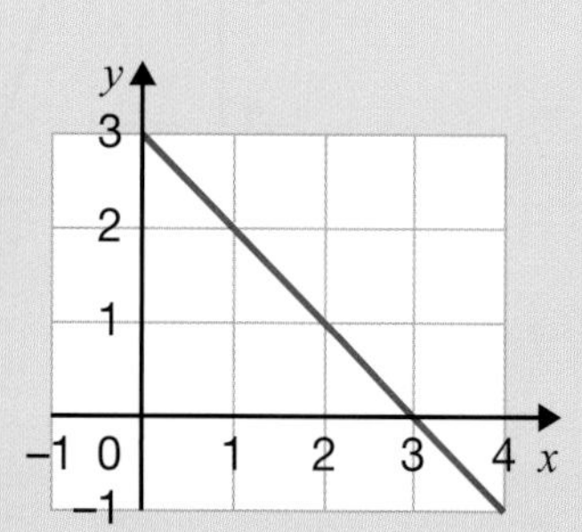

(d)

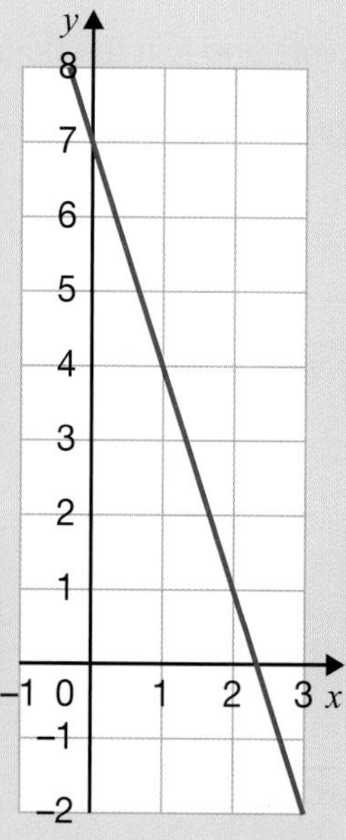

TIP When drawing graphs of straight lines or finding their equations, find the gradient and the point where the graph crosses the y-axis.

(e)

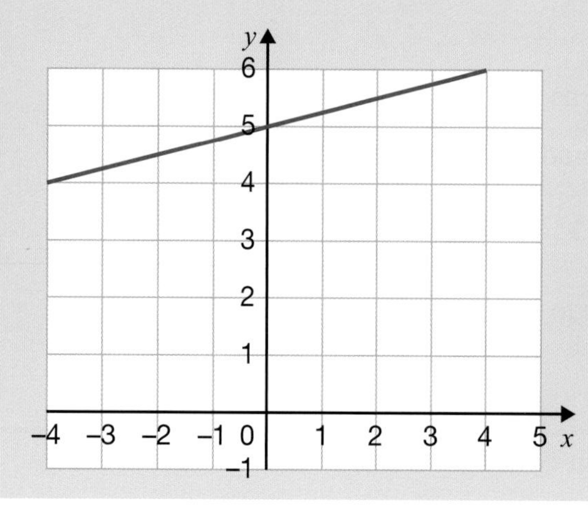

(f)

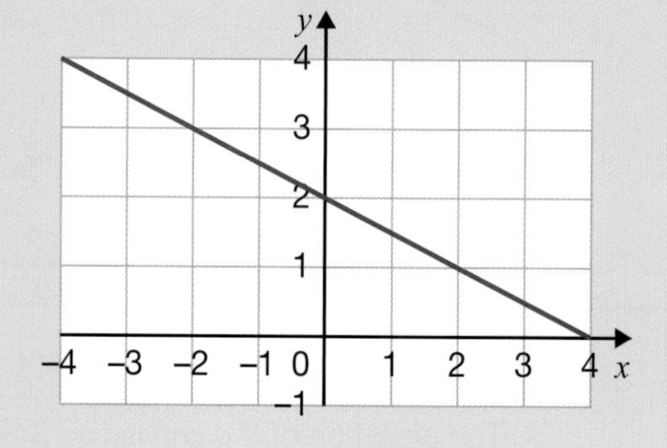

Parallel and perpendicular lines

Parallel lines have the same gradient: they have the same value of m.

CAM

The product of the gradients of two perpendicular lines is –1. If the gradient of one line is m, the gradient of the line perpendicular to it is $-\frac{1}{m}$.

Worked example

1. Find the equation of a line parallel to the line $y=3x+2$ that passes through the point (–1, 3).

CAM

2. Find the equation of a line that goes through the coordinates (4, 3) and is perpendicular to the line passing through the coordinates (1, 3) and (–2, –9).

Answer

1. The gradient of the line will be the same, $m=3$.

   So the equation of the line will be $y=3x+c$.

   Substitute the coordinates of the point that the parallel line passes through into this equation to find the value of c.

   $3=3\times-1+c$
   $3=-3+c$
   $c=6$

   So the equation of the parallel line is $y=3x+6$.

CAM

2. Gradient, m, of line passing through (1, 3) and (–2, –9) is $\frac{3--9}{1--2}=\frac{12}{3}=4$.

   Gradient of perpendicular line is $-\frac{1}{m}=-\frac{1}{4}$.

   Equation of line is $y=-\frac{1}{4}x+c$.

   Substitute coordinates the line passes through to find c:

   $3=-\frac{1}{4}\times4+c$
   $3=-1+c$
   $c=4$

   So the equation of the line is $y=4-\frac{1}{4}x$.

Test yourself

1. Find the equation of the line parallel to each of the following lines, that goes through the point given.

   (a) $y=2x-5$, (3, 2) (b) $y=3x+6$, (4, 6) (c) $y=0.5x+2$, (2, 1)

   (d) $y=3-4x$, (–1, 3) (e) $y=\frac{3-x}{4}$, (4, 1) (f) $x+2y=6$, (4, 5)

CAM

2. Find the equation of the line passing through the first pair of coordinates that is perpendicular to the line passing through the second and third pairs of coordinates.

   (a) (3, 8), (2, 4), (5, 10) (b) (6, –2), (3, 5), (6, –4)

   (c) (2, –2), (–3, –4), (9, 2) (d) (1, 11), (–3, –1), (3, –2)

Conversion graphs

You can use a conversion graph to convert between different quantities and different currencies. Find the value in the first quantity and read the value of the second one from the graph.

You can plot conversion graphs from data.

Sometimes you need to interpolate values that lie outside the range plotted on the graph.

Test yourself

1. The graph is used to convert between litres and pints. Use the graph to convert:

   (a) 2 litres to pints (b) 5.5 litres to pints (c) 15 litres to pints

   (d) 5 pints to litres (e) 8.5 pints to litres (f) 30 pints to litres.

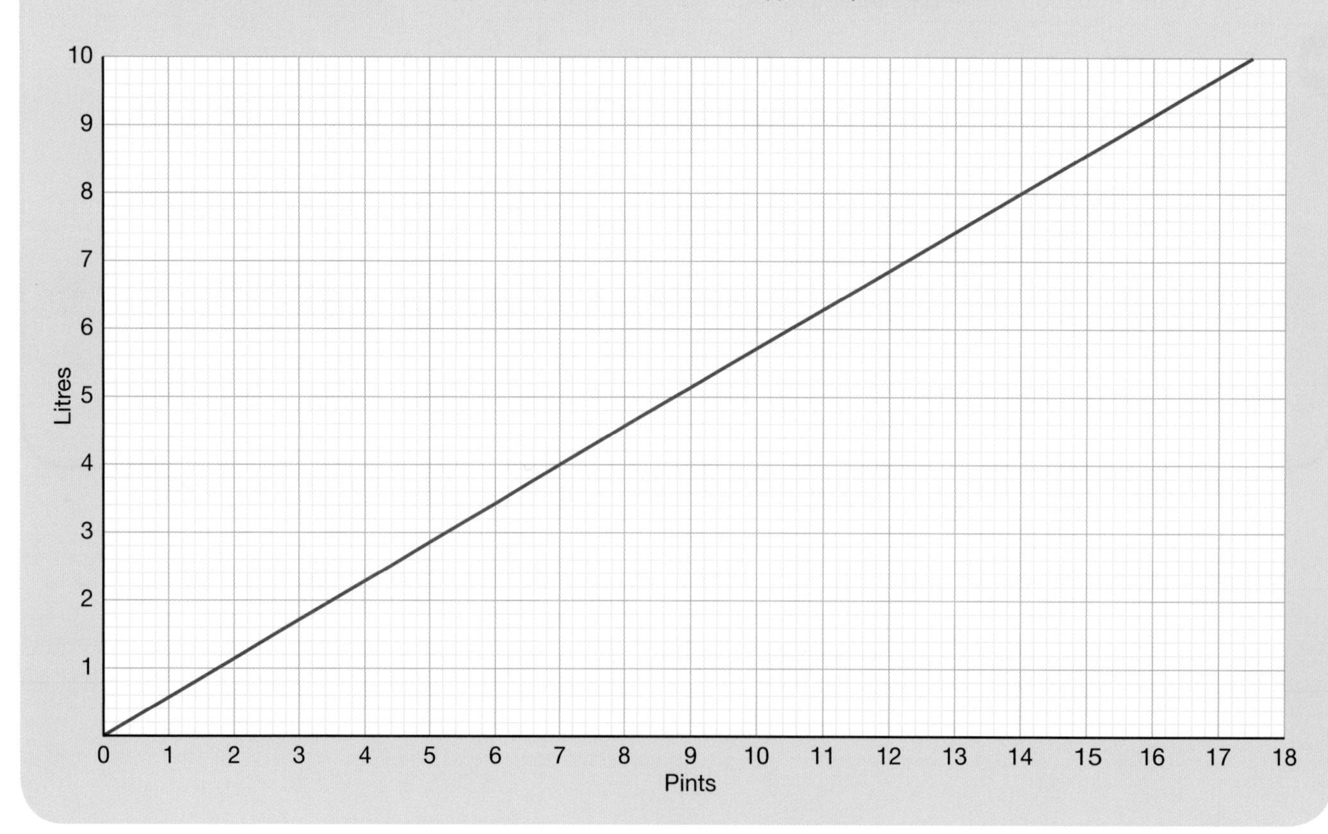

2. The conversion graph shows how much euros (€) are worth in South African rand. Use the graph to convert:

(a) €5 to rand
(b) €8.50 to rand
(c) €75 to rand
(d) 15 rand to euros
(e) 80 rand to euros
(f) 250 rand to euros.

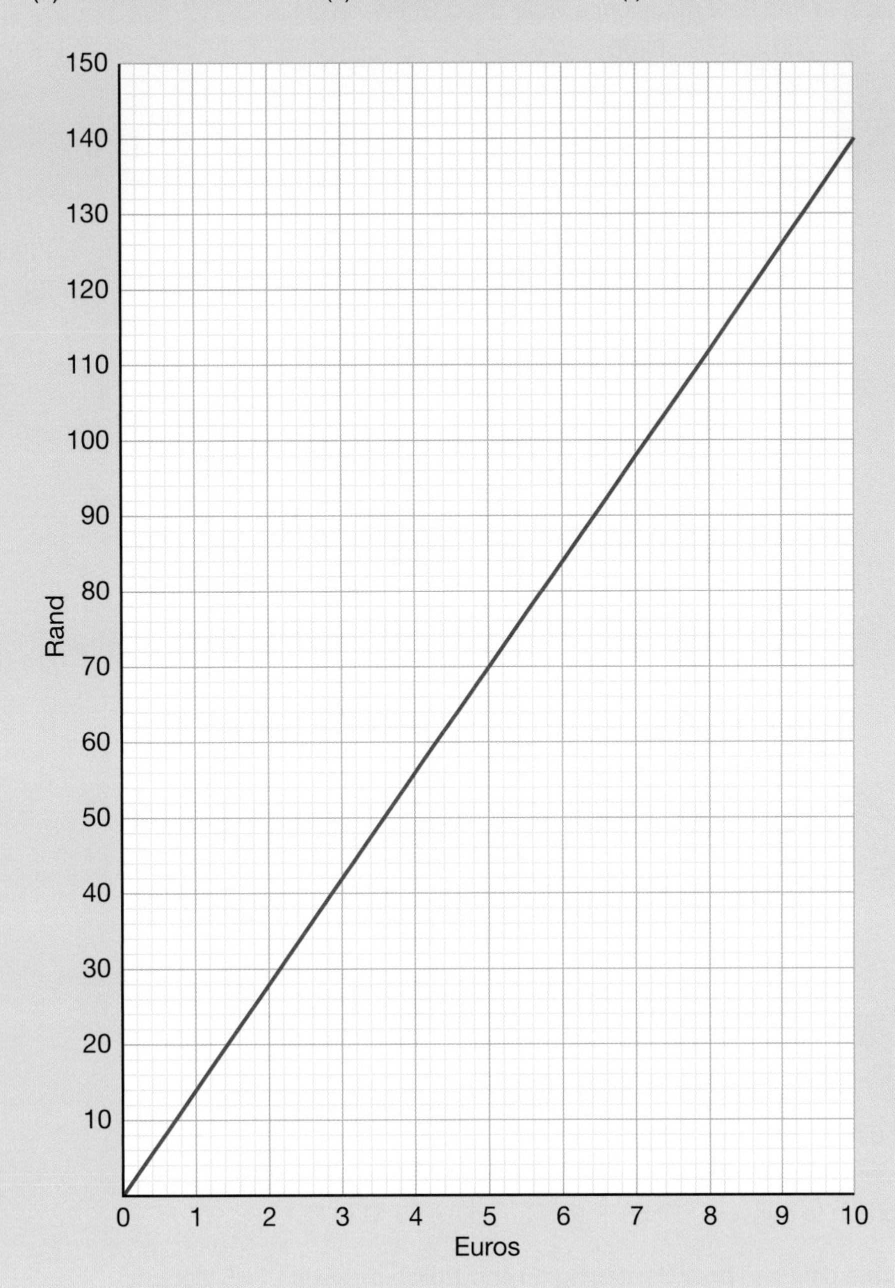

3. The graph shows the number of units of electricity used and the cost.

(a) Use the graph to find the cost of:

(i) 125 units (ii) 400 units (iii) 2500 units

(b) Use the graph to find how many units were used when the bill is:

(i) £25 (ii) £80 (iii) £200

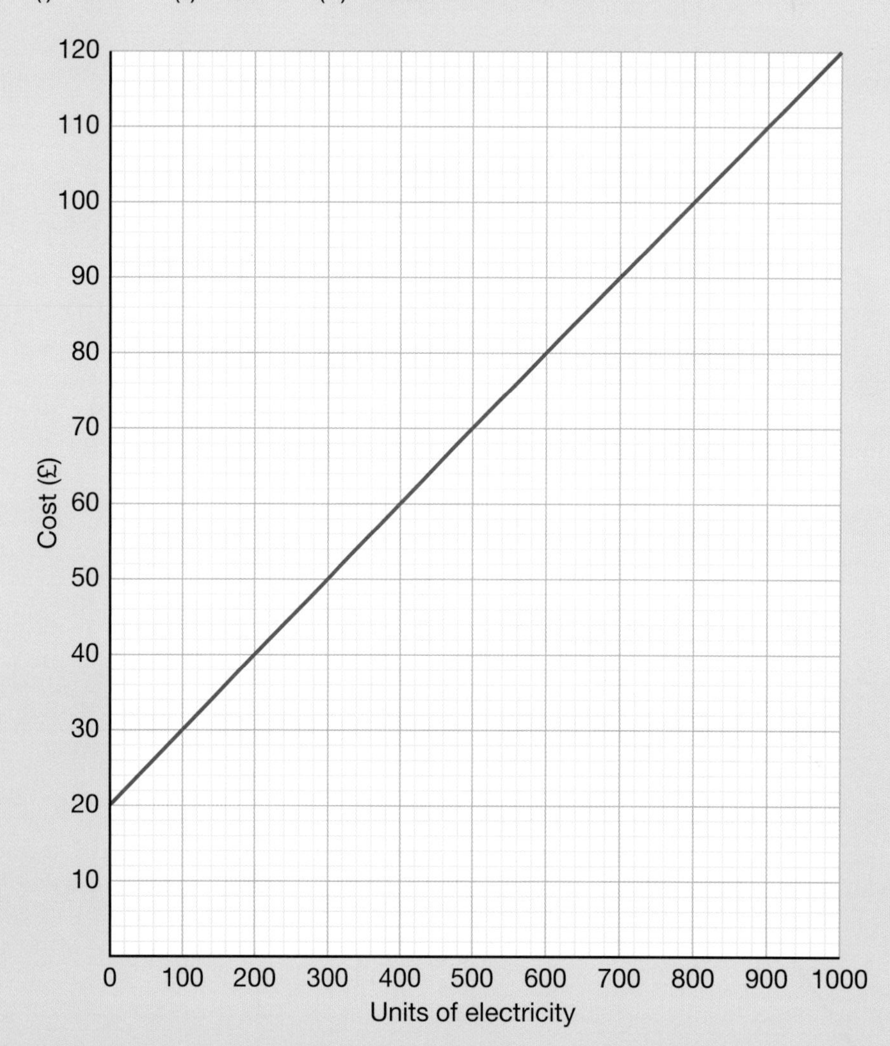

4. Bill knows that 0 °C is 32 °F and 100 °C is 212 °F.

(a) Use this information to plot a conversion graph between °C and °F.

(b) Use your graph to convert: (i) 68 °F to °C (ii) 35 °C to °F.

5. The exchange rate between pounds sterling (£) and Polish zlotys is £1 = 5 zloty.

(a) Use this information to plot a conversion graph between £ and zlotys.

(b) Use your graph to convert: (i) £8 to zlotys (ii) 68 zloty to £.

6. The cost of a conference is based on the number of people attending. The cost of 50 people attending is £500. The cost of 500 people attending is £2750.

(a) Use this information to plot a graph showing the number of people and cost.

(b) Use your graph to find the cost of 300 people attending a conference.

(c) A conference cost £900. How many people attended?

Check that your answer makes sense. Convert your answer back again. Does it give the original value?

Travel graphs

Information about a journey can be shown on a travel graph.

These graphs can show distance on the y-axis and time on the x-axis (distance–time graph) or speed on the y-axis and time on the x-axis (speed–time graph).

Average speed is given by total distance travelled $\div$ total time taken.

The slope of a travel graph shows how fast the distance or speed is changing. The slope of a distance–time graph gives speed. The slope of a speed–time graph gives acceleration – how quickly something is speeding up or slowing down.

On a distance–time graph, a horizontal line means the object is stationary.

On a speed–time graph, a horizontal line means that the object is moving at a constant speed.

Negative acceleration is also called deceleration.

The area under a speed–time graph is the total distance travelled for that journey.

You need to remember how to find the distance under a speed–time graph, and how to calculate average speed.

Worked example

1. The distance–time graph for a car journey is shown.

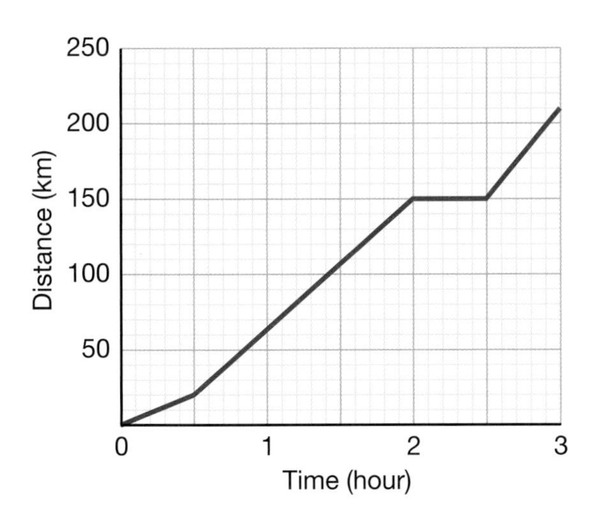

(a) How long was the break?

(b) What was the total time taken for the journey?

(c) What was the average speed in the first 30 minutes? Give your answer in km/h.

(d) What was the average speed for the whole journey?

2. This is a speed–time graph for a train's journey between two stations.

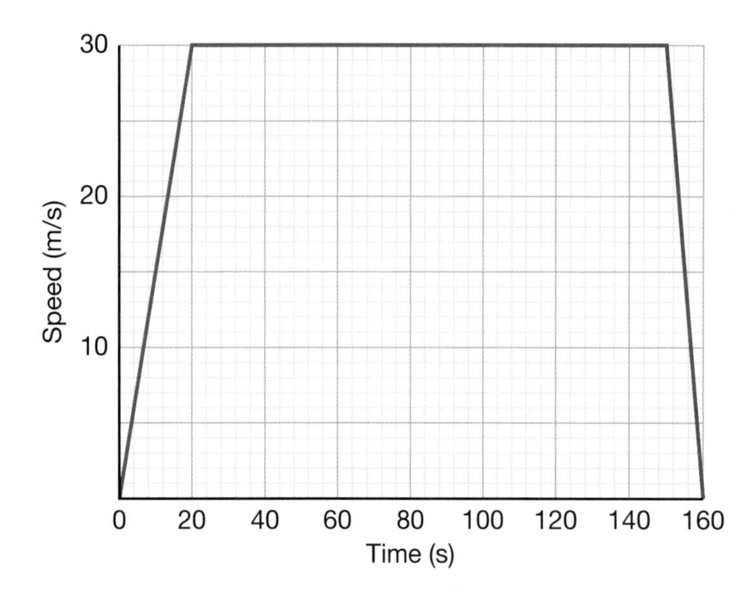

(a) What is the acceleration of the train in the first part?

(b) What is the acceleration of the train in the last part of the journey?

(c) How far did the train travel?

Answer

1. (a) During the break, the car was not moving so the line is horizontal. This happens between 2 and 2.5 hours. So the break was 30 minutes.

(b) Read the time at the end of the journey: 3 hours.

(c) Car travelled 20 km in 30 minutes.

Speed = distance ÷ time = 20 km ÷ 0.5 hour = 40 km/h

TIP Remember that 30 minutes is 0.5 hours.

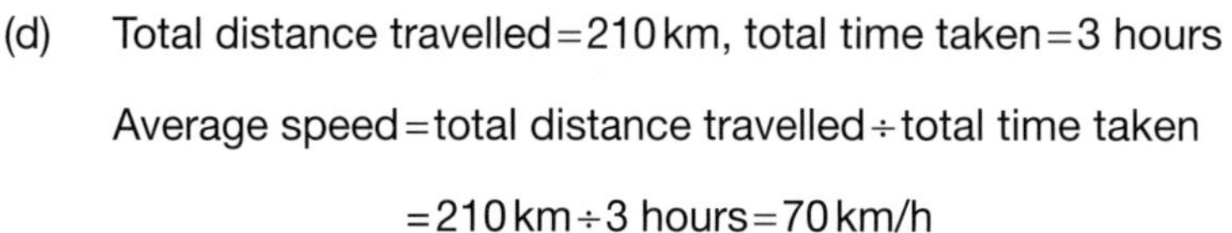

(d) Total distance travelled = 210 km, total time taken = 3 hours

Average speed = total distance travelled ÷ total time taken

= 210 km ÷ 3 hours = 70 km/h

2. (a) Acceleration = change in speed ÷ time taken for change in speed

$= 30\,\text{m/s} \div 20\,\text{s} = 1.5\,\text{m/s}^2$

(b) Acceleration $= -30\,\text{m/s} \div 10\,\text{s} = -3.0\,\text{m/s}^2$

TIP Remember to check the scales on graphs before reading values from them.

(c) Distance = area under graph

= area of triangle on left + area of rectangle in middle + area of triangle on right

$= \frac{1}{2} \times 20\,\text{s} \times 30\,\text{m/s} + 130\,\text{s} \times 30\,\text{m/s} + \frac{1}{2} \times 10\,\text{s} \times 30\,\text{m/s}$

= 300 m + 3900 m + 150 m

= 4350 m (or 4.35 km)

Test yourself

1. The distance–time graph shows a journey by car.

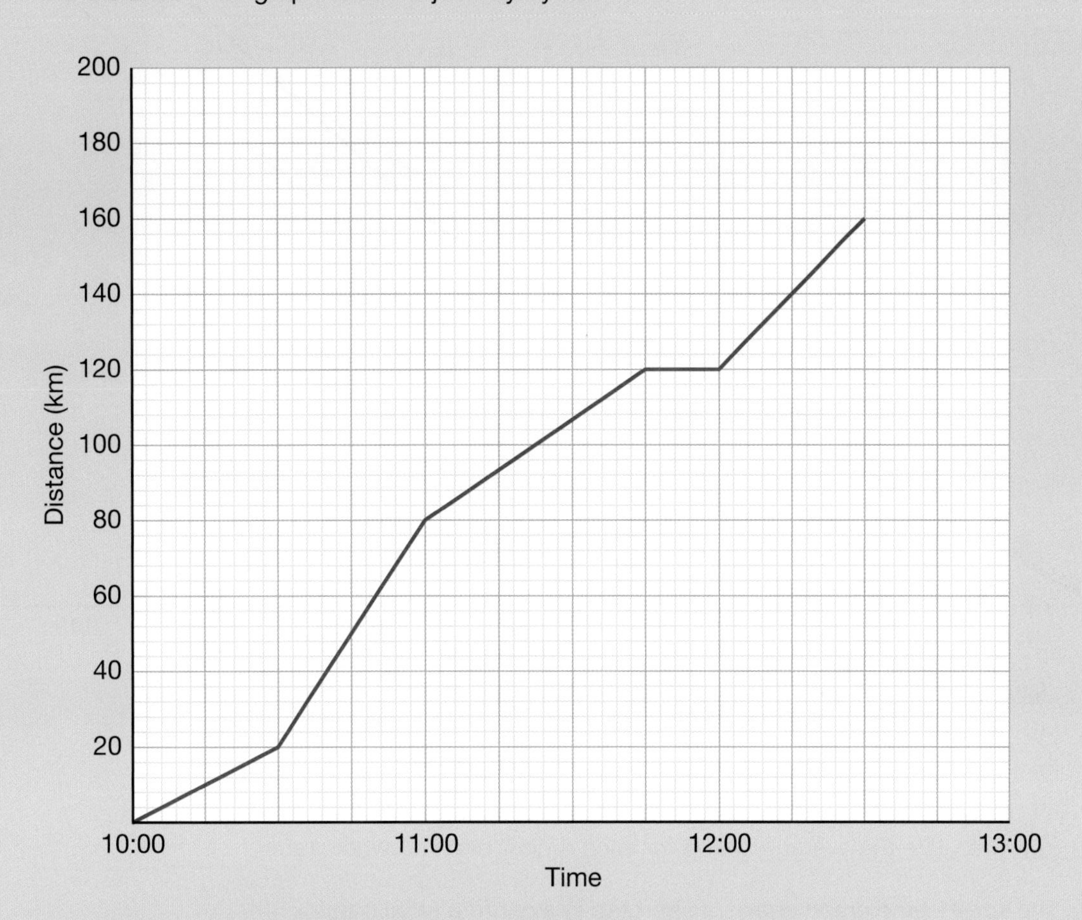

(a) What is the highest average speed reached?

(b) Between what times was the highest speed reached?

(c) What is the average for the whole journey?

(d) What happened between 11:45 and 12:00?

2. The distance–time graph shows three people running an 800 m race.

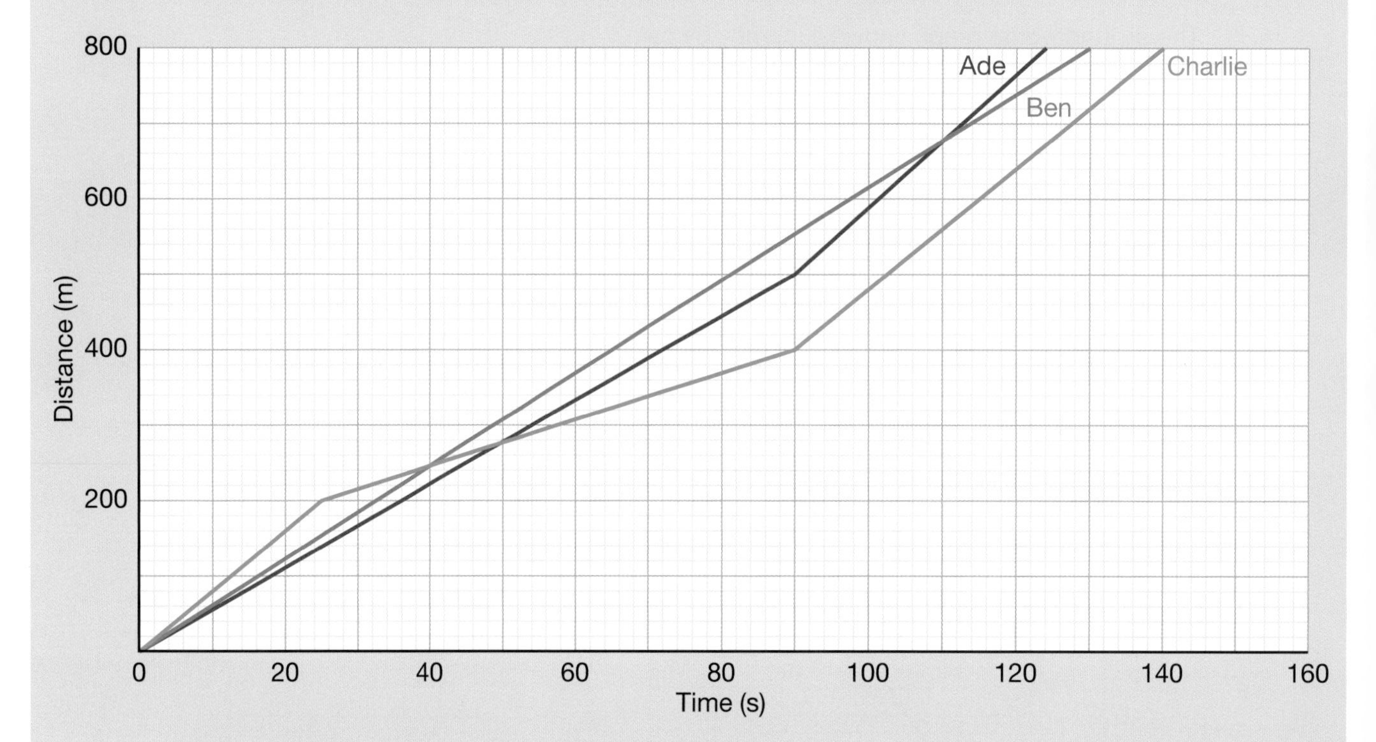

(a) Who ran the fastest?

(b) Between which times did this runner run the fastest?

(c) Calculate this speed.

(d) Calculate the average speed for each runner over the whole race.

3. The speed–time graph shows a short trip in a car to a retail park.

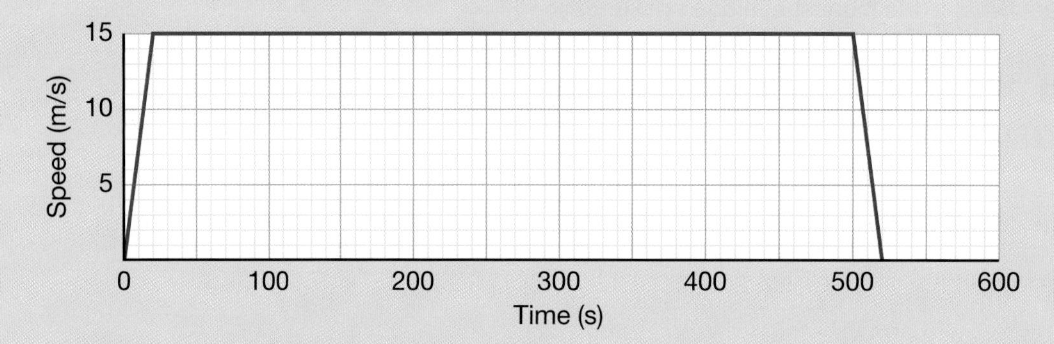

(a) What is the maximum speed of the car?

(b) What is the deceleration of the car?

(c) How far is it to the retail park?

(d) What is the average speed of the car?

4. The speed–time graph shows a short journey of an aeroplane.

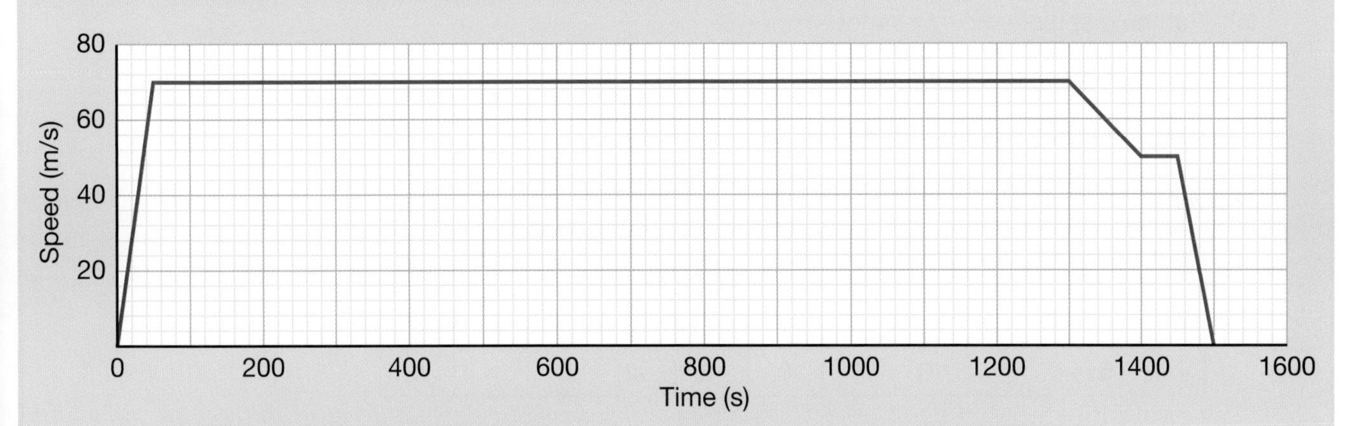

(a) What is the acceleration of the aeroplane in the first part of the journey?

(b) What is the initial deceleration of the aeroplane?

(c) What is the total distance travelled by the aeroplane?

5. Sumi is walking to school from home. She walks 400 m in 4 minutes. She stops for 2 minutes while she waits for her friend. Then she walks 800 m in 9 minutes.

(a) Show this information on a distance–time graph.

(b) What was Sumi's average speed for the whole journey? Give your answer in km/h.

6. Sasha drives to an appointment. The distance is 60 km and takes 45 minutes. The appointment lasts for 1.5 hours. Sasha then drives home taking 40 minutes for the return journey.

(a) Draw a distance–time graph for the journey.

(b) Calculate Sasha's average speed for the return journey.

Remember that you may not get all the marks for just writing down the correct answer. There are usually marks for showing your working.

Quadratic graphs

The graph of a quadratic function is always a parabola – it is a smooth curve.

To draw the graph of a quadratic equation:

- draw up a table of values
- plot the points and join them up with a smooth curve.

Worked example

(a) Pot the graph of $y=x^2-5x+4$ for $-1 \leqslant x \leqslant 6$.

(b) Use your graph to find the value of y when $x=3.5$.

(c) Use your graph to solve the equation $x^2-5x+4=5$.

Answer

(a) Draw up a table of values.

x	–1	0	1	2	3	4	5	6
$y=x^2-5x+4$	10	4	0	–2	–2	0	4	10

Plot the points and join them with a smooth curve.

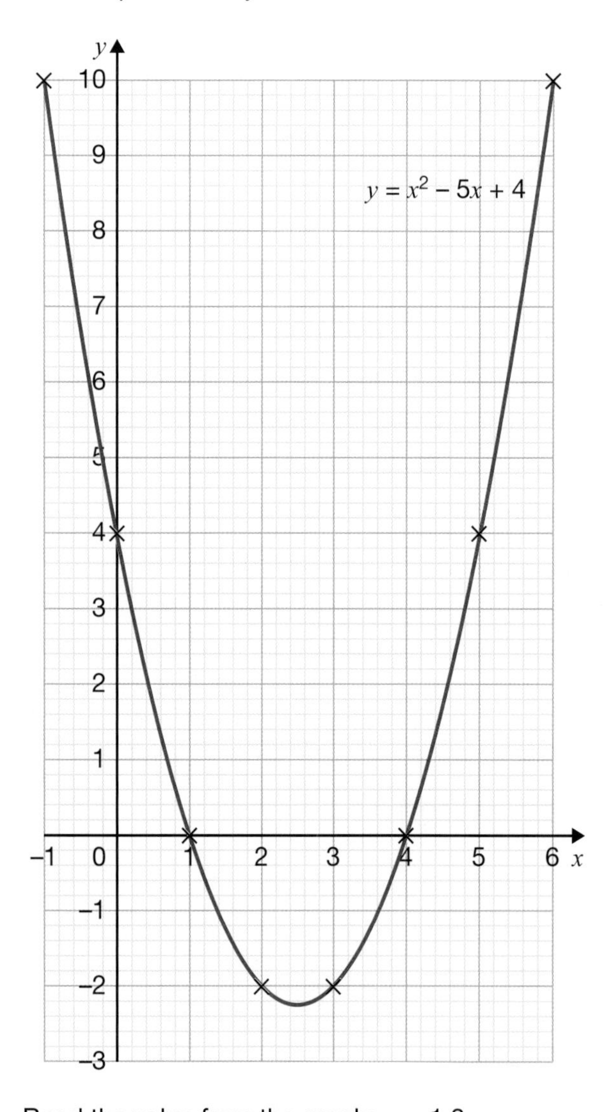

(b) Read the value from the graph: $y=-1.3$

(c) There are two solutions. Read the values from the graph: $x=-0.2$ and 5.2

Both of these answers will depend on how accurately you have drawn your graph!

Test yourself

1. (a) Plot the graph of $y=x^2+4x-7$ for $-6 \leqslant x \leqslant 2$.
   (b) Use your graph to find the value of y when $x=-3.8$.
   (c) Use your graph to solve the equation $x^2+4x-7=-5$.

2. (a) Plot the graph of $y=2x^2-x-2$ for $-3 \leqslant x \leqslant 3$.
   (b) Use your graph to find the value of y when $x=2.4$.
   (c) Use your graph to solve the equation $2x^2-x-2=6$.

3. (a) Plot the graph of $y=-x^2+2x+3$ for $-3 \leqslant x \leqslant 5$.
   (b) Use your graph to find the value of y when $x=-0.5$.
   (c) Use your graph to solve the equation $-x^2+2x+3=-3$.

4. (a) Plot the graph of $y=-2x^2-4x+6$ for $-4 \leqslant x \leqslant 2$.
   (b) Use your graph to find the value of y when $x=-1.4$.
   (c) Use your graph to solve the equation $-2x^2-4x+6=4$.

Cubic graphs

A cubic function contains a term in x^3 as the highest power of x.

You can plot a graph of a cubic function in the same way as a quadratic function.

Worked example

(a) Plot the graph of $y=x^3+x^2-4x-3$ for $-2 \leqslant x \leqslant 2$.

(b) Use your graph to solve the equation $x^3+x^2-4x-3=-1$.

Answer

(a) Draw up a table of values.

x	−2	−1.5	−1	−0.5	0	0.5	1	1.5	2
$y=x^3+x^2-4x-3$	1	1.9	1	−0.9	−3	−4.6	−5	−3.4	1

Plot the points and join them with a smooth curve.

(b) Read the values from the graph:
$x=-2.3$, -0.4 and 1.8

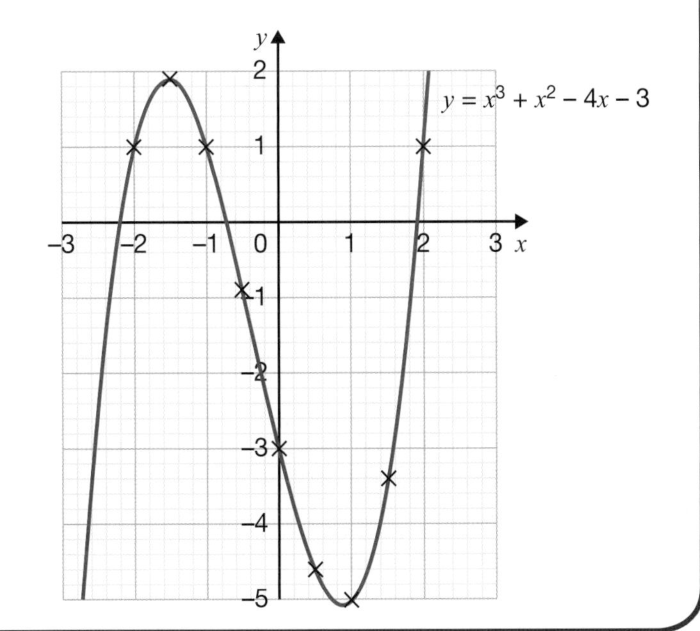

Test yourself

1. (a) Plot the graph of $y=x^3-4$ for $-2 \leqslant x \leqslant 2$.
   (b) Use your graph to solve the equation $x^3-4=-1$.

2. (a) Plot the graph of $y=x^3-2x^2-5x$ for $-2 \leqslant x \leqslant 3.5$.
   (b) Use your graph to solve the equation $x^3-2x^2-5x=0$.

3. (a) Plot the graph of $y=0.5x^3-3x+2$ for $-3 \leqslant x \leqslant 3$.
   (b) Use your graph to solve the equation $0.5x^3-3x+2=4$.

TIP

In a calculation with several steps, the memory and answer functions on your calculator can be useful, but make sure you know how to use them properly.

Reciprocal graphs

A reciprocal equation has a negative power of x, that is it is in the form $y=\frac{a}{x}$ or $y=\frac{a}{x^2}$.

You can plot the graph of a reciprocal equation in the same way as a quadratic equation.

You need to choose x-values carefully to make sure that you show the true shape of the graph. You cannot use $x=0$, because it is undefined and referred to as infinity.

The x- and y-axes are asymptotes – the graph gets closer and closer to them but never touches or crosses them.

The graphs are symmetrical.

Worked example

(a) Plot the graph of $y=\frac{5}{x}$ for $-5 \leqslant x \leqslant 5$.

(b) Use your graph to solve the equations: (i) $\frac{5}{x}=3.5$

(ii) $\frac{5}{x}=-4$

Answer

(a) Draw up a table of values.

You only need to work out the values of y for positive values of x as the graph is symmetrical.

x	1	1.5	2	3	4	5
$y=\frac{5}{x}$	5	3.33	2.5	1.67	1.25	1

Plot the points and join them with smooth curves.

The y-values for negative x-values are the same as for the positive x-values but with the opposite sign.

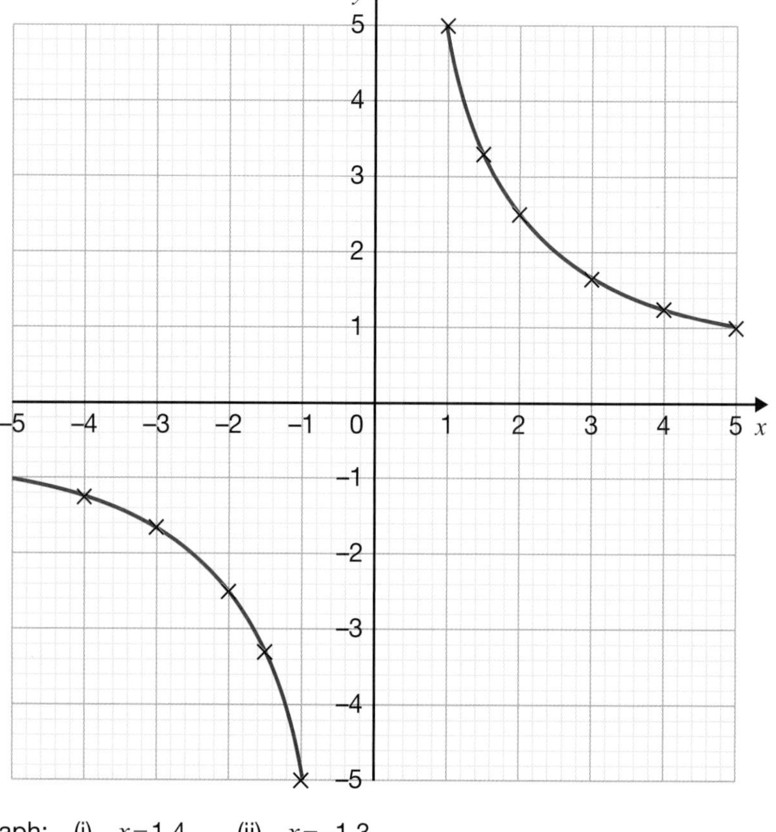

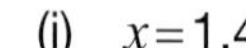
(b) Read the values from the graph: (i) $x=1.4$ (ii) $x=-1.3$

Test yourself

1. (a) Plot the graph of $y=\frac{8}{x}$ for $-8\leqslant x\leqslant 8$.

(b) Use your graph to solve the equations: (i) $\frac{8}{x}=1.5$ (ii) $\frac{8}{x}=-4.5$

2. (a) Plot the graph of $y=\frac{10}{x^2}$ for $-5\leqslant x\leqslant 5$.

(b) Use your graph to solve the equation $\frac{10}{x^2}=3.5$.

For graphs of non-linear functions, *always* join the points with a smooth curve.

Tangents to curves

A tangent to a curve has the same gradient as the curve at the point where it touches.

You can estimate the gradient of a curve at a point by drawing a tangent to the curve and finding the gradient of the tangent.

Worked example

Look at the graph of $y=x^2-5x+4$ in the worked example in Quadratic graphs (page 80).

(a) Draw a tangent to the curve at (4, 0).

(b) Estimate the gradient of the curve at (4, 0).

Answer

(a) Draw the tangent at (4, 0) so that it has the same gradient as the curve at this point.

(b) Estimate the gradient at this point by drawing a triangle.

Gradient = difference in y ÷ difference in x

$=6\div 2=3$

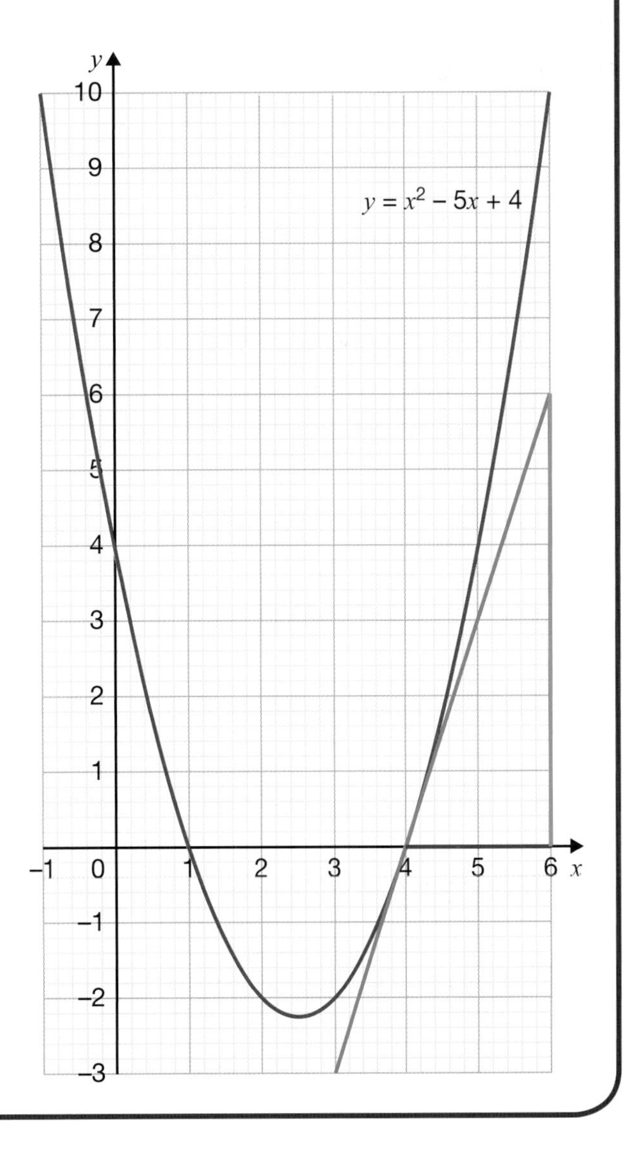

Test yourself

Use the graphs you have already drawn for the functions in the sections on quadratic, cubic and reciprocal graphs.

1. Use the graph of $y=2x^2-x-2$ from Quadratic graphs Q2.

(a) Draw a tangent to the curve at (2, 4).

(b) Estimate the gradient of the curve at (2, 4).

2. Use the graph of $y=-x^2+2x+3$ from Quadratic graphs Q3.

(a) Draw a tangent to the curve at (3, 0).

(b) Estimate the gradient of the curve at (3, 0).

3. Use the graph of $y=x^3-2x^2-5x$ from Cubic graphs Q2.

(a) Draw a tangent to the curve at (1, –6).

(b) Estimate the gradient of the curve at (1, –6).

4. Use the graph of $y=0.5x^3-3x+2$ from Cubic graphs Q3.

(a) Draw a tangent to the curve at (–2, 4).

(b) Estimate the gradient of the curve at (–2, 4).

5. Use the graph of $y=\frac{8}{x}$ from Reciprocal graphs Q1.

(a) Draw a tangent to the curve at (4, 2).

(b) Estimate the gradient of the curve at (4, 2).

Exponential graphs

An exponential function has the form $y = k^x$.

You can draw a graph of the function. Exponential functions always go through the point (0, 1).

Worked example

Draw the graph of $y = 2^x$ for $-2 \leqslant x \leqslant 4$.

Answer

Draw up a table of values:

x	−2	−1	0	1	2	3	4
$y = 2^x$	0.25	0.5	1	2	4	8	16

Plot the points and join them with a smooth curve.

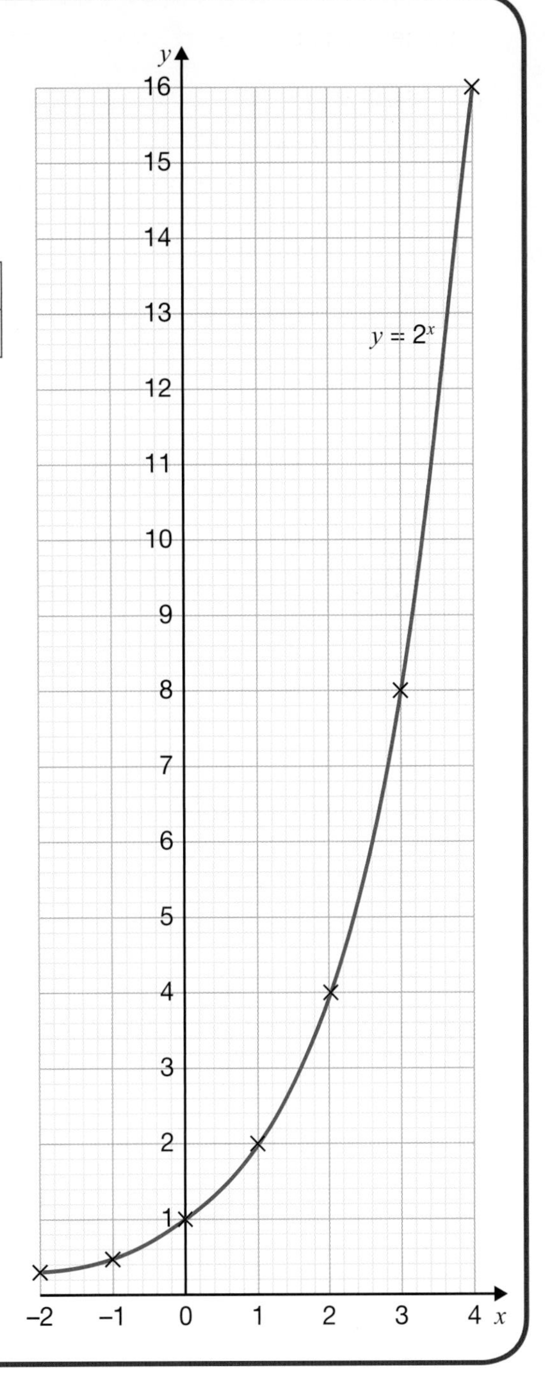

Test yourself

1. Draw the graph of $y = 3^x$ for $-2 \leqslant x \leqslant 2$.

2. Draw the graph of $y = 0.5^x$ for $-4 \leqslant x \leqslant 2$.

2.9 Inequalities

Inequalities

You should remember the symbols for inequalities from 1.6 Sets:

$<$	less than
$>$	greater than
$\leqslant$	less than or equal to
$\geqslant$	greater than or equal to

An inequality is an algebraic expression that uses at least one of these symbols.

You can solve inequalities in the same way that you solve equations.

The solution of an inequality will also be an inequality and will be a range of values.

Inequalities can be represented on a number line. A solid circle is used when the value is included and an empty circle when it is not included.

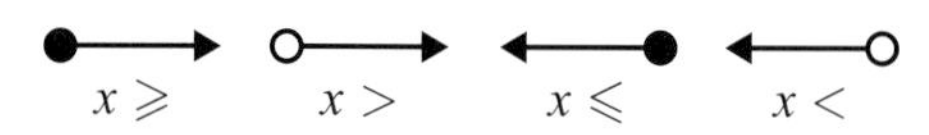

When you multiply both sides of an inequality by a negative number, the inequality sign is reversed.

Worked example

Solve the inequality $9-2x \leqslant 3$ and show the answer on a number line.

Answer

Subtract 9 from both sides: $9-9-2x \leqslant 3-9$

$-2x \leqslant -6$

Multiply both sides by −1 and reverse the inequality sign: $2x \geqslant 6$

Divide both sides by 2: $x \geqslant 3$

Show the answer on a number line:

0 1 2 3 4 5

The circle is solid because x can be equal to 3, so it is included in the range of values.

Test yourself

1. Solve the following inequalities and show the answer on a number line. Give your answers as fractions.

(a) $x-3 \leqslant 2$ (b) $x+5 \geqslant 3$ (c) $2x-5 \leqslant 4$

(d) $4x+3>7$ (e) $\frac{2y}{3}+2<6$ (f) $\frac{6t}{5}-4>-2$

(g) $3(2p-5)<21$ (h) $2(4y+3) \geqslant 12$ (i) $3(2-y) \leqslant 4$

(j) $4(5-2q)>4$ (k) $\frac{3(2y-4)}{5} \leqslant 18$ (l) $\frac{6-5y}{4}<3$

TIP

When a question asks you to give your answer as a fraction, give your answer as a fraction, *not* a decimal.

Inequalities on graphs

You can show inequalities on graphs by shading regions.

The boundary of the inequality is the line where the inequality sign has been replaced by an equals sign. Draw the line on the graph and shade the region shown by the inequality. Check that you have shaded the correct region by picking a point in this region and substituting the values into the inequality. If you have shaded the correct region, the inequality will be true.

If the values on the line are included (that is there is a $\leqslant$ or $\geqslant$ sign in the inequality), the line is solid. If the values are not included (there is a $<$ or $>$ sign in the inequality), the line is dashed.

Worked example

Show $x+y\geqslant 3$ on a graph.

Answer

The boundary line is $x+y=3$.

As the values on the line are included, draw it as a solid line.

Shade the region.

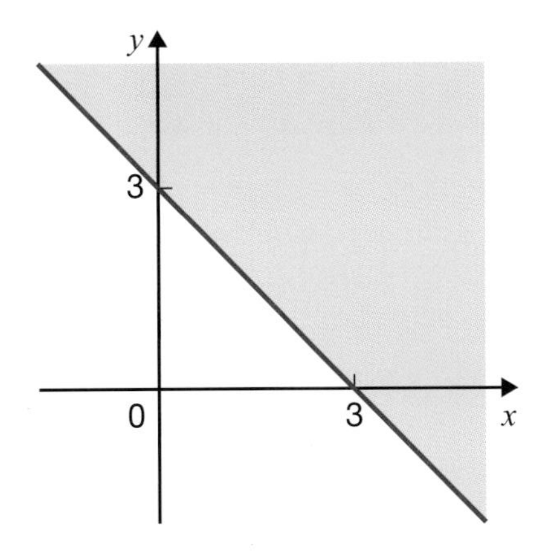

Test yourself

1. Show each of these inequalities on a graph.

(a) $x>6$ (b) $y\leqslant -2$ (c) $y\geqslant 3x-3$

(d) $y<\frac{x}{2}+3$ (e) $2x+3y\leqslant -12$ (f) $4y-2x<8$

More inequalities

You can show a region that satisfies two or more inequalities by drawing them all on one graph.

Regions that satisfy the inequalities will usually be shown as the area that is unshaded.

Regions that satisfy the inequalities will usually be shown as the area that is shaded.

Worked example

Show the following inequalities on a graph and shade the region that satisfies all three inequalities.

$2y-x<10$, $2y+x\geqslant-2$, $y\leqslant 2-4x$

Answer

Draw the graphs of $2y-x=10$, $2y+x=-2$ and $y=2-4x$.

Work out where each line crosses the x- and y-axes.

$2y-x=10$ crosses the axes at (–10, 0) and (0, 5) and has a gradient of 0.5. The line should be dashed as values on the line are not included.

$2y+x=-2$ crosses the axes at (–2, 0) and (0, –1) and has a gradient of –0.5. The line should be solid, as values on the line are included.

$y=2-4x$ crosses the axes at (0, 2) and (0.5, 0) and has a gradient of –4. The line should be solid, as values on the line are included.

Draw the lines.

Label each graph.

Shade the area that satisfies all three inequalities.

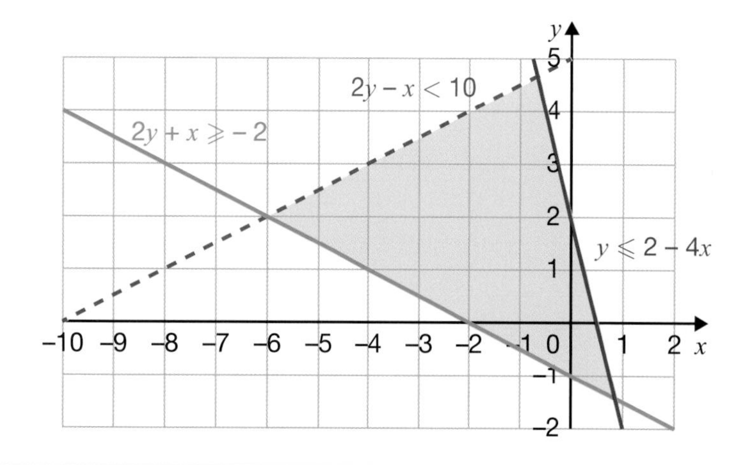

Test yourself

1. Show the following groups of inequalities on a graph and shade the region that satisfies all three inequalities.

(a) $x<3, y\geqslant-2, y\leqslant\frac{x}{2}-1$

(b) $x>2, y\geqslant-3, y<2-x$

(c) $x+y>5, x-y\geqslant5, y<2$

(d) $2x+5y>10, y\leqslant2x+3, x<2$

(e) $y>5x-3, 4y-x<3, y+x\geqslant-3$

(f) $2x-10y<20, y-8x\leqslant1, y+3x\leqslant4$

Quadratic inequalities

You can solve inequalities that contain quadratic expressions. The solutions will have a range of values with two bounds as there are two solutions to a quadratic equation.

The solutions can often be written in the form $p<x<q$ or $p>x>q$.

Worked example

Solve the inequality $x^2 < 81$ and show the answer on a number line.

Answer

Change the inequality to an equals sign: $x^2 = 81$

Take square roots on both sides of the equation: $x = \pm 9$

So $x > -9$ and $x < +9$.

This can be written as $-9 < x < 9$.

On a number line, it is shown as follows. Open circles are used because –9 and +9 are not included in the range.

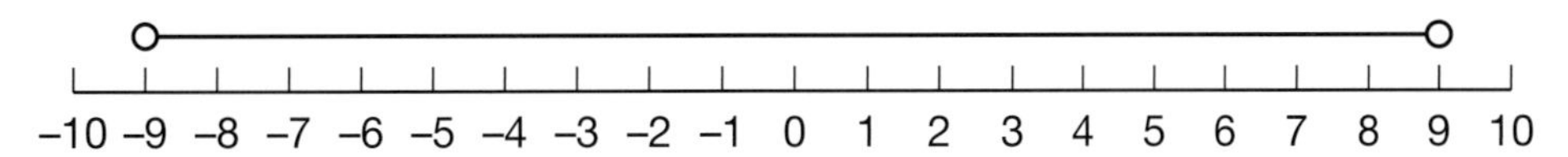

Test yourself

1. Solve each of the following inequalities and show the answer on a number line.

(a) $x^2 < 49$ (b) $x^2 > 1.44$ (c) $4x^2 \geqslant 36$

(d) $5x^2 \leqslant 125$ (e) $x^2 - 36 > 0$ (f) $2x^2 - 128 \leqslant 0$

(g) $27 - 3x^2 < 0$ (h) $64 - 4x^2 \geqslant 0$

CAM

Linear programming

There are many practical situations with constraints that can be shown as inequalities.

Linear programming involves using the constraints written as inequalities and plotting them on a graph to solve practical problems.

Worked example

A woman is buying tables and chairs for her cafe. Chairs cost £20 and tables cost £50.

She needs at least 4 tables and 10 chairs.

She has £500 to spend. Find the different ways that she can spend the money.

Answer

Write the constraints as inequalities.

Let x=number of chairs and y=number of tables.

Write the total cost as an inequality: $20x+50y \leqslant 500$

This simplifies to: $2x+5y \leqslant 50$

Write the minimum numbers of tables and chairs as inequalities: $x \geqslant 10$, $y \geqslant 4$

Draw the graphs of $2x+5y=50$, $x=10$ and $y=4$ on the same axes.

All three graphs should be drawn as solid lines because the values on the lines are included.

Shade the region.

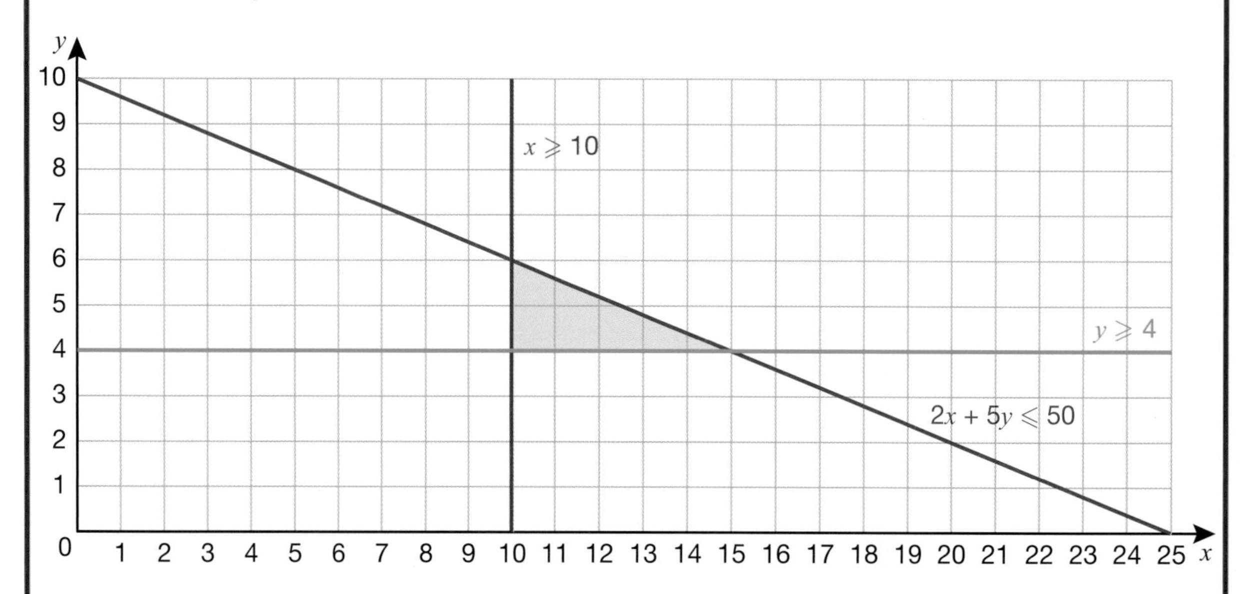

There are 10 possible ways of spending the money:

Number of chairs	10	10	10	11	11	12	12	13	14	15
Number of tables	4	5	6	4	5	4	5	4	4	4

Test yourself

1. A bus company has 45 seater coaches and minibuses. A coach is 12 m long and a minibus is 5 m long.

At the depot, there is 100 m of parking space. The company must have at least 5 coaches and 3 minibuses.

(a) Write these constraints as inequalities and show them on a graph.

(b) Find the number of different ways that the depot can take coaches and minibuses that satisfy these constraints.

2. Tickets at a theme park cost £30 for adults and £20 for children. The maximum capacity of the theme park is 5000. In one day the ticket sales were over £125 000. There is at least one child for every adult.

(a) Write these constraints as inequalities and show them on a graph.

(b) What is the minimum number of adult tickets sold?

3. Cartons of milk cost 60p and bottles of water cost £1. Shelagh has £10 to spend. She needs to buy at least 3 bottles of water and 2 cartons of milk.

(a) Write these constraints as inequalities and show them on a graph.

(b) What is the maximum total number of cartons of milk Shelagh can buy?

4. In a football league, a team gets 3 points for a win, 1 point for a draw and no points for a loss. A team has scored at least 34 points and has lost at least 5 games out of the 20 games played so far.

(a) Express these constraints as inequalities and draw them on a graph.

(b) What is the minimum number of games the team has won?

In problems like this, the solutions will always be integers – you cannot have a fraction of a coach, a fraction of a match or a fraction of a person.

2.10 Sequences

Sequences

A sequence is a set of numbers where there is a rule for finding every number in the sequence.

Each number in the sequence is called a term.

To find the pattern in a sequence, look at the differences between consecutive terms. You can then use this to work out the other terms in the sequence.

Sequences can be linear (increase or decrease by a fixed number) or geometric (increase or decrease by the power of a number, or be multiplied or divided by a number).

Worked example

Find the rule for the sequence and write down the next three terms.

128, 64, 32, 16, …

Answer

The difference between consecutive terms is 64, 32 and 16.

Each term has been divided by 2.

So the rule is divide by 2.

The next three terms are 8, 4, 2.

Test yourself

1. Find the rule for each sequence and then write down the next three terms.
   (a) 3, 7, 11, 15, ... (b) 6, 15, 24, 33, ... (c) 2, 8, 32, 128, ..
   (d) 10, 50, 250, 1250, ... (e) 3, 6, 12, 24, ... (f) 1000, 500, 250, 125, ...
   (g) 729, 243, 81, 27, ... (h) 64, 58, 52, 46, ...

Finding the *n*th term

You can find any term in a sequence when you know the rule for the nth term of the sequence.

The rule for the nth term will always be in the form $An \pm B$.

To find A, find the difference between consecutive terms.

To find B, find the difference between A and the first term of the sequence.

The nth term can also be written as u_n

Worked example

Find the nth term and then the 50th term of the following sequence.

66, 62, 58, 54, ...

The difference between terms is –4.

First term $= An \pm B = -4 \times 1 + B = 66$

$B - 4 = 66$

So $B = 70$

Rule for the nth term is $70 - 4n$

50th term $= 70 - 4 \times 50 = 70 - 200 = -130$

TIP: When the sequence increases, A is positive. When the sequence decreases, A is negative.

Test yourself

1. Find the nth term and then the 50th term of the following sequences.

(a) 5, 8, 11, 14, ... (b) 3, 11, 19, 27, ... (c) 22, 27, 32, 37, ...

(d) 7, 11, 15, 19, .. (e) 99, 96, 93, 90, ... (f) 125, 119, 113, 107, ...

2. Write down the first five terms of the following sequences.

(a) $2n^2$ (b) n^2+5 (c) $n(n+1)$ (d) $\dfrac{n-1}{n+2}$

Number patterns

You can find general rules from patterns.

Worked example

The following patterns are made of squares.

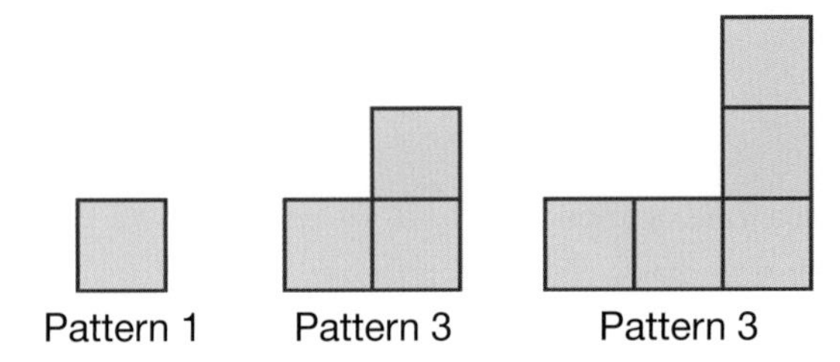

(a) Find the number of squares in the nth pattern.

(b) How many squares are there in the 40th pattern?

Answer

(a) The number of squares in the pattern increases by 2 each time, so $A=2$.

Number of squares in first pattern $=1=An+B=2\times1+B$

So $B=1-2=-1$

Number of squares in nth pattern $=2n-1$

(b) Number of squares in 40th pattern $=2\times40-1=80-1=79$

Test yourself

1. People can be seated around tables as shown. Six people can sit at one table.

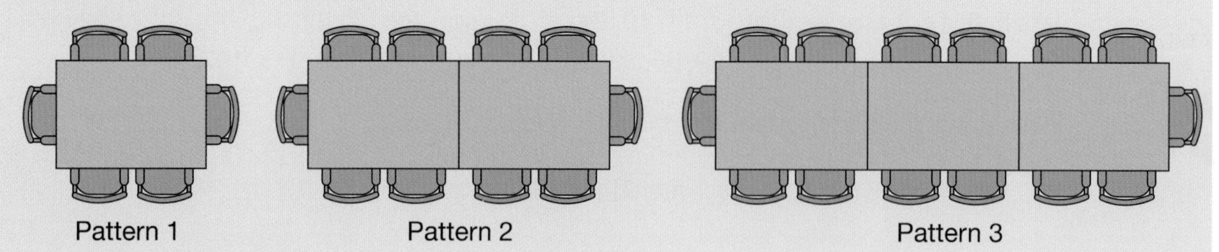

(a) Find the expression for the number of people that can be seated at n tables.

(b) Calculate the number of people that can be seated at 12 tables.

2. Patterns of hexagons are made using matchsticks as shown.

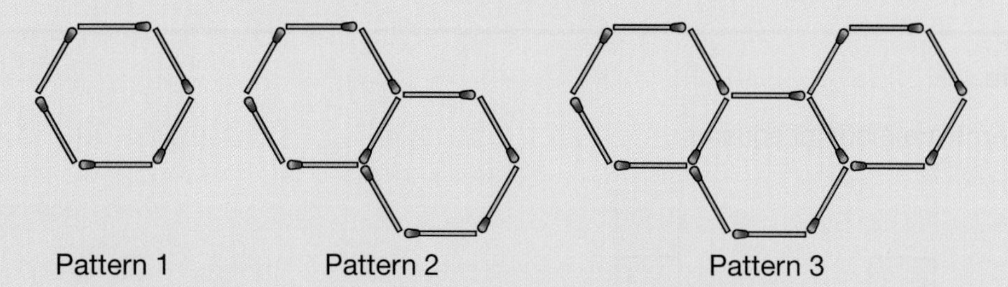

(a) How many matchsticks are needed to make n hexagons?

(b) Calculate the number of matchsticks needed to make the 50th pattern.

3. Patterns are made of squares as shown.

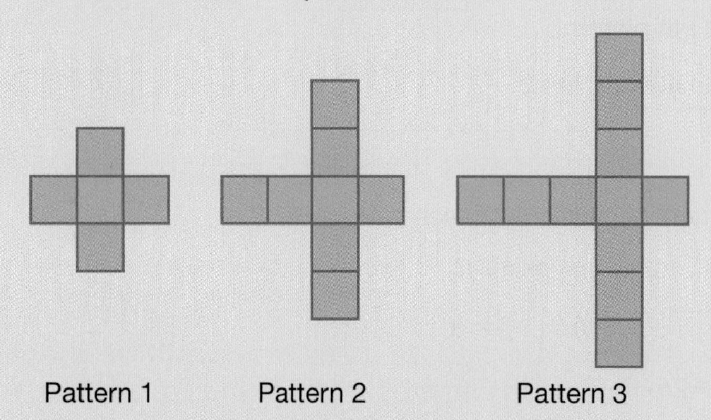

(a) Find the number of squares in the nth pattern.

(b) Calculate the number of squares in the 75th pattern.

4. Triangular patterns of matchsticks are made as shown.

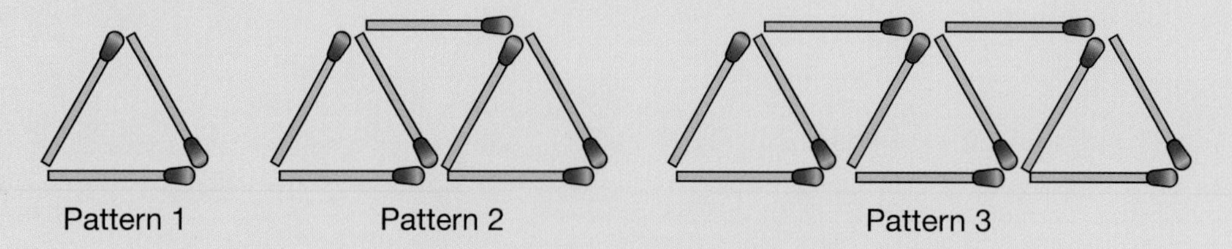

(a) Find the number of matchsticks needed to make the nth pattern.

(b) How many matchsticks are needed to make the 30th pattern?

2.11 Functions

Function notation

In the equation $y=ax^2+bx+c$, y is a function of x.

$y=$ can also be written as $f(x)=$ and $f:x\mapsto$.

$f(a)$ means the value of the function when $x=a$. Substitute a into the function and work out its value.

When there is more than one function, other letters can be used instead of f, e.g. $g(x)$, $h(x)$.

Worked example

$f(x)=\sqrt{x-5}$

Find: (a) $f(9)$ (b) x when $f(x)=-3$.

Answer

(a) Substitute $x=9$ into the function: $f(9)=\sqrt{9-5}=\sqrt{4}=\pm2$

(b) Put $f(x)=-3$: $-3=\sqrt{x-5}$

Square both sides of the equation: $9=x-5$

Solve for x: $x=9+5=14$

Test yourself

1. $f(x)=5x+3$. Find:
(a) $f(2)$ (b) $f(9)$ (c) $f(-6)$ (d) $f\left(\frac{1}{5}\right)$

2. $f(x)=2x^2-7x$. Find:
(a) $f(3)$ (b) $f(8)$ (c) $f(-4)$ (d) $f\left(\frac{1}{2}\right)$

3. $f(x)=2x^3+3x-2$. Find:
(a) $f(3)$ (b) $f(-2)$ (c) $f(10)$ (d) $f(0)$

4. $f:x\mapsto\dfrac{10}{x+2}$. Calculate:
(a) $f(3)$ (b) $f(8)$ (c) $f(-1)$ (d) $f\left(\frac{1}{2}\right)$

5. $f:x\mapsto\dfrac{x+3}{x-1}$. Calculate:
(a) $f(3)$ (b) $f(9)$ (c) $f(-3)$ (d) $f\left(\frac{1}{2}\right)$

6. $f:x\mapsto\sqrt{x+3}$. Calculate:
(a) $f(1)$ (b) $f(6)$ (c) $f(-2)$ (d) $f(3.25)$

Inverse functions

An inverse function is a function that reverses the original function. It is written as $f^{-1}(x)$.

To find the inverse of a function:

- Write the function as $y=f(x)$.
- Rearrange the equation to make x the subject.
- Replace y by x and x by y in the rearranged equation.

Worked example

$f: x \mapsto \frac{2x+4}{3}$. Find $f^{-1}(x)$.

Answer

Put $y=f(x)$: $y=\frac{2x+4}{3}$

Rearrange to make x the subject.

Multiply both sides by 3: $3y=2x+4$

Subtract 4 from both sides: $3y-4=2x$

Divide both sides by 2: $\frac{3y-4}{2}=x$

Replace y by x and x by y in the rearranged equation: $y=\frac{3x-4}{2}$

So $f^{-1}(x)=\frac{3x-4}{2}$

Test yourself

1. Find the inverses of the following functions.

(a) $f(x)=3x+2$ (b) $f(x)=\frac{x}{2}+5$ (c) $f(x)=3(2x+3)$ (d) $f(x)=\frac{2x-7}{4}$

2. $f: x \mapsto \frac{2}{x+5}$. Find:

(a) $f^{-1}(3)$ (b) $f^{-1}(10)$ (c) $f^{-1}(-5)$ (d) $f^{-1}\left(-\frac{1}{2}\right)$

TIP Finding an inverse involves rearranging a formula to make a new letter the subject of the formula. Make sure you collect all terms containing this letter on one side of the equals sign.

Composite functions

A composite function is two or more functions acting on x.

When working out a composite function, apply the last function first, then work to the left.

$fg(x)$ means apply function g to x first, then function f.

Worked example

$f(x)=(x+3)^2$, $g(x)=x-5$. Find: (a) $fg(x)$ (b) $gf(x)$ (c) $gg(x)$

Answer

(a) Start with $g(x)$ and substitute it into $f(x)$: $fg(x)=((x-5)+3)^2$
Simplify: $=(x-2)^2=x^2-4x+4$

(b) Start with $f(x)$ and substitute it into $g(x)$: $gf(x)=(x+3)^2-5$
Simplify: $=x^2+6x+9-5=x^2+6x+4$

(c) Start with $g(x)$ and substitute it into $g(x)$: $gg(x)=(x-5)-5$
Simplify: $=x-10$

Test yourself

1. $f(x)=2x+1, g(x)=\frac{x}{3}$. Find:
(a) $fg(3)$ (b) $gf(3)$ (c) $fg(x)$ (d) $gf(x)$

2. $g(x)=\frac{3}{x}, h(x)=x+2$. Find:
(a) $gh(2)$ (b) $gh(5)$ (c) $gh(x)$ (d) $hg(x)$

3. $g(x)=\frac{x-5}{2}, h(x)=2x-4$. Find:
(a) $gh(6)$ (b) $hg(6)$ (c) $gh(x)$ (d) $hg(x)$

4. $f(x)=2x^2+x$, $g(x)=2x-3$. Find:
(a) $fg(3)$ (b) $fg(8)$ (c) $fg(x)$ (d) $gf(x)$

5. $f(x)=5-x$, $g(x)=x^2-5x$. Find:
(a) $fg(x)$ (b) $gf(x)$ (c) $fg(4)$ (d) $gf(4)$

6. $f(x)=\frac{1}{x+5}, g(x)=2x-5$. Find:
(a) $fg(x)$ (b) $gf^{-1}(x)$ (c) $fg(3)$ (d) $gf^{-1}(2)$

EDE

Domain and range of a function

A function links two sets of numbers: the domain and the range. The domain is the set of values that you put into the function – the values of x.

The range is the set of values you obtain from putting the values of x into the function.

The function maps the domain onto the range.

With some functions, certain values have to be excluded from the domain, because you cannot find the range for these values.

Worked example

1. $f: x \mapsto \frac{x}{x-5}$

   What number must be excluded from the domain of f?

2. $f(x) = \sqrt{x-5}$

   (a) What is the domain of f?

   (b) Find the range for the domain {9, 14, 30}.

Answer

1. When $x=5$, the denominator is 0. $\frac{1}{0}$ is not defined, so $x \neq 5$.

2. (a) You cannot find the square root of a negative number, so x cannot be less than 5.

   The domain of x is $\{x: x \geqslant 5\}$.

   (b) $f(9)=\pm 2, f(14)=\pm 3, f(30)=\pm 5$

   So the range is {–5, –3, –2, 2, 3, 5}.

Test yourself

1. What are the domains of the following functions?

(a) $f(x) = \sqrt{x}$ (b) $f(x) = \sqrt{x+6}$ (c) $h: x \mapsto \sqrt{\frac{x-3}{2}}$

(d) $f: x \mapsto \frac{1}{x+2}$ (e) $p(x) = \frac{2x}{3x+9}$ (f) $f(x) = \frac{2}{\sqrt{x-9}}$

2. The domain is {1, 9, 36, 100}. Find the ranges of the following functions for this domain.

(a) $f(x) = 2x+1$ (b) $g(x) = 2x^2 - 9x$ (c) $f(x) = x^3 - 5x + 3$

(d) $h(x) \mapsto \sqrt{x}$ (e) $f: x \mapsto \frac{1}{x+2}$ (f) $p(x) = \frac{2x}{3x+9}$

EDE

2.12 Calculus

Differentiation

The gradient of a curve at a point is the rate of change of y with respect to x.

You can find the gradient of a curve at a point by differentiating the equation of the curve and substituting the x-value of the point into the differentiated equation.

The notation for the gradient of a curve y that is a function of x is $\frac{dy}{dx}$.

To differentiate an equation, for each term in x:

- multiply the term by the power of x
- reduce the power of x by 1
- if the power of x is zero, then the term is left out.

In general terms, when $y = ax^n$, $\frac{dy}{dx} = nax^{n-1}$.

Worked example

What is the gradient of the curve $y = 2x^2 + \frac{3}{x}$ at the point (2, 9.5)?

Answer

Rewrite the equation in index form: $y = 2x^2 + 3x^{-1}$

Differentiate with respect to x: $\frac{dy}{dx} = 2 \times 2x + -1 \times 3x^{-2} = 4x - \frac{3}{x^2}$

Substitute $x = 2$ into the equation: $4 \times 2 - \frac{3}{2^2} = 8 - \frac{3}{4} = 7\frac{1}{4}$

So the gradient at the point (2, 9.5) is $7\frac{1}{4}$.

Test yourself

1. Find the gradient of each of the following curves at the point given for each curve.

(a) $y = x^2 + 2x + 5$ at (4, 29)

(b) $y = 2x^3 + 6x^2 - 3$ at (–3, –3)

(c) $y = 4x^4 - 8x^2$ at (2, 32)

(d) $y = 2x + \frac{5}{x}$ at (5, 11)

(e) $y = 2x^2 + \frac{2}{x^2}$ at (–2, 8.5)

(f) $y = 2x(x^2 - 5)$ at (–5, 200)

2. A curve has the equation $y = 3x + \frac{4}{x} + 2$. Show that there are two points on the curve where the rate

of change in y with respect to x is –1. Find the coordinates of the points.

Turning points

A turning point is where the gradient of a curve, $\frac{dy}{dx}$, is zero.

A turning point is a minimum where the gradient is going from negative to positive around the point as x increases.

A turning point is a maximum where the gradient is going from positive to negative around the point as x increases.

To find whether a turning point is a maximum or a minimum, calculate the gradient at one point on each side of the turning point.

You can also sketch the curve by finding the coordinates of a couple of points on either side of the turning point.

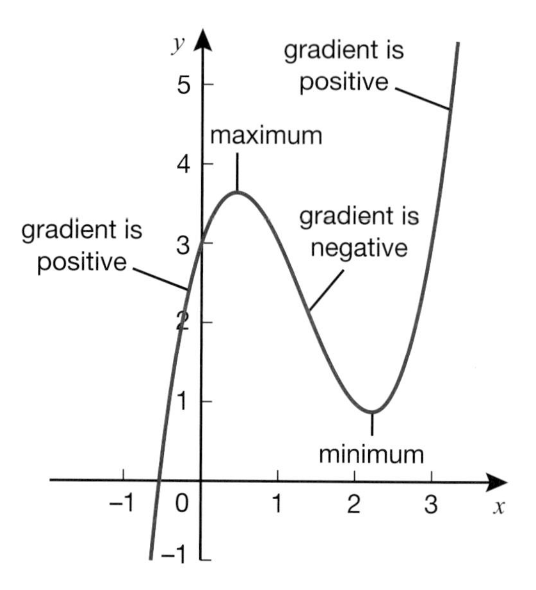

Worked example

Find the turning points of $y=2x^3-6x+10$. Give the coordinates and state whether each one is a maximum or a minimum.

Answer

$$\frac{dy}{dx}=6x^2-6$$

At a turning point $\frac{dy}{dx}=0$ so $6x^2-6=0$.

Solve equation for x:

$$6x^2=6$$
$$x^2=1$$
$$x=\pm 1$$

Substitute the values of x into the original equation:

$x=-1$: $y=-2+6+10=14$
$x=1$: $y=2-6+10=6$

The coordinates of the turning points are (–1, 14) and (1, 6).

To find out whether each point is a maximum or a minimum, calculate the gradient at a point on each side of the turning point:

x	−2	−1	0	1	2
$\frac{dy}{dx} = 6x^2 - 6$	18	0	−6	0	18
Gradient	positive /	–	negative \	–	positive /

So (−1, 14) is a maximum and (1, 6) is a minimum.

Or calculate the coordinates of a point on each side of the turning points:

x	−2	−1	0	1	2
$y = 2x^3 - 6x + 10$	6	14	10	6	14

Plot the points:

You can see from the graph that (−1, 14) is a maximum and (1, 6) is a minimum.

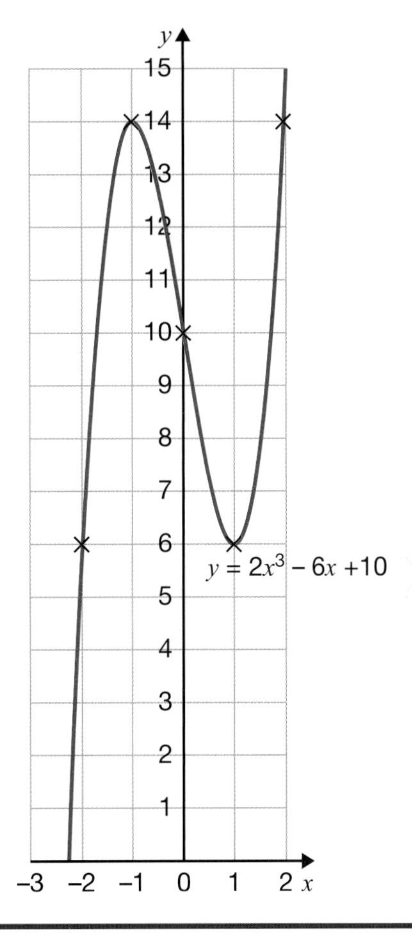

Test yourself

1. Find the coordinates of the turning point or points for each of the following curves. State whether each turning point is a maximum or a minimum.

(a) $y = 2x^2 + 6x - 5$ (b) $y = 10 + 3x - 4x^2$ (c) $y = x^3 + 5x^2 + 3$

(d) $y = 6 - 6x^2 - x^3$ (e) $y = 2x + \frac{8}{x} + 3$ (f) $y = 2x + \frac{8}{x^2} - 5$

Practical problems

Equations can be used to describe the motion of a particle moving in a straight line as a function of time, t.

As velocity is the rate of change of displacement (distance), differentiate the equation for displacement to find an equation for velocity.

As acceleration is the rate of change of velocity, differentiate the equation for velocity to find an equation for acceleration.

Worked example

The displacement of a particle, in metres, is given by the equation $s=2t^2-3t+2$, where t is in seconds and $t \geqslant 0$.

(a) Find the velocity of the particle at 2 seconds.

(b) Find the acceleration of the particle at 2 seconds.

(c) When is the velocity 0 m/s?

Answer

(a) $v=\frac{ds}{dt}=4t-3$

At 2 seconds, $v=4\times2-3=5$ m/s.

(b) $a=\frac{dv}{dt}=4$ m/s^2 (Note that the acceleration is constant.)

(c) Velocity $=0=4t-3$

$t=0.75$ seconds

The velocity is 0 at 0.75 seconds.

Test yourself

1. The displacement of a particle is given by the equation $s=3t^2-6t+5$ where s is in metres, t is in seconds and $t \geqslant 0$.

(a) At what time does the turning point happen?

(b) What is the displacement and acceleration at the turning point?

2. When a ball is dropped, its displacement in metres is given by the equation $s=4.9t^2$ where t is in seconds and $t \geqslant 0$.

(a) Find the velocity of the ball at $t=5$ s.

(b) Find the acceleration of the ball at $t=5$ s.

3. The displacement in metres of a particle at t seconds is given by $s=12t-t^2$ for $0 \leqslant t \leqslant 12$.

(a) Find the velocity and acceleration of the particle at 10 seconds.

(b) When is the particle stationary?

(c) What is the maximum displacement of the particle?

4. The displacement of a particle is given by the equation $s=2t^2(6-t)$, where s is in metres, t is in seconds and $0 \leqslant t \leqslant 6$.

(a) At what time does the turning point occur?

(b) When is the acceleration zero?

5. Th displacement in metres of a particle is given by the equation $s=\frac{t}{2}+\frac{10}{t}$ where t is in seconds and $0<t\leqslant 20$.
   (a) When is the velocity 0?
   (b) What is the minimum displacement of the particle?
   (c) What is the velocity and acceleration of the particle at 10 seconds?

6. The displacement in metres of a particle is given by the equation $s=t^4-6t+9$, where t is in seconds and $t\geqslant 0$.
   (a) When is the velocity 0 m/s?
   (b) What is the acceleration when the velocity is 0 m/s?

You should now be able to:

★ use the rules of indices (see page 45)
★ expand and factorise algebraic expressions (see page 47)
★ manipulate algebraic fractions (see page 50)
★ substitute numbers into expressions (see page 51)
★ solve linear equations (see page 54)
★ use direct and indirect variation and proportion (see page 56)
★ solve quadratic equations by factorisation, the quadratic formula and completing the square (see page 60)
★ solve simultaneous equations (see page 63)
★ find the gradient, midpoint and length of a line segment (see page 67)
★ find the equation of a straight line and a straight line parallel to it passing through a stated point (see pages 68 and 71)
★ draw graphs of linear, quadratic, cubic and reciprocal functions (see pages 68, 79, 81 and 82)
AM ★ find the equation of a line perpendicular to a straight line (see page 71)
★ draw and use conversion graphs (see page 72)
★ draw and interpret distance–time and speed–time graphs (see page 75)
DE ★ use the domain and range of a function (see page 81)
★ estimate gradients by drawing tangents to curves (see page 83)
★ solve linear inequalities (see page 86)
DE ★ solve quadratic inequalities (see page 89)
AM ★ solve problems using linear programming (see page 90)
★ find the nth term of a sequence (see page 92)
★ use function notation and find the inverse and composite functions (see page 95)
★ differentiate equations and find the maximum and minimum points of graphs (see page 99).

Practice questions

1. The force, F, between two particles varies inversely as the square of the distance, d, between them. $F=0.5$ when $d=1.6$.

Find F when $d=2.8$. **(3)**

2. $v=\sqrt{\dfrac{k+u}{d}}$

(a) Find v when $d=3.5$, $k=6$ and $u=-2$. **(2)**

(b) Make u the subject of the formula. **(3)**

3. A train travelled for 10 minutes at 100 km/h and then slowed down to 40 km/h over 1 minute. It travelled at this speed for 3.5 minutes and then slowed to a stop over 30 seconds.

The speed–time graph shows this journey.

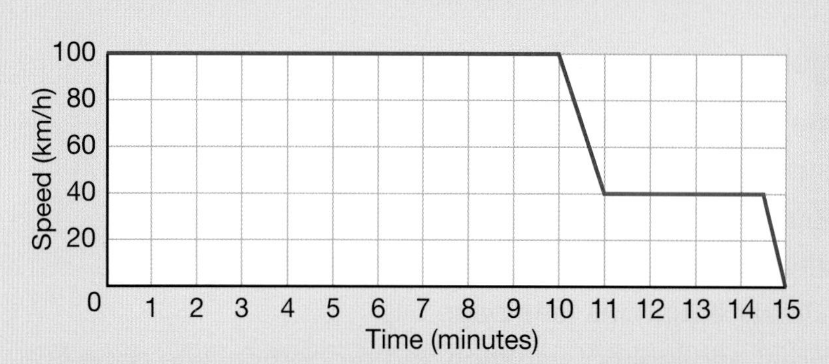

(a) Calculate the total distance travelled by the train. **(4)**

(b) Calculate the average speed of the train. Give your answer in km/h. **(2)**

4. The coordinates of A, B and C are shown on the diagram, which is not to scale.

Not to scale

y

C (2, 7)

B (7, 0)

x

A (4, –3)

(a) Work out the coordinates of the midpoint of AB. **(1)**

(b) Find the length of the line BC. **(3)**

(c) Find the equation of the line AC. **(3)**

5. $f(x)=x(x-1)$, $g(x)=2x^3-3$, $h(x)=\frac{1}{x-2}$, $(x \neq 2)$

(a) Work out $gh(1)$. **(2)**

(b) Find $g^{-1}(x)$. **(2)**

(c) Solve the equation $f(x)=12$. **(3)**

6. Factorise completely $pq+rq+ps+rs$. **(2)**

7. A sequence is given by $u_1=\sqrt{5}, u_2=\sqrt{8}, u_3=\sqrt{11}, u_4=\sqrt{14}$.

(a) Find a formula for the nth term. **(2)**

(b) Find u_{34}. **(1)**

8. Write as a single fraction in its simplest form: $\frac{8}{x+8}-\frac{2}{x+2}$. **(3)**

9. The region R is bounded by three lines. Write down the three inequalities which define the region R. **(5)**

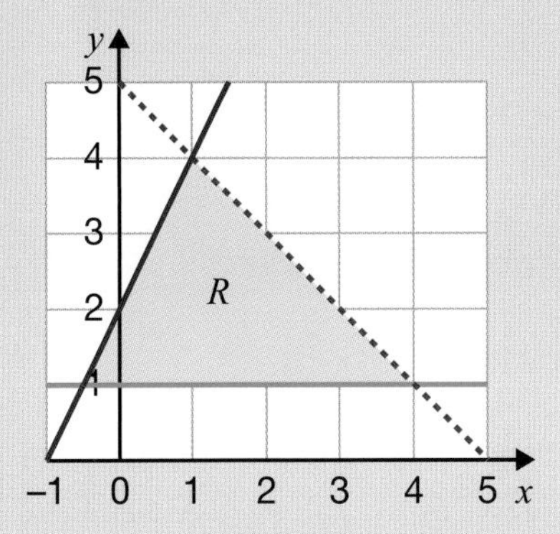

10. $p=\frac{q}{\sqrt{rs}}$

(a) Find p when $q=6\times10^3$, $r=1.8\times10^{-7}$ and $s=8\times10^4$. **(3)**

(b) Rearrange the formula to make r the subject. **(3)**

11. Solve the simultaneous equations: $2x+3y=13$, $4x+2y=14$. **(3)**

12. $bx=ax+by$

Write x in terms of a, b and y. **(3)**

13. The time, t, for a pendulum to swing varies directly as the square root of its length, l.

When $l=25$, $t=1$.

(a) Find a formula for t in terms of l. **(2)**

(b) Find t when $l=144$. **(1)**

14. Write as a single fraction, in its simplest form: $\frac{2+x}{x}-\frac{2x+3}{2x-1}$ **(4)**

15. Car A accelerates from 0 m/s to 30 m/s in 12 seconds and then travels at a constant speed of 30 m/s. Car B accelerates from 0 m/s to 30 m/s in 20 seconds.

(a) Calculate the acceleration of car A in the first 12 seconds. **(2)**

(b) Calculate the difference in the distance that the two cars travel in the first 20 seconds. **(4)**

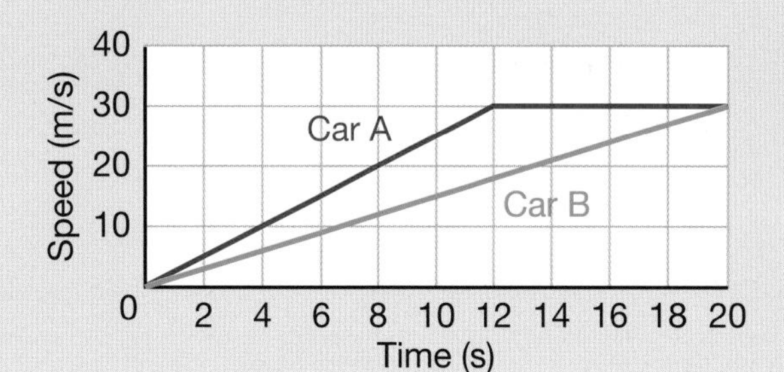

16. (a) Find the integer values for x which satisfy the inequality $-4 < 3x + 2 \leqslant 8$. **(3)**

(b) Simplify $\dfrac{x^2 - 36}{x^2 - 9x + 18}$. **(3)**

(c) Show that $\dfrac{3}{x-5} - \dfrac{2}{x-1} = 4$ simplifies to $4x^2 - 25x + 13 = 0$. **(3)**

(d) Solve the equation $4x^2 - 25x - 13 = 0$, giving your answer to two decimal places. **(4)**

17. (a) Copy and complete the table for the function $f : x \mapsto \dfrac{x^3}{4} - 5x + 1$ for $-5 \leqslant x \leqslant 5$. **(6)**

x	−5	−4	−3	−2	−1	0	1	2	3	4	5
$f : x$	−5.25		9.25		5.75		−3.75				7.25

(b) Draw the graph of $y = f : x \; -5 \leqslant x \leqslant 5$. **(4)**

(c) Use your graph to solve $f : x = 4$. **(3)**

(d) Find the inequalities for k such that $f : x = k$ has only one answer. **(2)**

(e) On the same grid, draw the graph of $y = 2x - 3$ for $0 \leqslant x \leqslant 5$. **(3)**

(f) The equation $\dfrac{x^3}{4} - 5x + 1 = 2x - 3$ can be written in the form $x^3 + bx + c = 0$.

Find the values of b and c. **(2)**

(g) Use your graph to find the positive solutions to $\dfrac{x^3}{4} - 5x + 1 = 2x - 3$. **(2)**

18. Mr Smith has been asked to supply coaches for a school trip. There are 360 students and teachers going on the trip. He needs x small coaches and y large coaches.

A small coach can take 30 people and a large coach 45 people.

There are 6 large coaches and 6 small coaches available.

(a) Write inequalities to show the following:

(i) the number of large coaches he can use **(1)**

(ii) the number of small coaches he can use **(1)**

(iii) the number of people that can be taken on x small coaches and y large coaches. **(2)**

(b) Draw these inequalities on a graph. Shade the unwanted regions. **(5)**

(c) A small coach costs £350 and a large coach £500.

(i) Find the number of small coaches and large coaches that would give the minimum cost for this trip. **(2)**

(ii) Calculate the minimum cost. **(1)**

19. Solve $\frac{3x+2}{5}+\frac{x-4}{2}=5$. **(3)**

20. Solve $3x+4=5x+14$. **(2)**

21. $V=3x^2-12x+50$

(a) Find $\frac{dV}{dx}$. **(2)**

(b) Find the value of x for which V is a minimum. **(2)**

(c) Explain how you know this is a minimum. **(1)**

(d) Find the gradient of the curve when $x=5$. **(1)**

22. M is directly proportional to the cube of N.

When $N=4$, $M=12.4$.

(a) Find an equation linking M and N. **(2)**

(b) Find M when $N=3$. **(1)**

23. $f(x)=\frac{8}{x-4}$, $g(x)=3x+5$

(a) Find $f^{-1}(x)$. **(2)**

(b) Find $gf(x)$. Simplify your answer. **(2)**

24. The diagram shows the graph of $y = f(x)$

where $f(x) = -\frac{2}{x} + x^2$ for $-3 \leqslant x \leqslant 0$.

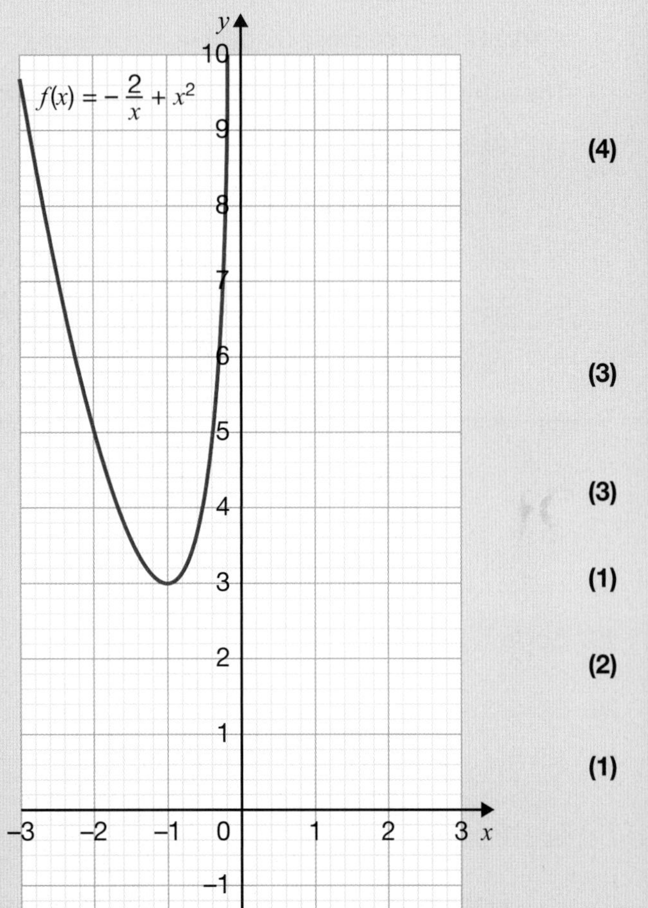

(a) Copy and complete the table for $f(x) = -\frac{2}{x} + x^2$ for $0.2 \leqslant x \leqslant 3$. **(4)**

x	0.2	0.4	0.6	1	2	3
$f(x)$	–10			–1		

(b) Copy and complete the graph of $y = f(x)$ for $-3 \leqslant x \leqslant 3$. **(3)**

(c) By drawing a tangent, work out an estimate of the gradient of the graph where $x = -2$. **(3)**

(d) Write down the inequality satisfied by k when $f(x) = k$ has three answers. **(1)**

(e) Draw the line $y = x - 6$ on the grid for $-3 \leqslant x \leqslant 3$. **(2)**

(f) Use your graph to solve the equation $-\frac{2}{x} + x^2 = x - 6$. **(1)**

(g) Rearrange $x^3 - x^2 - 2x - 2 = 0$ in the form $-\frac{2}{x} + x^2 = ax + b$ where a and b are integers. **(2)**

(h) Write down the equation of the line that could be drawn on the graph to solve $x^3 - x^2 - 2x - 2 = 0$. **(1)**

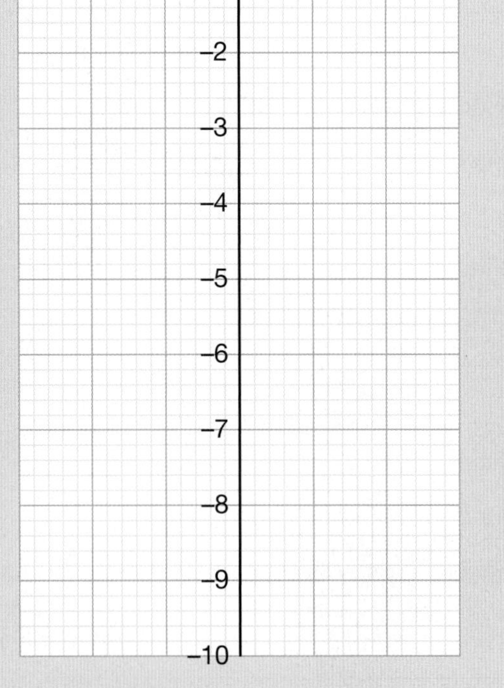

Section Three

3 Geometry and measure

You will be expected to:

- ★ know the properties of angles, polygons, symmetrical 2-D and 3-D shapes and circles
- ★ construct geometrical shapes and loci
- ★ use three-figure bearings and Pythagoras
- ★ calculate perimeters, surface areas and volumes of 2-D and 3-D shapes
- ★ use units of mass, length, area, volume and capacity and convert between different units
- ★ use similarity to solve problems
- ★ use vectors
- ★ identify and describe a range of transformations.

3.1 Lines and angles

Angles and triangles

An acute angle is between 0° and 90°.

A right angle is exactly 90°.

An obtuse angle is between 90° and 180°.

A reflex angle is between 180° and 360°.

The angles on a straight line add up to 180°.

The angles at a point add up to 360°.

The angles in a triangle add up to 180°.

An equilateral triangle has all three angles the same size and all three sides the same length.

An isosceles triangle has two angles the same size and two sides the same length.

A scalene triangle has all three angles different sizes and all three sides different lengths.

A right-angled triangle has one right angle.

The exterior angle in a triangle makes a straight line with the side of the triangle.

In the triangle, $a+b+c=d+c=180°$. $d=a+b$

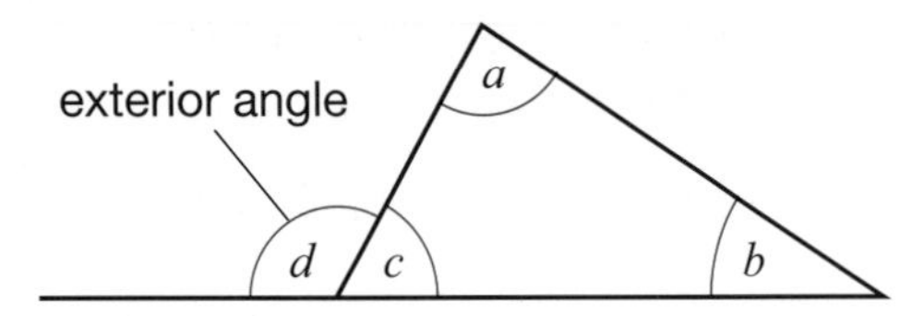

Test yourself

1. Explain whether a right-angled triangle is always a scalene triangle.
2. Find the sizes of the angles shown.

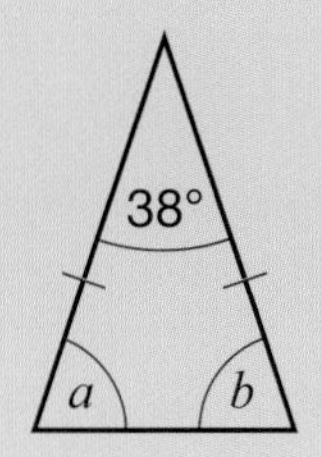

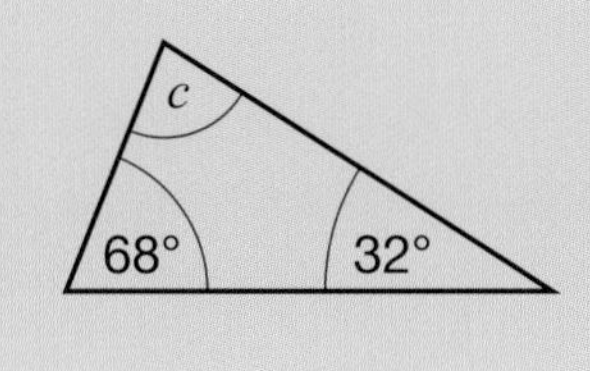

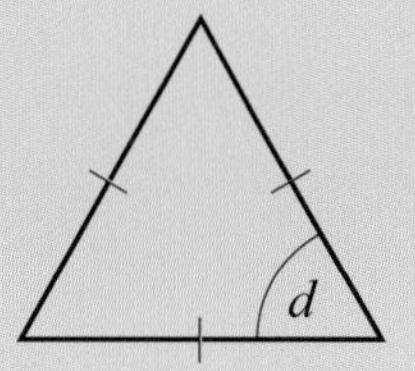

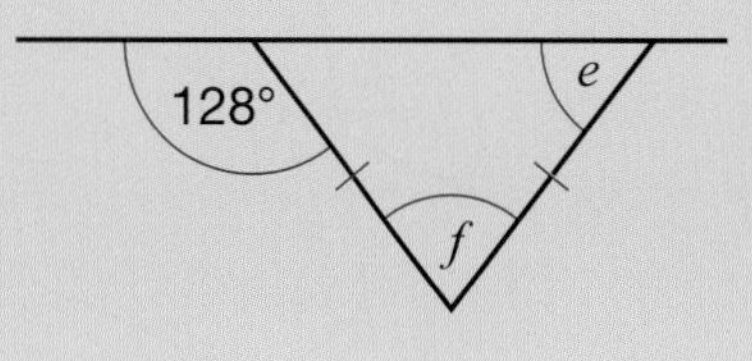

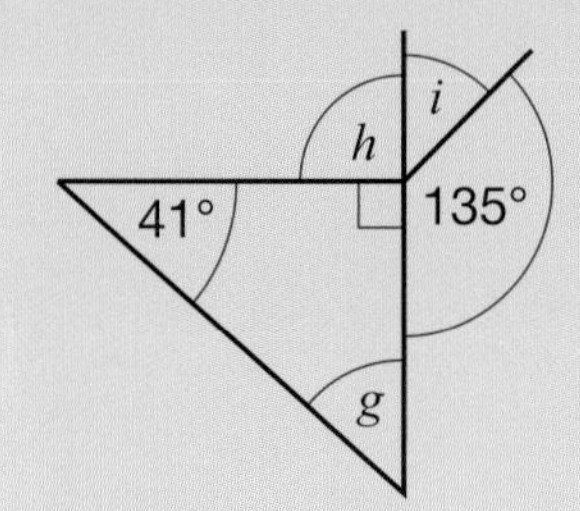

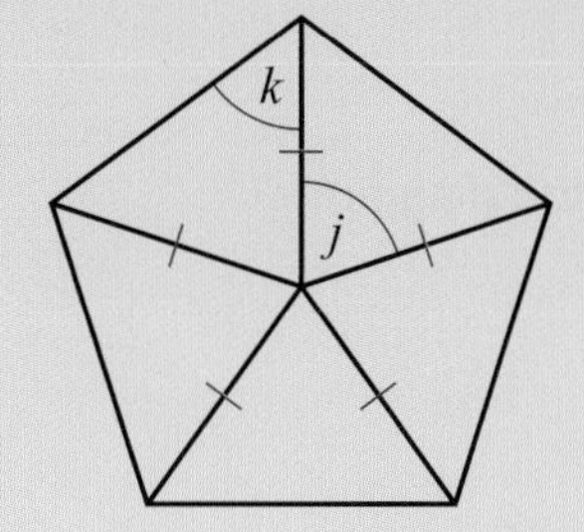

Lines and angles

A transversal is a line that crosses two or more parallel lines.

Angles d and f are alternate angles – alternate angles are equal.

Angles a and e are corresponding angles – corresponding angles are equal.

Angles c and f are interior angles – interior angles are on the same side of the transversal and inside the parallel lines. They add up to 180°.

Angles a and c are opposite angles – opposite angles are equal.

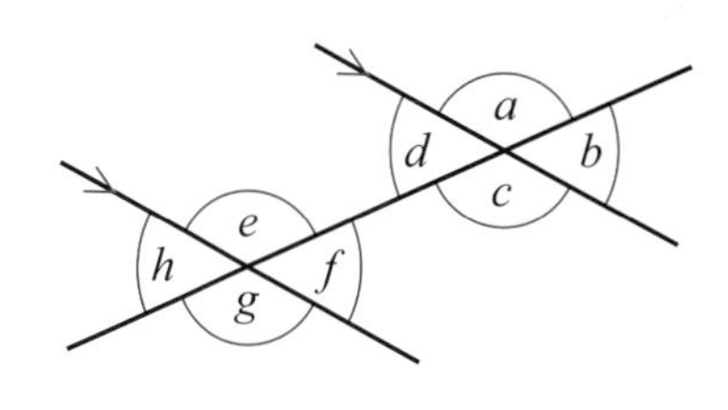

Worked example

In the diagram above, angle $a = 142°$.

Find the sizes of angles b to h.

TIP Note that there are two, and sometimes three or four, different ways of finding each angle.

Answer

$b = 180° - 142° = 38°$ (angles on a straight line add up to 180°)

$c = a = 142°$ (opposite angles); or $b + c = 180°$ (angles on a straight line)

$d = b = 38°$ (opposite angles); or $a + d = 180°$ (angles on a straight line)

$e = a = 142°$ (corresponding angles); or $e = c$ (alternate angles) or $d + e = 180°$ (interior angles)

$f = d = 38°$ (alternate angles); or $f = b$ (corresponding angles); or $c + f = 180°$ (interior angles); or $e + f = 180°$ (angles on a straight line)

$g = c = 142°$ (corresponding angles); or $g = e$ (opposite angles); or $f + g = 180°$ (angles on a straight line)

$h = f = 38°$ (opposite angles); or $h = d$ (corresponding angles); or $e + h = g + h = 180°$ (angles on a straight line)

Test yourself

1. Find the sizes of the marked angles in the diagram.

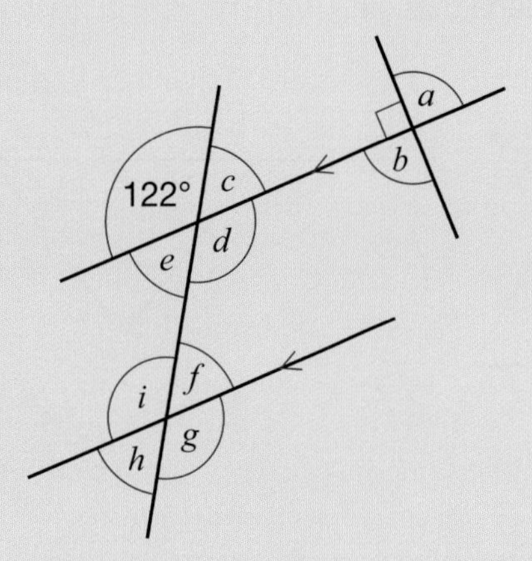

2. Find the sizes of the marked angles in the diagram.

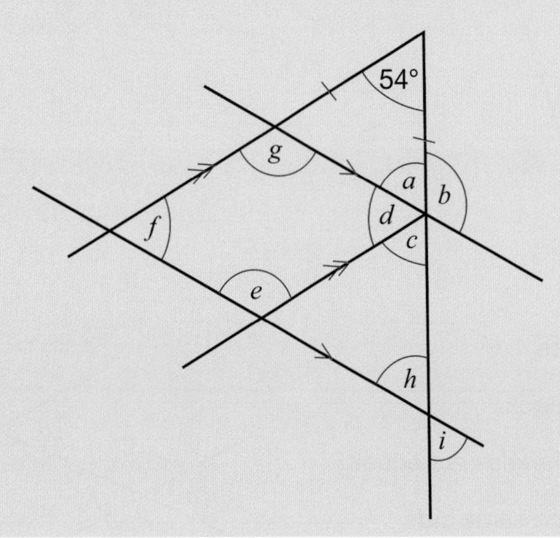

3.2 Polygons

Quadrilaterals

The properties of a square, rectangle, parallelogram, rhombus, trapezium and kite are shown in the diagrams.

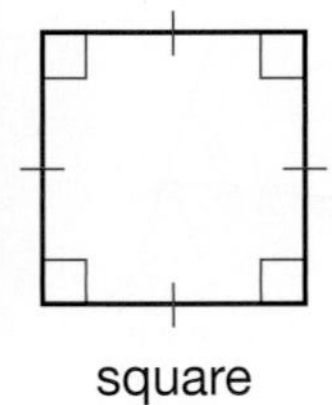
square

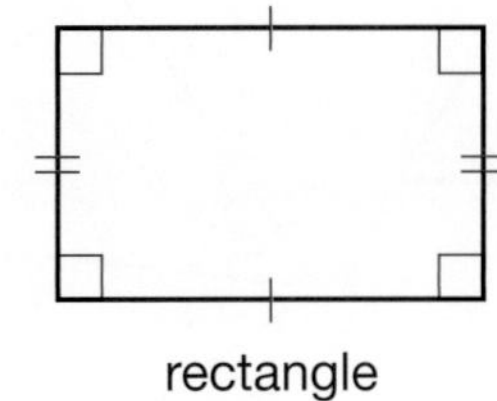
rectangle

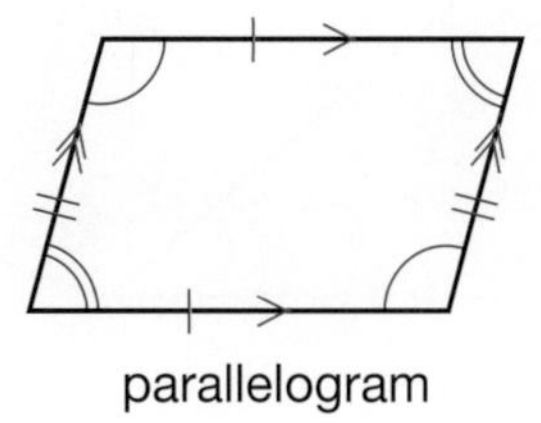
parallelogram

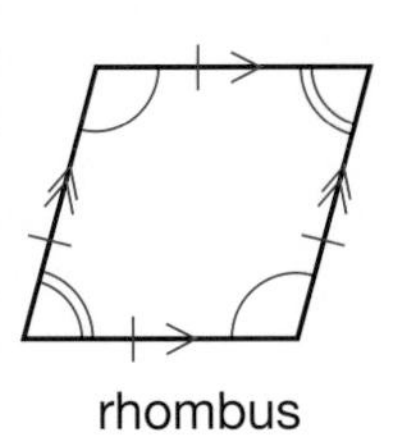
rhombus

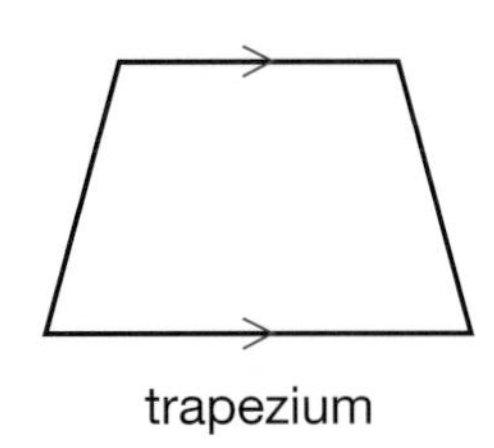
trapezium

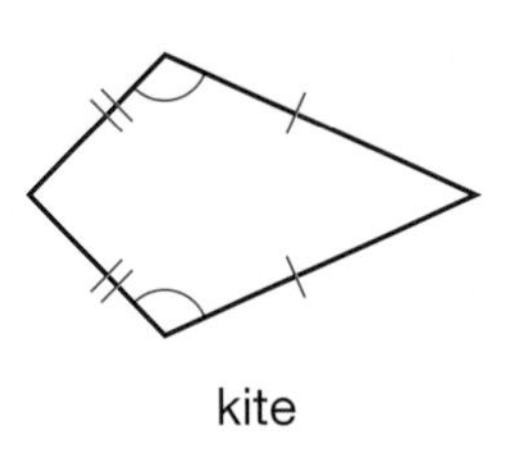
kite

The sum of the interior angles in a quadrilateral is 360°.

Worked example

Find the sizes of the marked angles in the diagram.

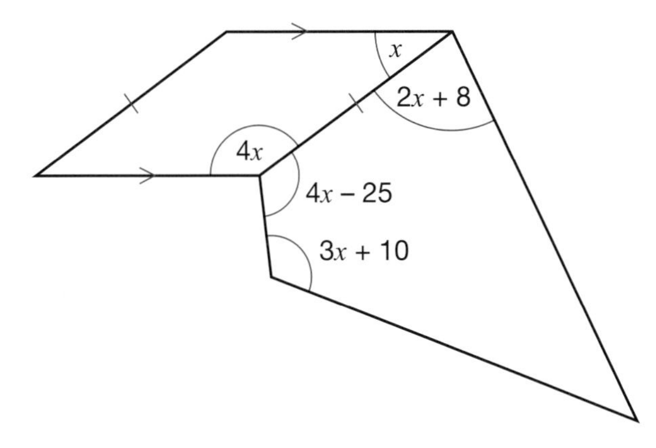

Answer

The angles $4x$ and x are interior angles so $4x+x=180°$

$$5x=180°$$

$$x=36°$$

So the two angles are 36° and 144°.

$2x+8=2\times36+8=80°$

$4x-25=4\times36-25=119°$

$3x+10=3\times36+10=118°$

Test yourself

1. Find the sizes of the marked angles in the diagrams.

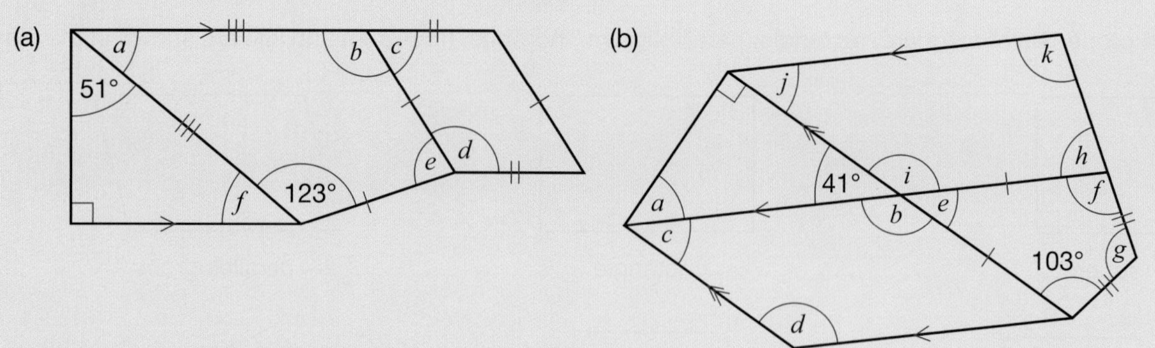

2. Find the sizes of the marked angles in the diagrams.

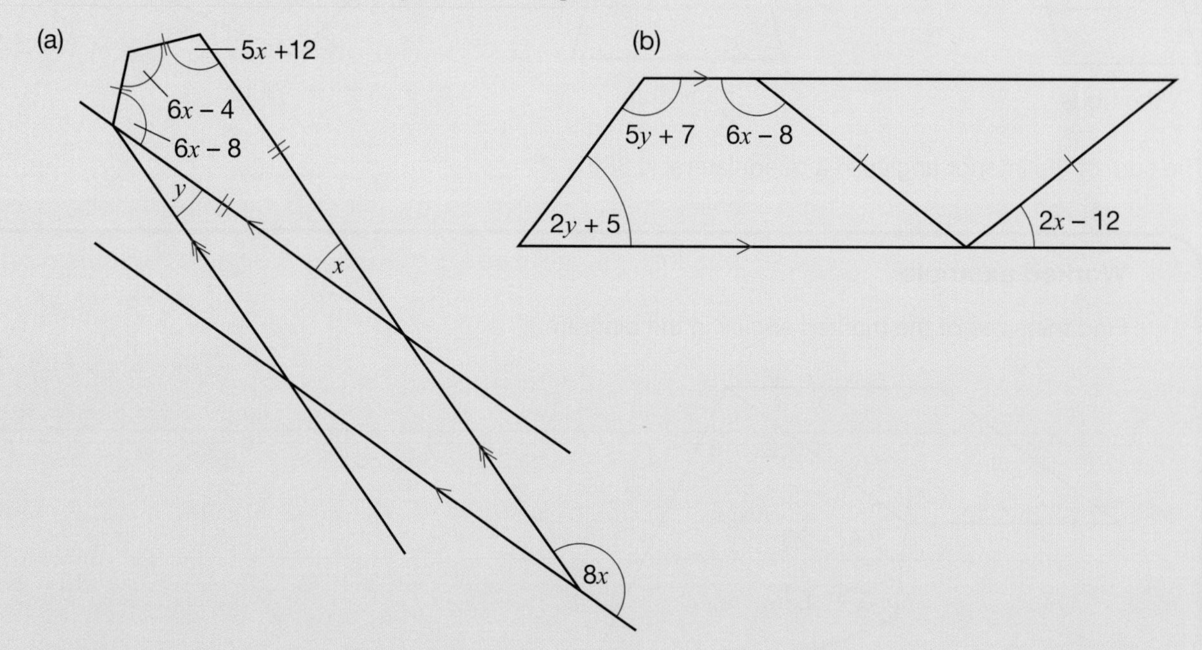

3. The four angles of a quadrilateral are $(x+15)°$, $(x+20)°$, $(2x-10)°$ and $(3x-15)°$. Find the value of x.

4. Explain whether all squares are rectangles.

5. Explain whether all rhombuses are parallelograms.

6. Explain whether all squares are rhombuses.

7. Explain whether all kites are rhombuses.

Polygons

A polygon is a shape with three or more sides.

A regular polygon has all sides the same length and all interior angles the same size.

The angle sum of the interior angles of an n-sided polygon is $s=180(n-2)°$ or $(2n-4)$ right angles.

The exterior angle of a regular n-sided polygon is $\frac{360°}{n}$.

The sum of the exterior and interior angles of a polygon is 180°.

Polygons which have the same shape and size are congruent.

TIP

If you cannot remember the formula for the sum of the interior angles of a polygon, split the polygon into triangles by drawing lines across the polygon from one vertex to each of the other vertices that is not already connected to it. The sum of the interior angles is the number of triangles multiplied by 180°. A hexagon splits into four triangles so, sum of interior angles $= 4 \times 180° = 720°$.

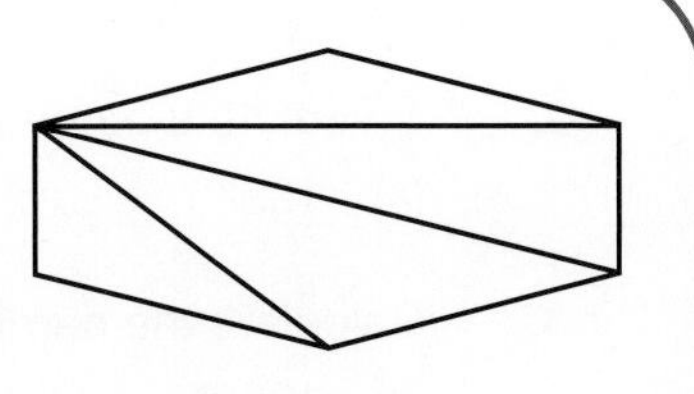

Worked example

1. The interior angle of a regular polygon is 160°. How many sides does the polygon have?
2. The sum of the interior angles of a polygon is 900°. How many sides does the polygon have?
3. Find the value of x in this shape.

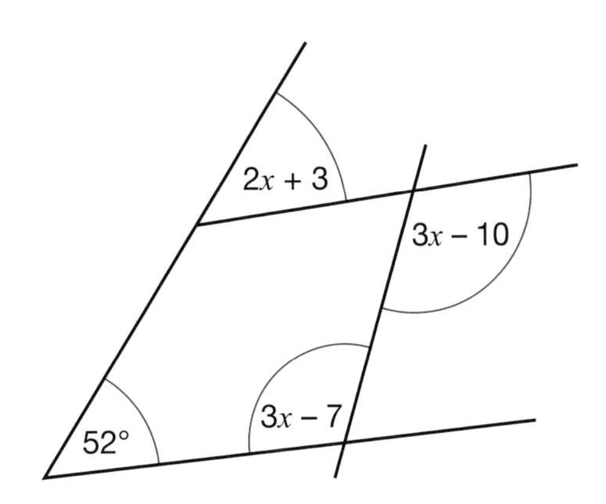

Answer

1. Exterior angle + interior angle = 180°

   Exterior angle $= 180° - 160° = 20°$

   Exterior angle $= \frac{360°}{n}$, so $n = \frac{360°}{20°} = 18$

   The polygon has 18 sides.

2. Sum of interior angles $= 180(n-2)°$

   So $900° = 180(n-2)°$

   Solving for n: $900 = 180n - 360$

   $180n = 1260$

   $n = 7$

   The polygon has 7 sides.

3. Use the sum of the interior angles = 360° and exterior angle + interior angle = 180°.

   $180 - (2x+3) + 180 - (3x-10) + 3x - 7 + 52 = 360$

   Solve for x. $180 - 2x - 3 + 180 - 3x + 10 + 3x - 7 + 52 = 360$

   $-2x - 3 - 3x + 10 + 3x - 7 + 52 = 0$

   $-2x + 52 = 0$

   $2x = 52$

   $x = 26$

Test yourself

1. Calculate the number of sides of a regular polygon when the exterior angle is:
   (a) 36° (b) 60° (c) 72°

2. Calculate the number of sides of a regular polygon when the interior angle is:
   (a) 135° (b) 150° (c) 156°

3. Calculate the number of sides in a polygon when the sum of the interior angles is:
   (a) 1260° (b) 1620° (c) 2160°

4. Find x in each of these shapes.

(a)

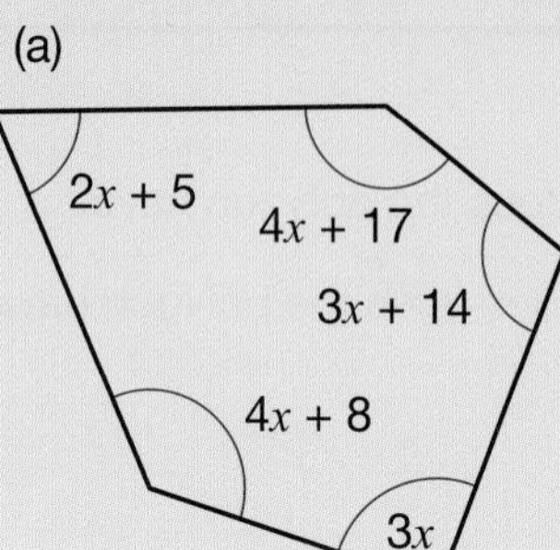

(b)

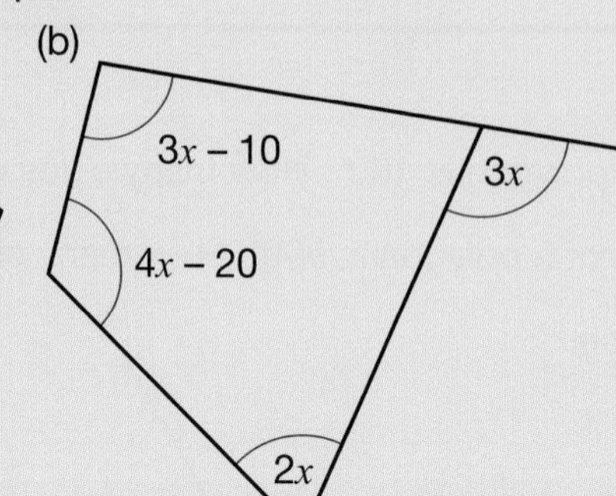

(c)

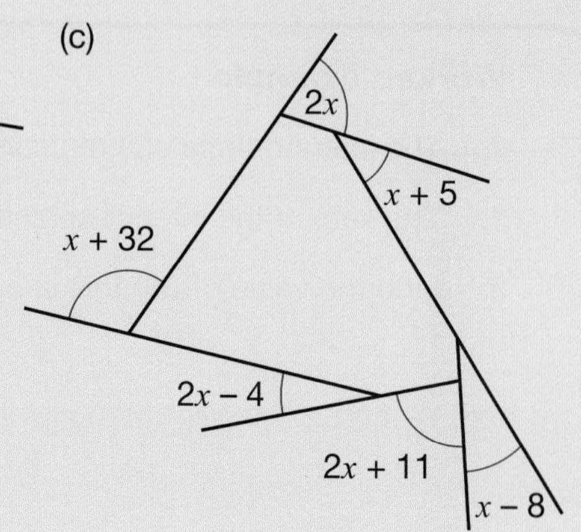

3.3 Construction

Construction

You can use a protractor to measure and draw any angle.

You can use a ruler to measure and draw line segments.

You can construct polygons using combinations of a ruler, compasses and a protractor.

Worked example

Construct a triangle with sides of length 6 cm, 5 cm and 4 cm.

Answer

1. Draw a line of length 6 cm using a ruler.
2. Set the compasses to a distance of 5 cm. Draw an arc from one end of the line segment.
3. Set the compasses to a distance of 4 cm. Draw an arc from the other end of the line segment.
4. Draw straight lines (using the ruler) from the point where the two arcs intersect to each end of the 6 cm line.

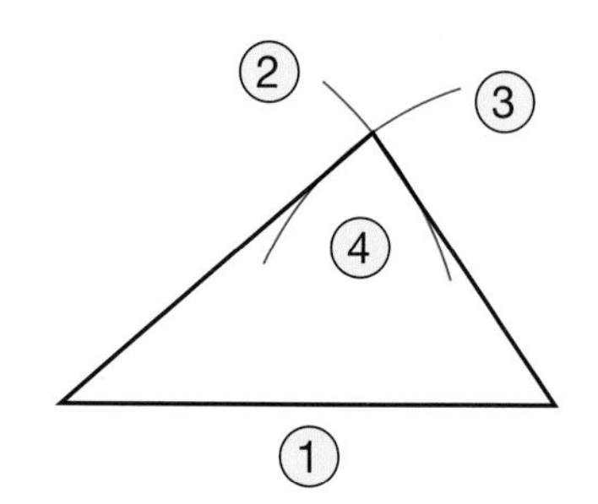

Test yourself

1. Use a protractor to measure the angles and a ruler to measure the lengths of the line segments.

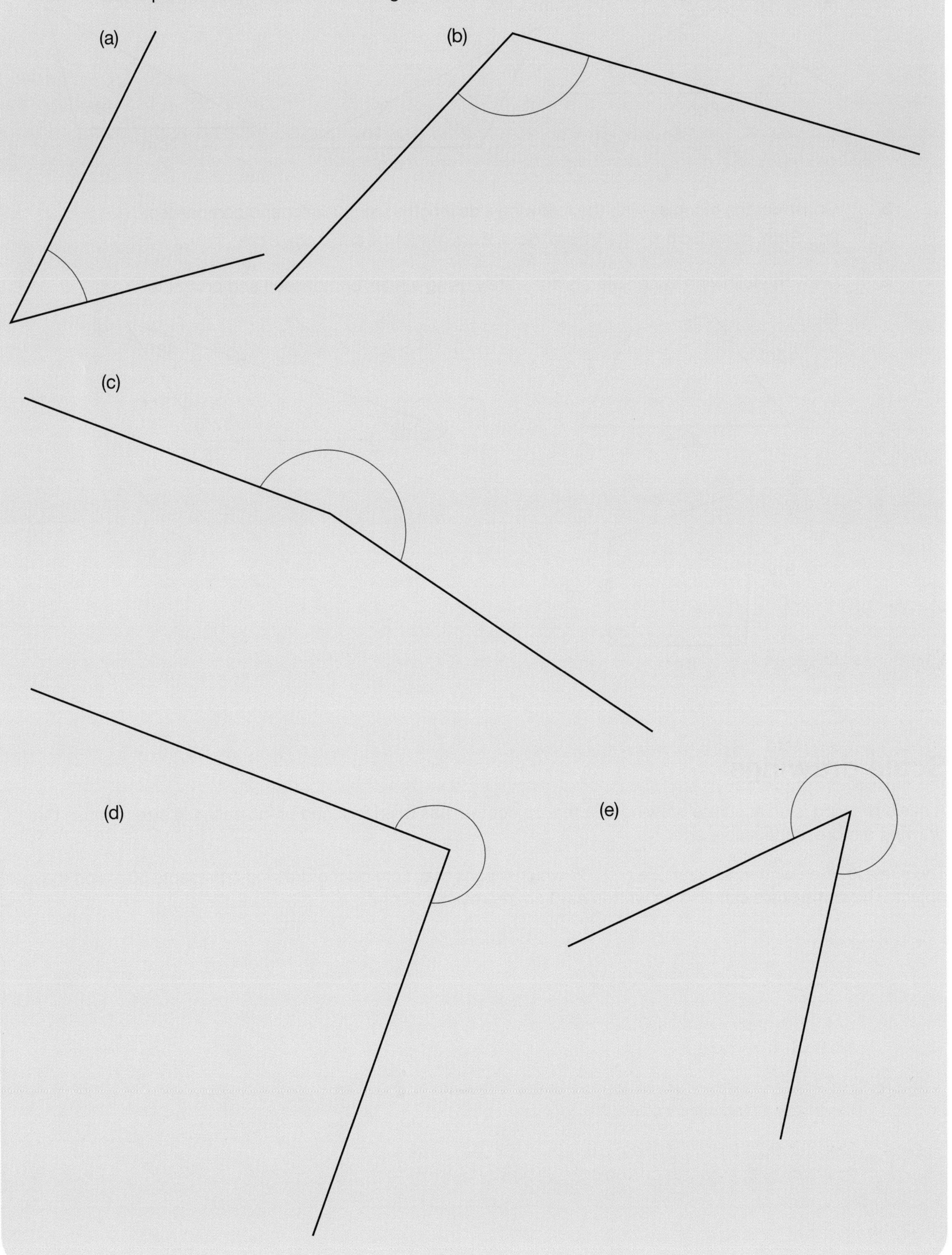

2. Use a ruler and a protractor to draw these triangles accurately. Then measure the sizes of the other angles and lengths of the other lines.

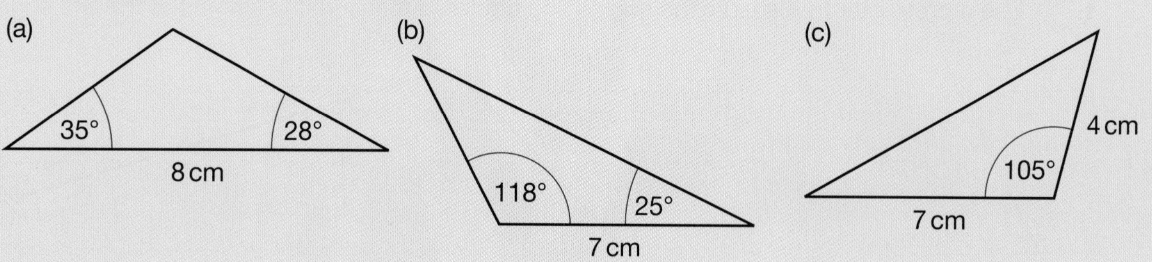

3. Construct the triangles with the following side lengths using a ruler and compasses.

(a) 3 cm, 4 cm, 5 cm (b) 5 cm, 6 cm, 8 cm (c) 6 cm, 3 cm, 8 cm

4. Draw the following quadrilaterals accurately using a ruler, compasses and protractor.

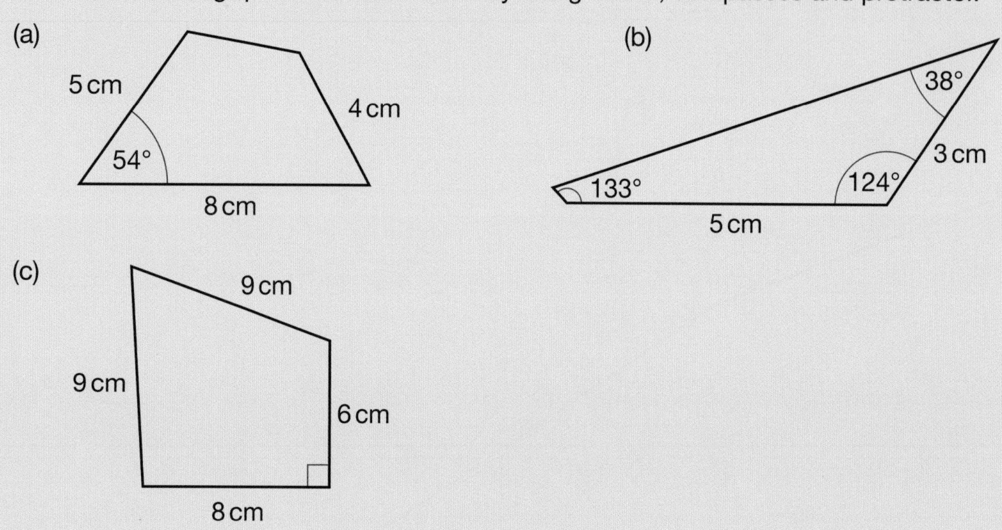

Scale drawings

A scale drawing is an accurate drawing of a real object that has been reduced or increased in size to make the drawing a more manageable size.

The scale is often written as a ratio, e.g. 1 : 50 which means that 1 cm on the drawing represents 50 cm on the real object. The same scale can also be written as '1 cm represents 50 cm'.

Test yourself

1. The diagram shows a plan of the units in Sam's new kitchen.
Scale: 1 cm represents 20 cm.

(a) What are the dimensions of the sink?
(b) How long is the work surface altogether?
(c) Sam wants to put a large fridge freezer in the space on the left. The fridge freezer is 90 cm wide. Will it fit?
(d) Write the scale as a ratio.

2. The diagram shows the positions of three cities. The scale is 4 cm to 100 km.

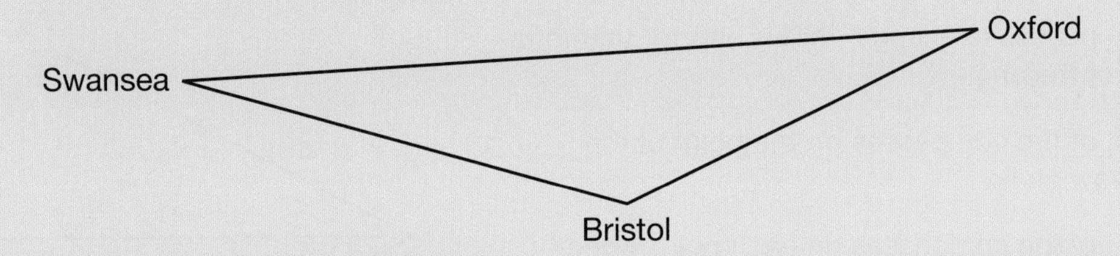

(a) What is the distance between:
(i) Bristol and Oxford (ii) Oxford and Swansea (iii) Bristol and Swansea?
(b) Express the scale as a ratio.

3. Draw each of the following diagrams accurately as a scale diagram, using the scale shown.

(a)

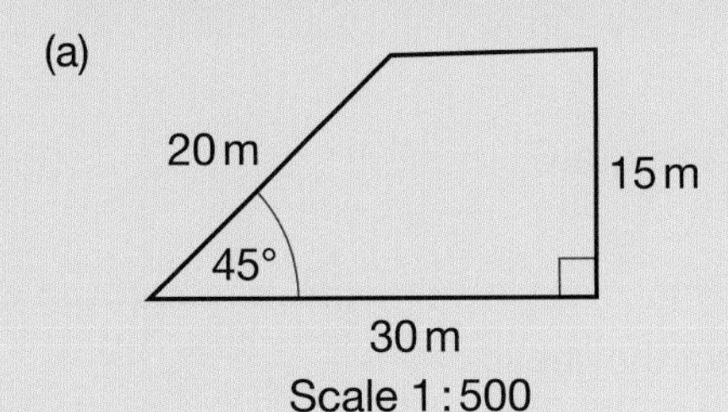

Scale 1 : 500

(b)

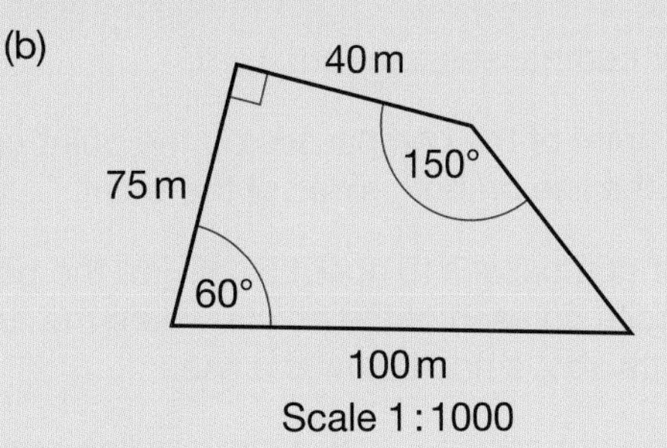

Scale 1 : 1000

Bisectors

You can use a ruler or straight edge and compasses to construct bisectors of lines and angles.

Constructing the bisector of a line segment or a perpendicular to a line produces a right angle.

Drawing an equilateral triangle produces an angle of 60°.

You can use combinations of these constructions to construct angles of 15°, 30°, 45°, 75° and 90°.

Worked example

1. Construct the bisector of a line segment.
2. Construct the bisector of an angle.
3. Construct a perpendicular from a point on a line.
4. Construct an angle of 60°.

TIP

When a question says 'construct', you must use compasses. Do NOT use a protractor.

Make sure that you show your construction arcs clearly so that the examiner can see what you have done.

Answer

1. Set your compasses to about three-quarters of the length of the line segment.

   Put the point of the compasses on each end of the line and draw two arcs – one above the line, the other below the line.

   Use a straight edge to draw a line between the two points where the arcs intersect.

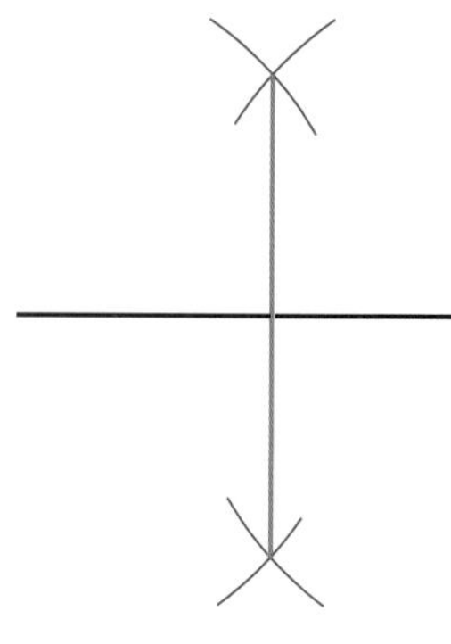

2. Set your compasses to a length that is shorter than one of the sides of the angle.

   Put the point of the compasses on the point of the angle and draw an arc.

   Put the point of the compasses on each point where the arc intersects the side of the angle and draw another arc.

   Use a straight edge to draw a line from the angle to the point where the two arcs intersect.

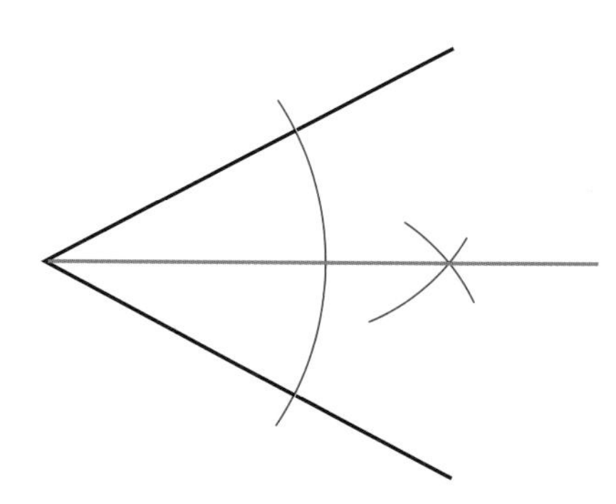

3. Set your compasses to about 3 cm.

   Put the point of the compasses on the point on the line and draw arcs on the line on both sides of the point.

   Set your compasses to about 5 cm. Put the point of the compasses on each of the points where the arcs intersect the line. Draw arcs above and below the line.

   Use a straight edge to draw a straight line between the points where the arcs intersect above and below the line.

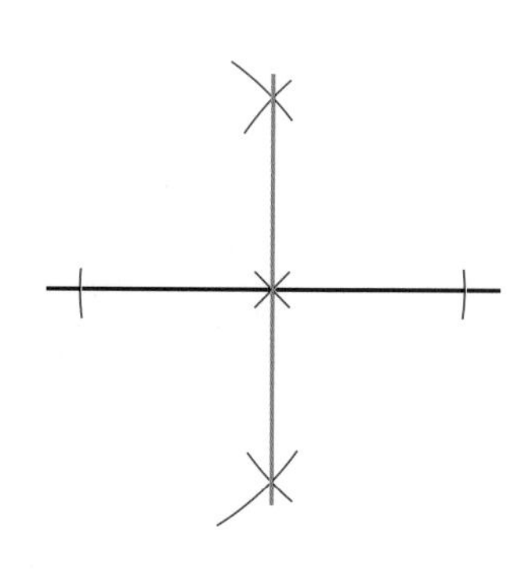

4. Draw a line segment.

   Set your compasses to the same length as the line segment. Draw arcs from each end of the line segment.

   Use a straight edge to draw a straight line from the point where the arcs intersect to one end of the line segment.

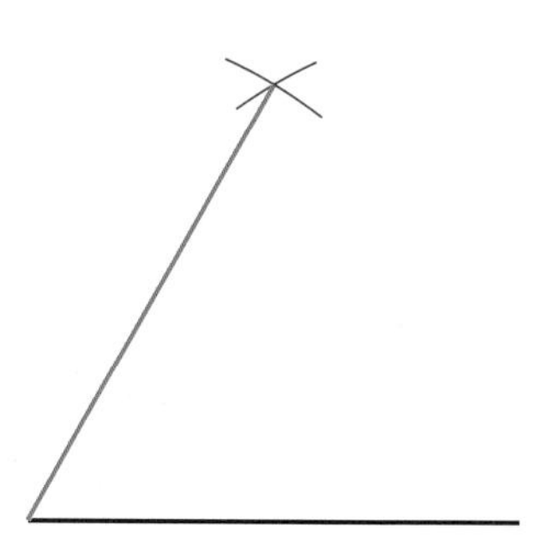

Test yourself

1. Draw a line 7.5 cm long. Bisect the line.

2. Construct the following angles.
(a) 30° (b) 45° (c) 165°

AM

Loci

A locus is a point that moves a fixed distance from a point or line or is equidistant between two fixed points or lines.

Worked example

1. A line segment is 6 cm long. A point moves so that it is always 4 cm from this line.

   Draw the locus of this point.

2. Draw the locus of a point that moves equidistant from the two lines shown in the diagram.

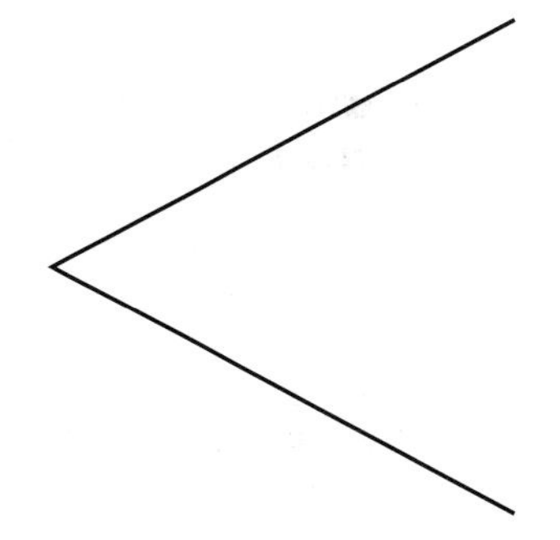

Answer

1. The point moves along lines that are 4 cm above and 4 cm below the line. These lines are parallel to the original line segment. Draw these two lines.

   The point will move in a semicircle around each end of the line segment.

   Set your compasses to 4 cm and draw semicircles at each end of the line segment.

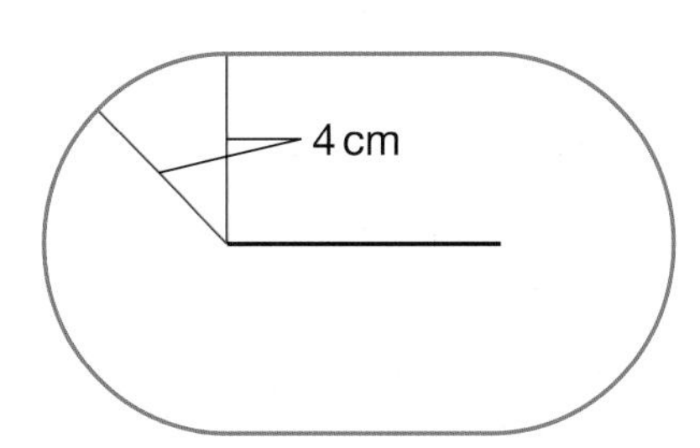

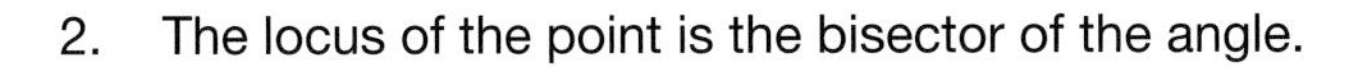

2. The locus of the point is the bisector of the angle.

   Construct the bisector of the angle.

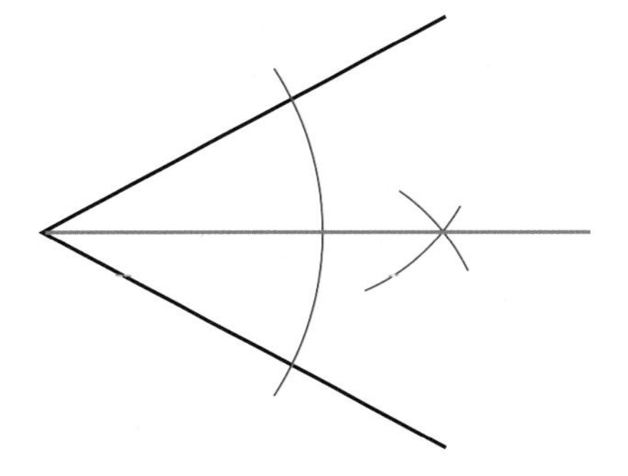

Test yourself

1. Draw the locus of a point that is 6 cm from a fixed point.

2. Draw the locus of a point that is 7 cm from the line segment shown in the diagram. The line segment is 5 cm long.

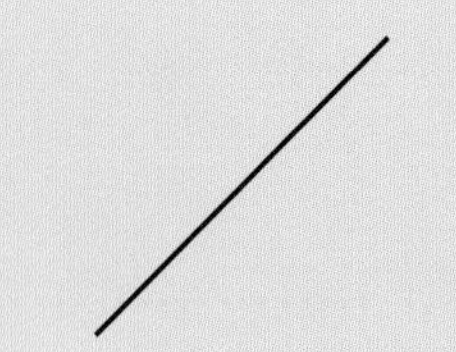

3. Draw the locus of a point that is 5 cm from the line segments shown in the diagram.

   Each line segment is 6 cm long. The line segments are perpendicular to each other.

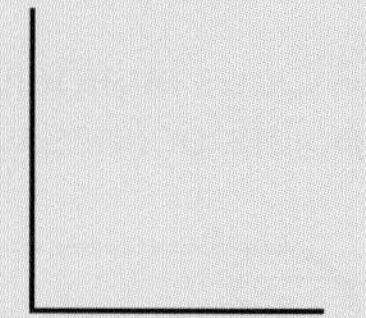

4. Draw the locus of a point that is equidistant from points P and Q as shown in the diagram.

5. Draw the locus of a point that is equidistant from the two lines shown in the diagram.

6. The diagram shows a field. A goat is tethered at point P with a rope that is 25 m long. Can the goat eat the grass at point G?

   Draw an accurate scale drawing of the field to help you.

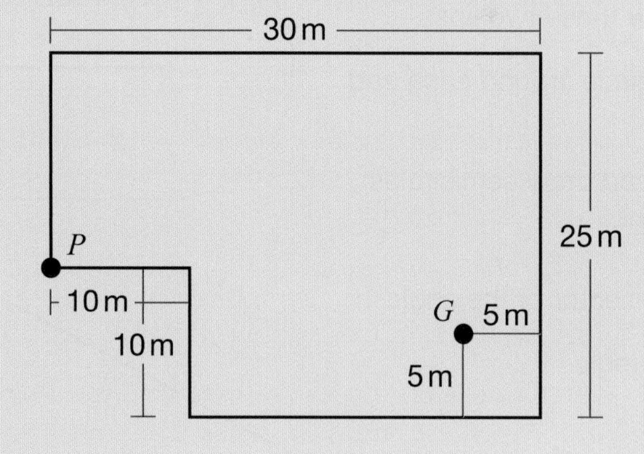

3.4 Circles

Circles, tangents and chords

The names for different parts of a circle are shown in the diagram.

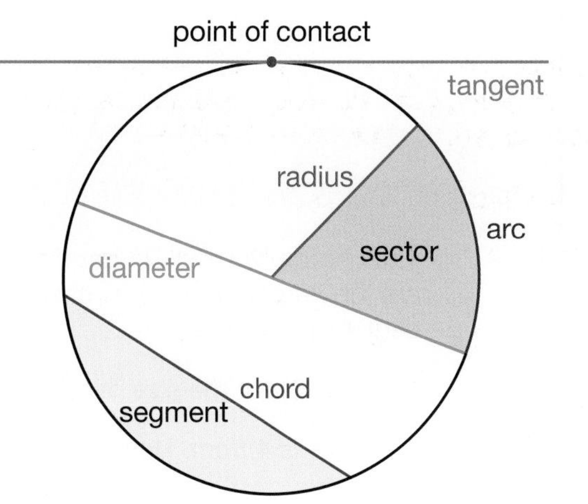

A diameter divides a circle into two semicircles.

A tangent (AB) to a circle is perpendicular to the radius (OT) that goes to the point of contact.

The lengths of two tangents drawn from a point to a circle are equal. $PC = PD$

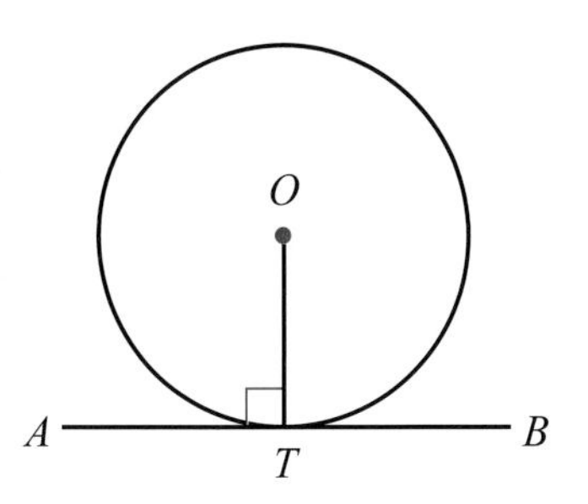

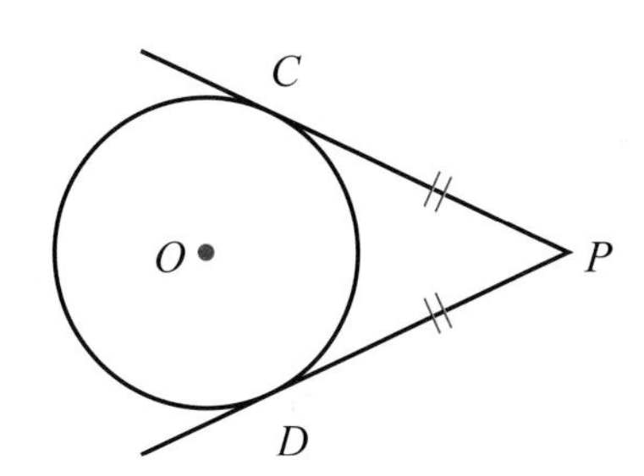

The perpendicular bisector of a chord passes through the centre of the circle.

Equal chords are equidistant from the centre.

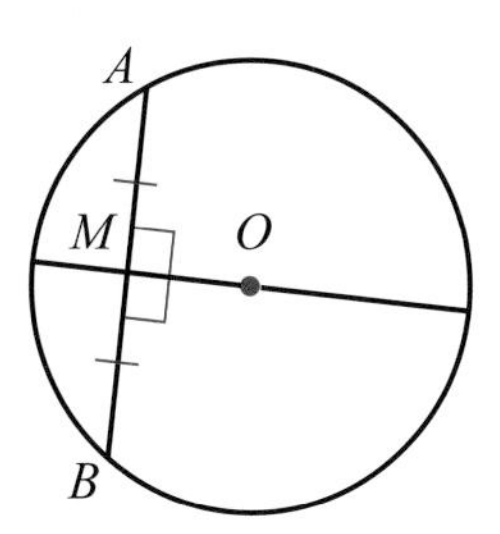

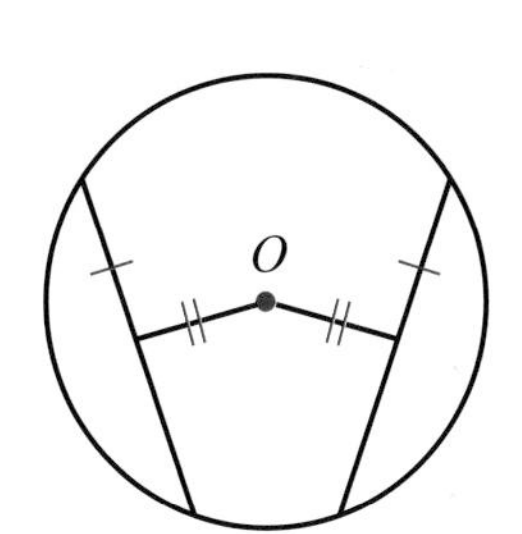

When two chords intersect, the product of the lengths of the two parts of one chord is equal to the product of the lengths of the two parts of the other chord. In the diagram, $ab = cd$.

This also applies when the chords are outside the circle, and when one of them is a tangent to the circle. In the diagram, $mn = pq$ and $rs = t^2$.

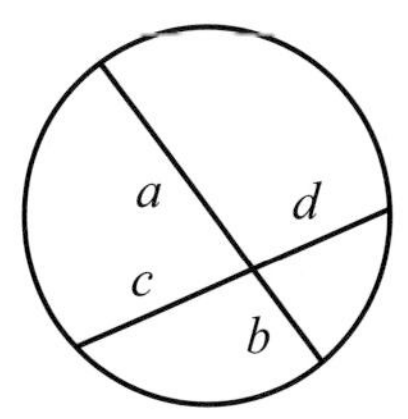

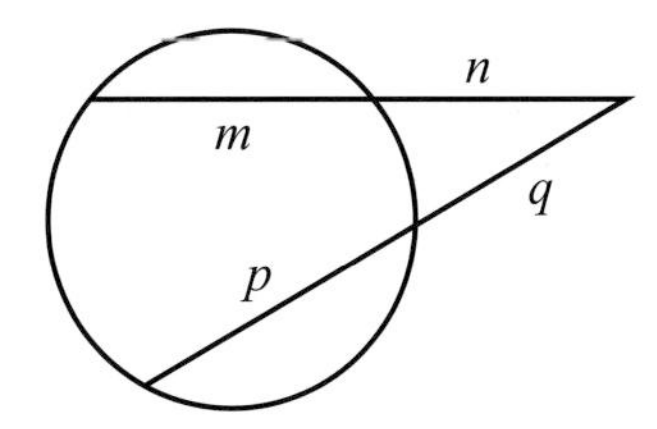

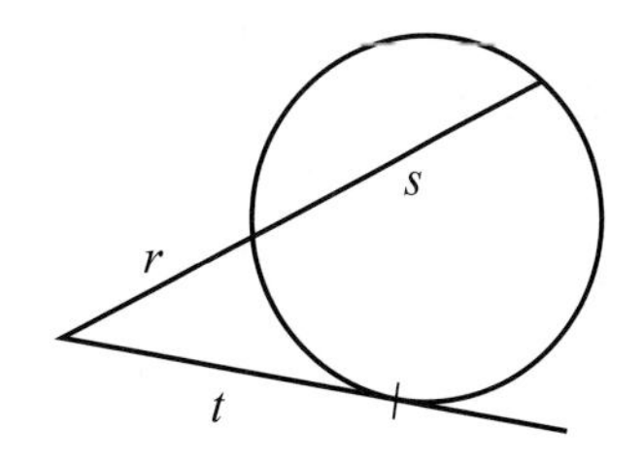

Worked example

1. Work out the size of a. O is the centre of the circle.

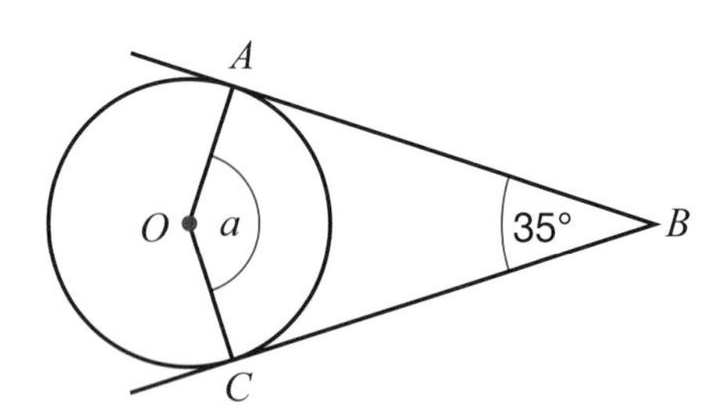

2. The chords BD and DF are the same length, AE and CG are the perpendicular bisectors of the chords. O is the centre of the circle.

   (a) Work out the size of angle a.

   (b) OX is 4.5 cm. How long is OY?

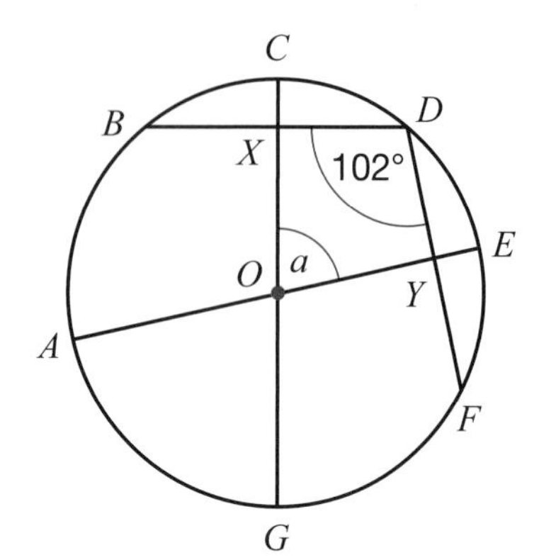

EDE

3. Work out x.

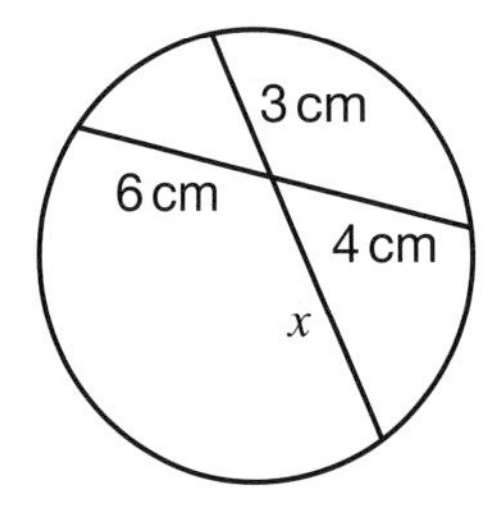

Answer

1. $OABC$ is a quadrilateral, so the sum of the internal angles is 360°.

   As OA and OC are radii that go through the points of contact for the tangents AB and CB, angles OAB and OCB are right angles.

   So $a = 360° - 35° - 2 \times 90° = 360° - 215° = 145°$

2. (a) Angles OXD and OYD are right angles.

   $OXDY$ is a quadrilateral, so the angles add up to 360°.

   $a = 360° - 2 \times 90° - 102° = 360° - 282° = 78°$

   (b) As chords BD and DF are the same length, they are the same distance from the centre of the circle. So $OY = OX = 4.5$ cm.

EDE

3. $x \times 3 = 6 \times 4$

   So $x = (6 \times 4) \div 3 = 24 \div 3 = 8$ cm

Test yourself

1. Work out the sizes of the marked angles. O is the centre of the circle.

(a)

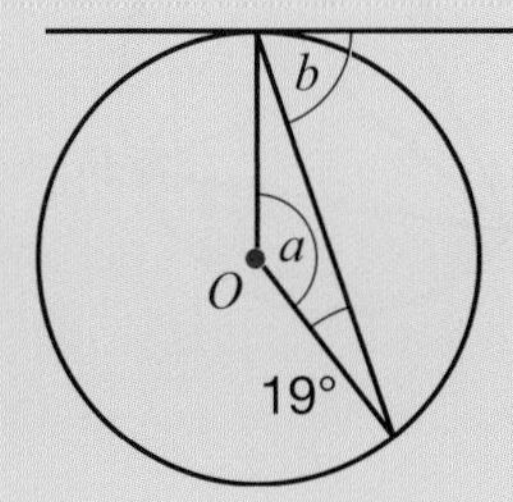

(b)

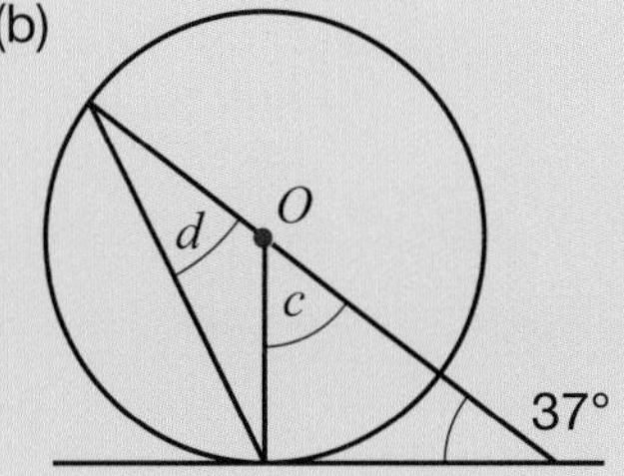

(c)

O 4x
x

2. O is the centre of the circle. AB is the perpendicular bisector of chord CD.

(a) Work out the sizes of the marked angles.

(b) The radius of the circle is 8 cm. AX is 3 cm. What is the length of OY?

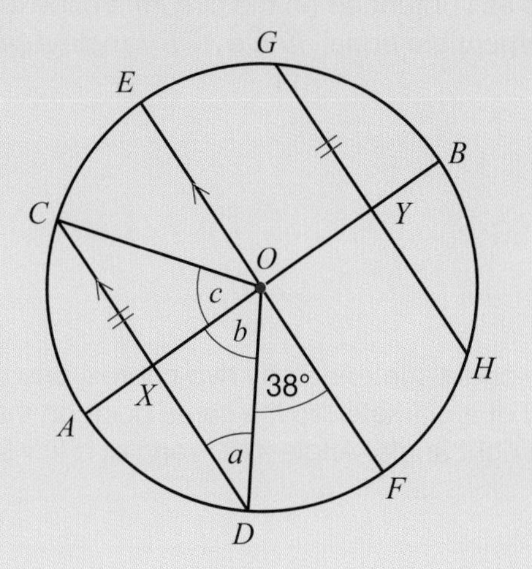

3. O is the centre of the circle. The chords AC and DF are the same length.

EG is the perpendicular bisector of both chords.

(a) Calculate the size of angle a.

(b) AB is 8 cm long. How long is BC?

(c) YC is 3.5 cm and OY is 1 cm. What are the lengths of:

(i) AY (ii) OX?

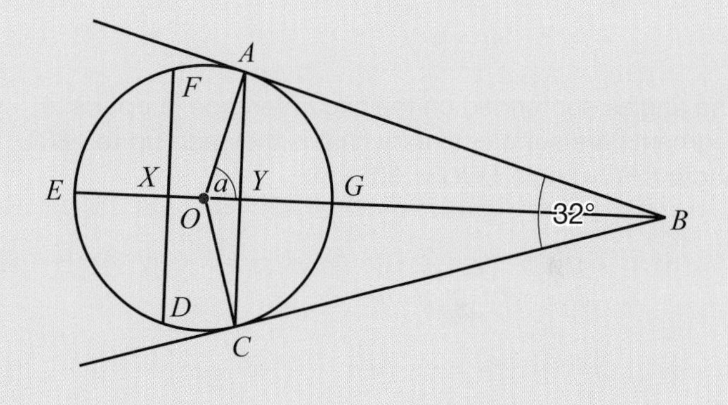

4. Work out x in these circles.

(a)

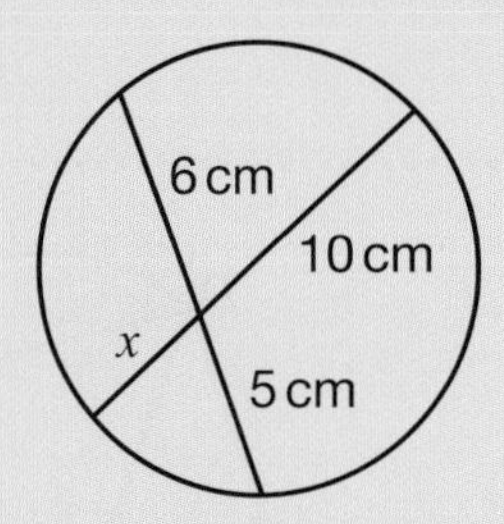

(b)

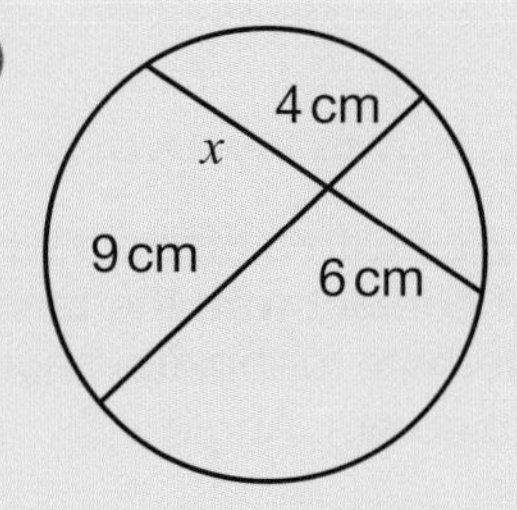

(c)

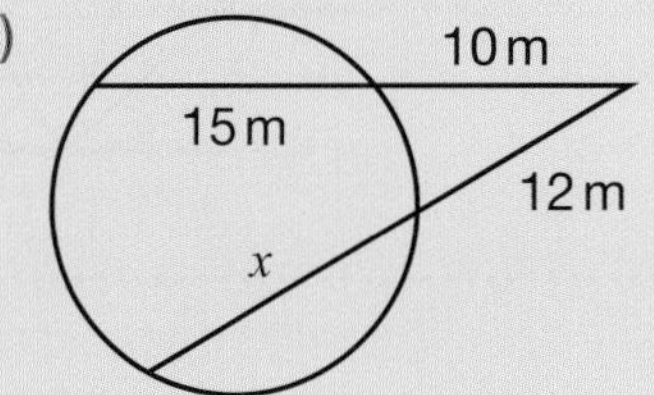

(d)

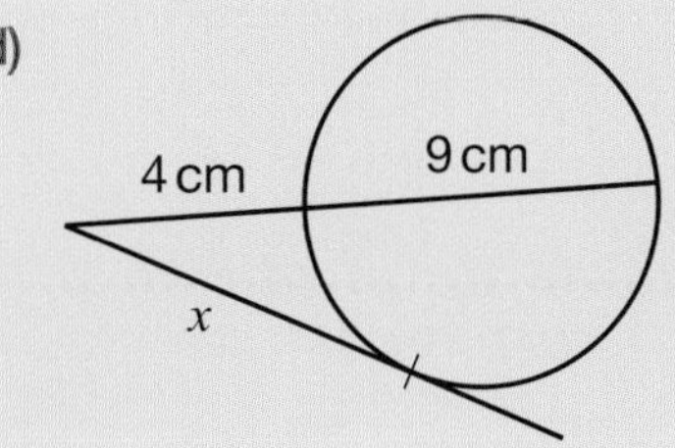

Circle theorems

The angle subtended at the centre of a circle is twice the angle subtended at the circumference when the angles are in the same segment. Angle $AOB = 2 \times$ angle APB

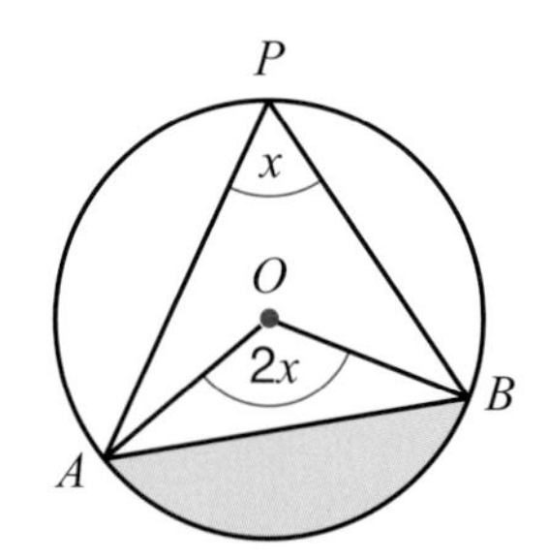

Angles subtended on the circumference of a circle in the same segment are equal. Angle $APB =$ angle AQB

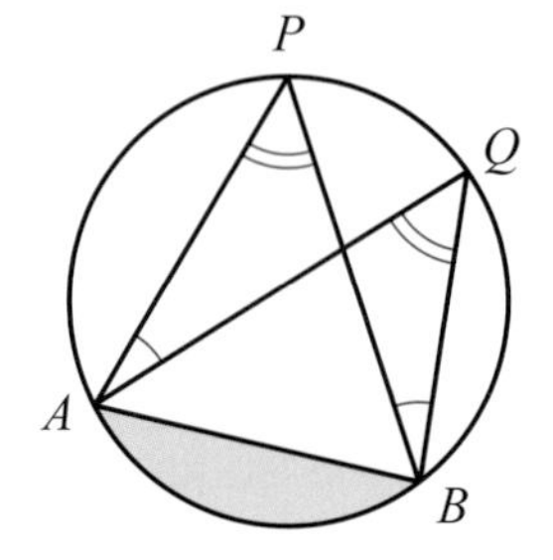

The angle subtended by two chords, one drawn from each end of a diameter, to the same point on the circumference, is a right angle. Angle $ABC =$ angle $ADC = 90°$

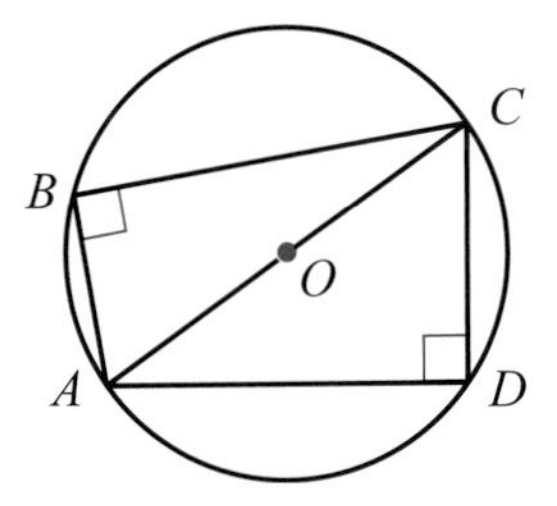

The angles subtended on the circumference in opposite segments are supplementary, that is they add up to 180°. Angle $EFG +$ angle $EHG = 180°$

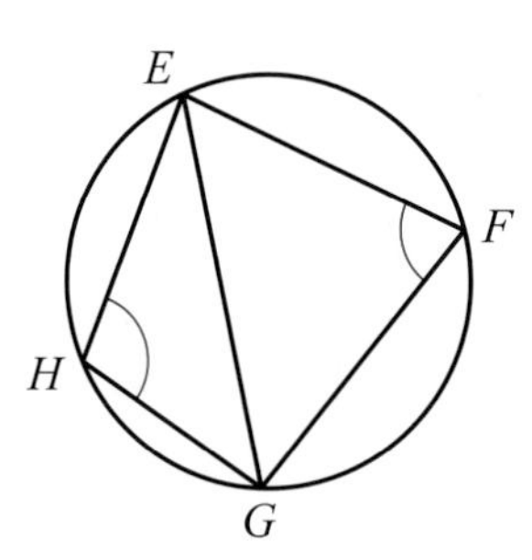

A cyclic quadrilateral is a quadrilateral where all four vertices lie on the circumference of the same circle. $ABCD$ and $EFGH$ are cyclic quadrilaterals.

EDE

The angle that a chord makes with a tangent where one end of the chord is at the point of contact with the tangent is equal to the subtended angle in the alternate (opposite) segment. This is known as the alternate segment theorem. Angle $ATD =$ angle TED and angle $BTE =$ angle DCT

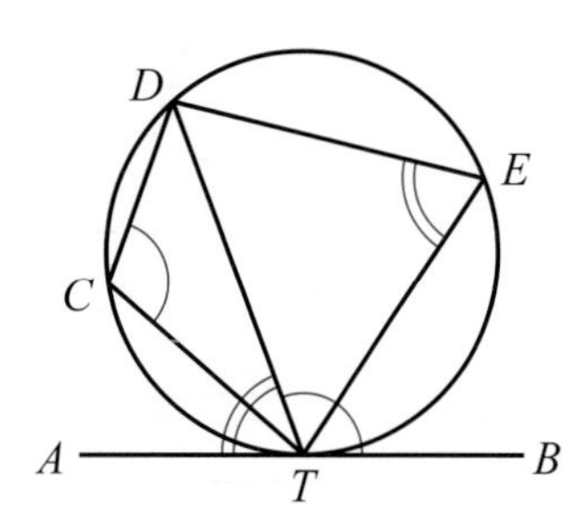

Worked example

1. Find the sizes of angles a, b and c. O is the centre of the circle.

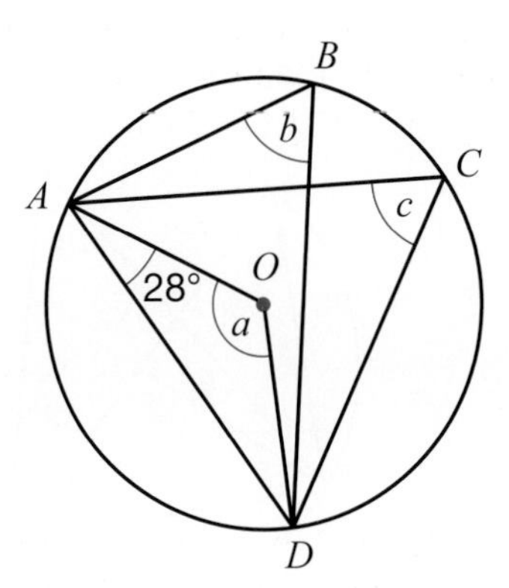

2. Angle $GDE = 69°$. Find the sizes of angles a, b and c.

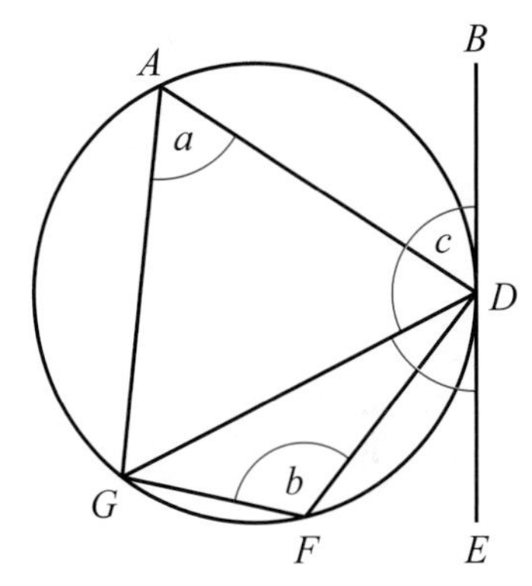

Answer

1. Triangle OAD is an isosceles triangle so angle OAD = angle ADO.

   So $a = 180° - 2 \times 28° = 180° - 56° = 124°$

   The angle subtended at the centre is twice the angle subtended at the circumference, so $a = 2b$ and $b = a \div 2 = 124° \div 2 = 62°$

   Angles subtended on the circumference are equal so $c = b = 62°$

2. Angle a is subtended in the alternate segment from the angle the chord makes with a tangent where one end of the chord is at the point of contact with the tangent and so is equal to angle $GDE = 69°$

   Angle b is the opposite angle in a cyclic quadrilateral, so $a + b = 180°$, and $b = 180° - 69° = 111°$.

   Angle c is the angle that a chord makes with a tangent where one end of the chord is at the point of contact with the tangent and angle b is in the alternate segment, so $c = b = 111°$.

   Or, angle $GDE + c = 180°$
   So angle $c = 180° - 69° = 111°$

   Angle b is subtended in the alternate segment from the angle the chord makes with a tangent where one end of the chord is at the point of contact and so is equal to $c = 111°$.

Test yourself

1. Find the sizes of angles a to p. O is the centre of each circle. Give reasons for your answers.

(a)

(b)

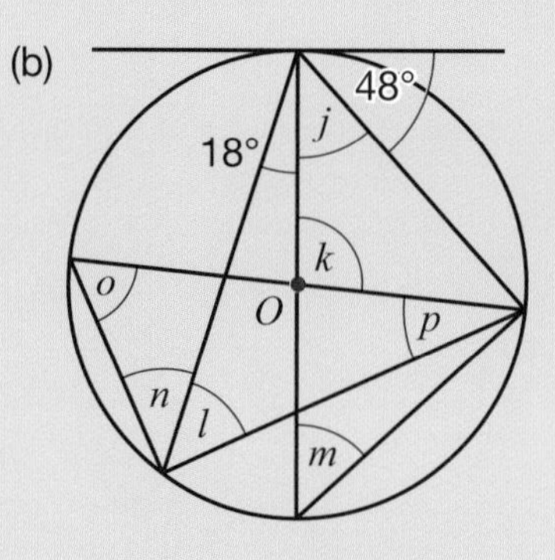

EDE

2. Find the sizes of angles a to k. O is the centre of the circle in (b). Give reasons for your answers.

(a)

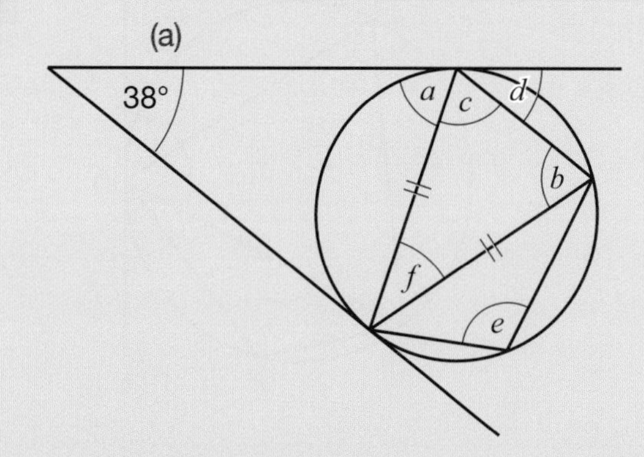

(b)

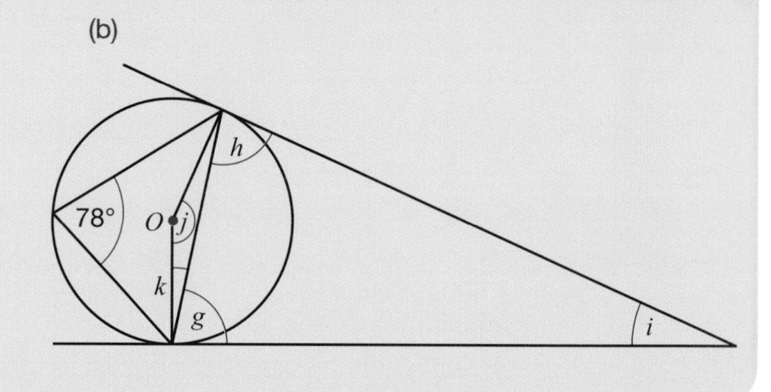

3.5 Trigonometry and Pythagoras' theorem

Three-figure bearings

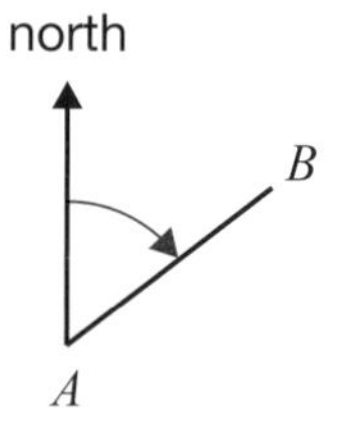

The bearing of one point from another is the clockwise angle turned from due north to a line joining the two points.

Bearings are between 0° and 360°, and are usually given with three digits.

Some common bearings and directions are shown in the diagram below.

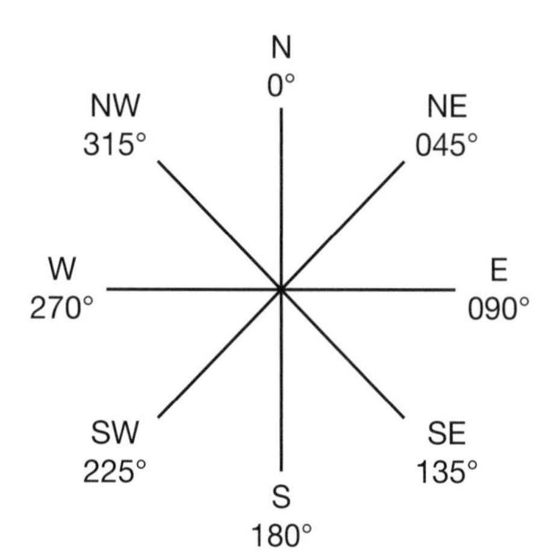

Worked example

The bearing of B from A is 088°. The bearing of C from A is 227°.

(a) Sketch these bearings on a diagram.

(b) Write down the bearing of: (i) A from B (ii) A from C.

Answer

(a)

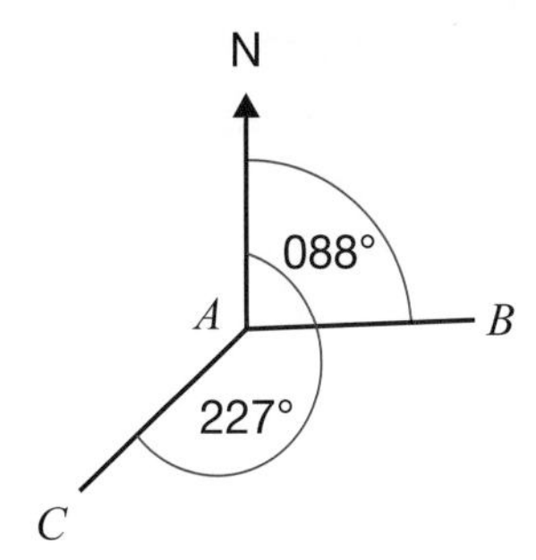

(b) (i) The bearing of A from B is in the opposite direction from the bearing of B from A.

When a bearing is in the opposite direction, add 180° when the original bearing is 180° or less; subtract 180° when the original bearing is between 180° and 360°.

So the bearing of A from B is $088° + 180° = 268°$.

(ii) The bearing of A from C is $227° - 180° = 047°$.

Test yourself

1. Write down the bearings of:

(a) Q from P (b) P from Q (c) R from P (d) P from R

(e) Q from S (f) T from Q (g) Q from R (h) S from T.

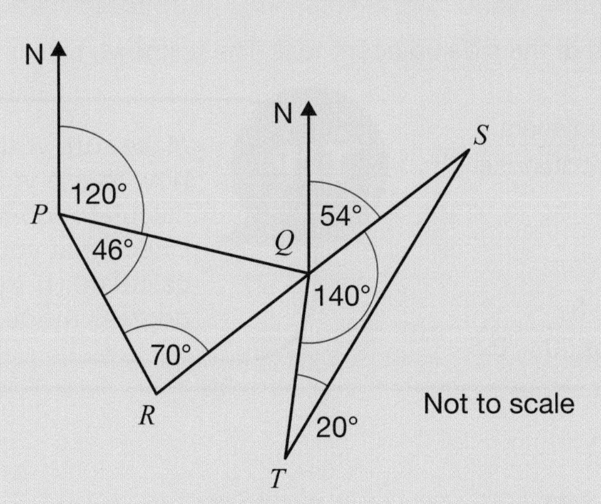

Not to scale

TIP Remember to write a zero at the start of the bearing when the bearing is less than 100°.

Pythagoras' theorem and right-angled triangles

Pythagoras' theorem is usually written as $c^2 = a^2 + b^2$. It applies only to right-angled triangles.

In the triangle:

$\tan A = \frac{\text{opposite}}{\text{adjacent}} = \frac{a}{b}$, $\sin A = \frac{\text{opposite}}{\text{hypotenuse}} = \frac{a}{c}$, $\cos A = \frac{\text{adjacent}}{\text{hypotenuse}} = \frac{b}{c}$

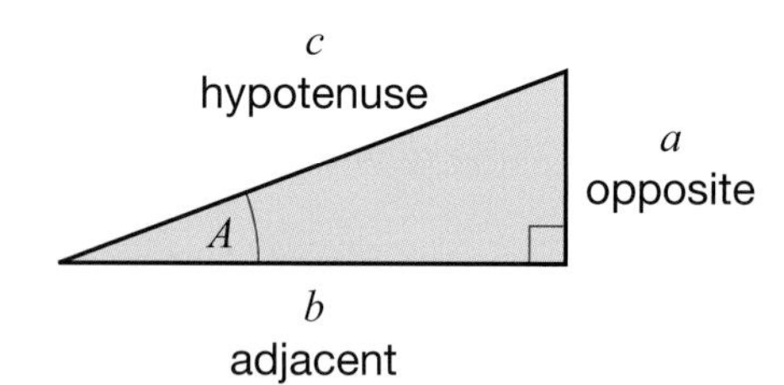

Worked example

1. Find the value of x in this triangle.

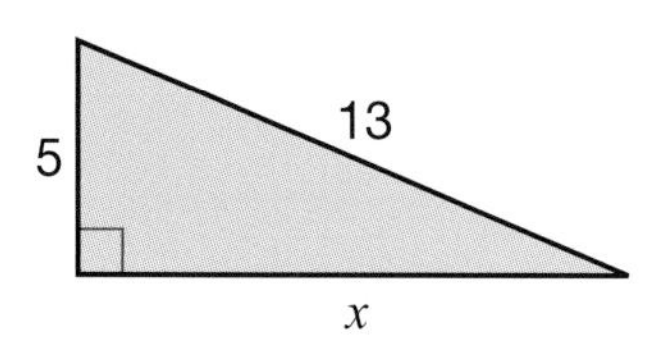

2. Find the length x in this triangle.

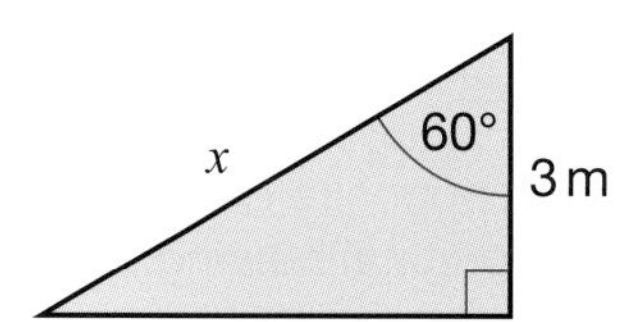

Answer

1. In Pythagoras' theorem, let $x = b$. Rearrange the theorem to make b the subject:

   $b^2 = c^2 - a^2$

   Substitute the values into the equation ($a = 5$, $c = 13$):

   $b^2 = 13^2 - 5^2 = 169 - 25 = 144$

   So $b = \sqrt{144} = 12$

2. First choose the correct ratio.

   We know the size of the angle and the length of the side adjacent to it. The unknown side is the hypotenuse.

   So use the cosine ratio: $\cos A = \frac{\text{adjacent}}{\text{hypotenuse}}$

   $\cos 60° = \frac{3}{x}$

   Rearrange to make x the subject: $x = \frac{3}{\cos 60°} = \frac{3}{0.5} = 6\text{ m}$

TIP

Make sure you know how to use your calculator correctly. Check that your calculator is in degrees mode.

Test yourself

1. Find the lengths of the missing sides in these triangles. Give your answers to 2 decimal places where appropriate.

(a)

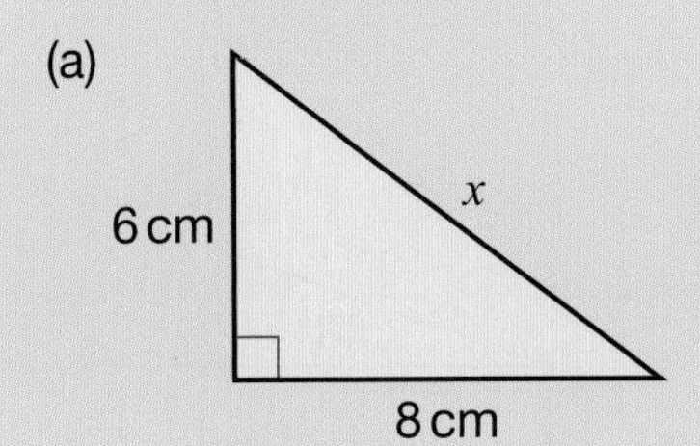

(b)

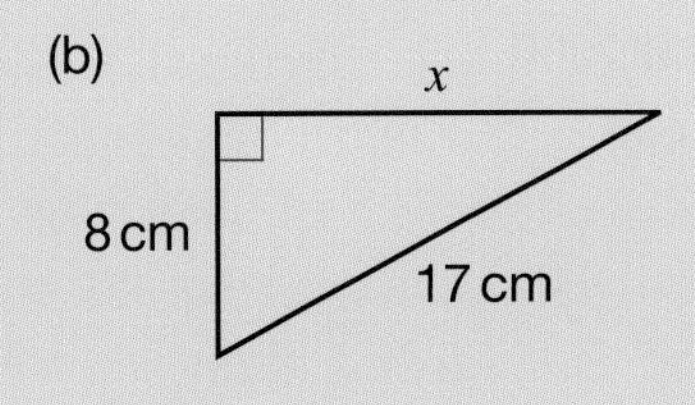

(c)

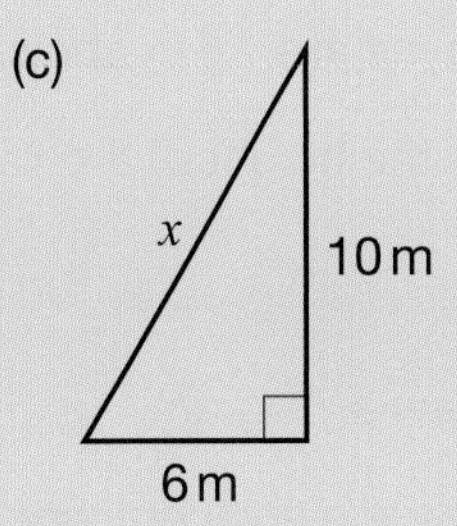

(d)

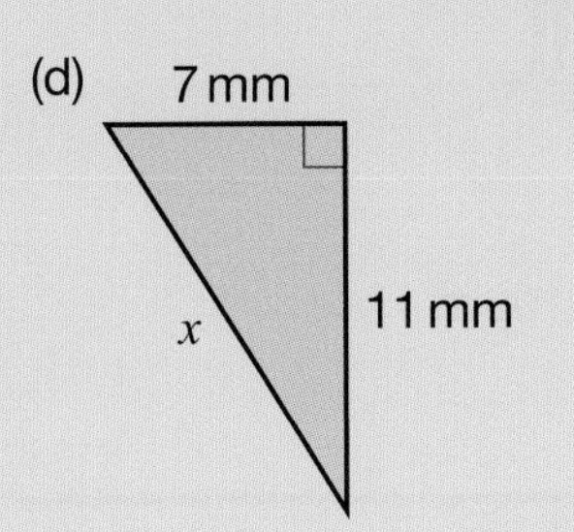

(e)

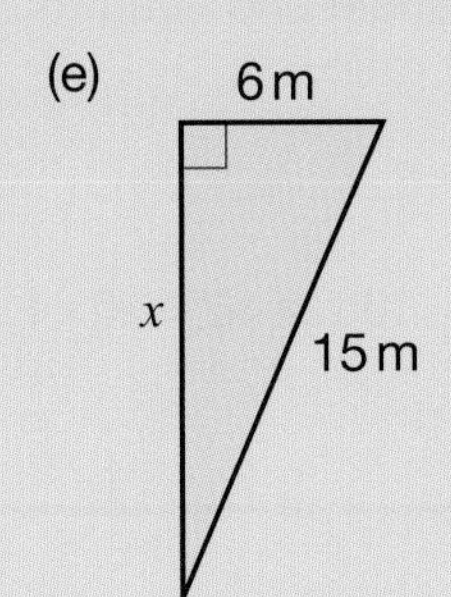

(f)

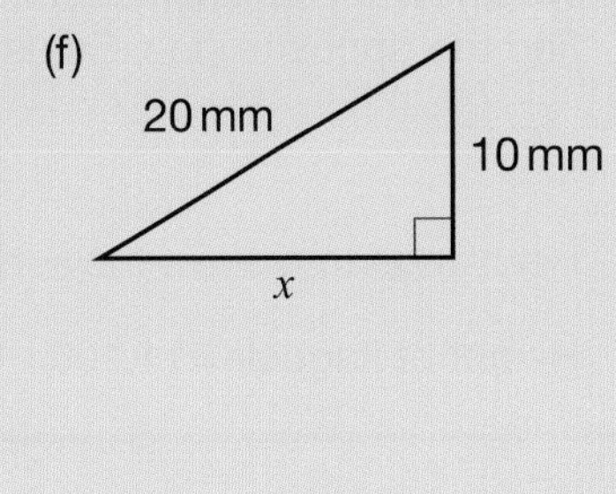

2. Find the missing sides in these triangles. Give your answers to 2 decimal places.

(a)

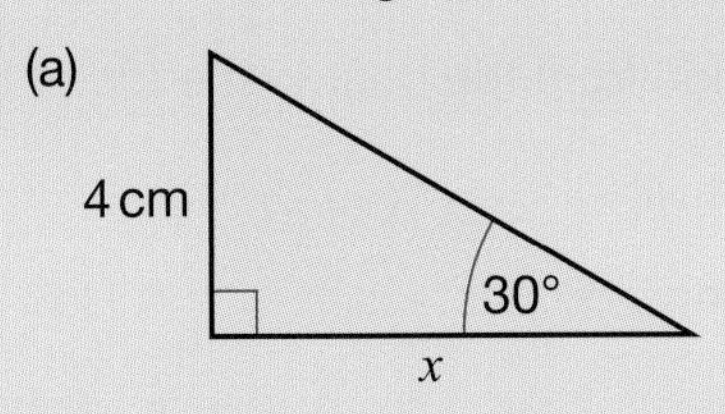

(b)

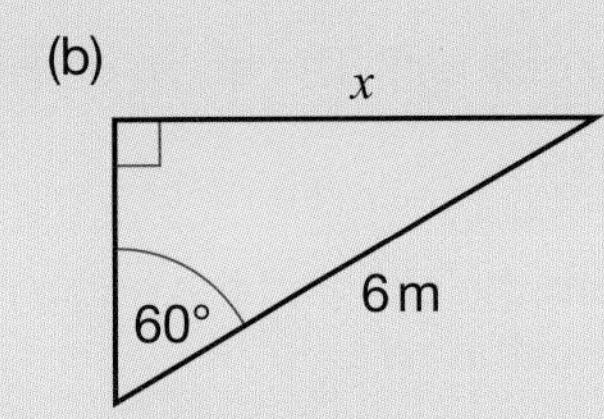

(c)

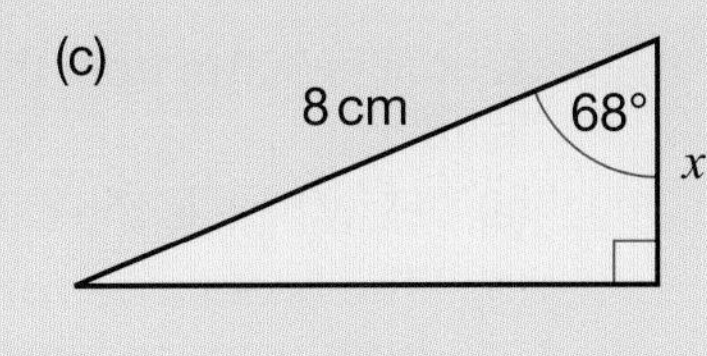

(d)

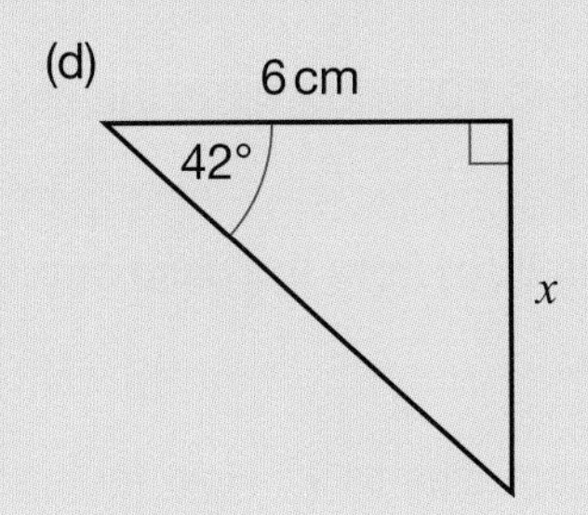

(e)

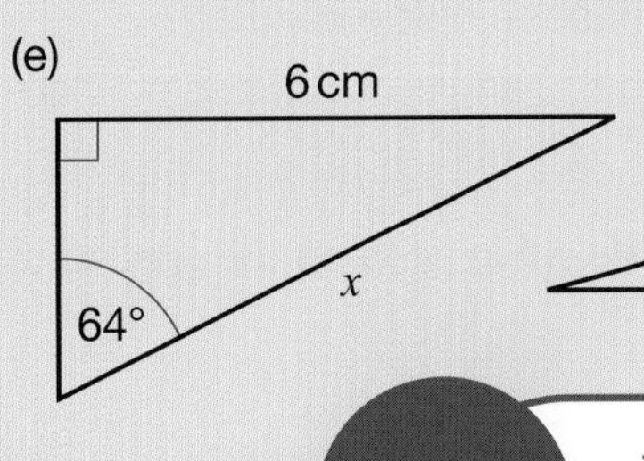

(f) 75° x 8 cm

TIP When the number of decimal places is specified, make sure you give your answers to the given number of decimal places.

Angles of depression and elevation

The angle of elevation is the angle when you look up at something and is measured from the horizontal.

The angle of depression is the angle when you look down at something and is measured from the horizontal.

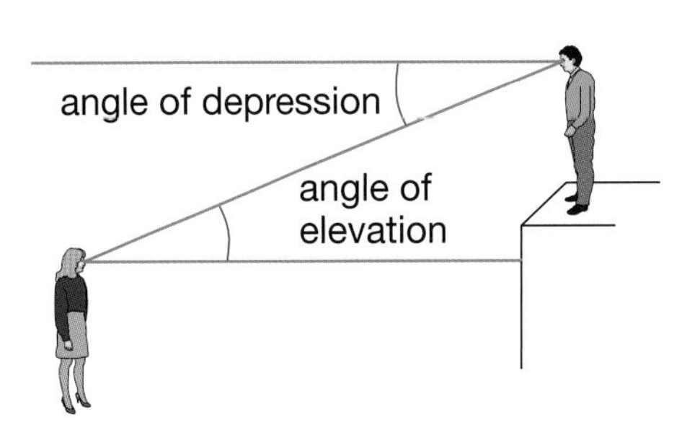

Worked example

Tina is 10 m from the base of a flagpole. She looks at the top of the flagpole. The angle of elevation is 48°.

Tina's eyes are 1.6 m above the ground.

What is the height of the flagpole?

Answer

First draw a diagram.

We know the adjacent side to the known angle and need to find the opposite side. So use the tangent ratio.

$$\tan 48° = \frac{x}{10}$$

Rearrange to make x the subject: $x = 10 \tan 48° = 10 \times 1.1106 = 11.106$ m

Height of flagpole $= 11.106 + 1.6$ m $= 12.71$ m

Test yourself

1. A boat is 500 m from the base of a cliff. The angle of elevation from the boat to the top of the cliff is 18°.
   (a) How high is the cliff?
   (b) The boat moves away from the cliff and the angle of elevation decreases to 10°. How far is the boat from the base of the cliff now?

2. Alex sees a car from the top of a building. The angle of depression is 35°. The building is 80 m high.
   (a) How far is the car from the base of the building?
   (b) The car starts moving and the angle of depression increases to 60°. How far is the car from the base of the building now?

3. Rachel looks at the top of a tree while lying on the ground. She is 80 m from the base of the tree and the angle of elevation is 25°.
   (a) How high is the tree?
   (b) She moves away from the tree and the angle of elevation decreases to 9°. How far is she from the tree now?

4. Ben is at the top of a 150 m high cliff and looks down at a boat. The angle of depression is 32°.
   (a) How far is the boat from the base of the cliff?
   (b) The boat moves and the angle of depression decreases to 15°. How far is the boat from the base of the cliff now?

Obtuse angles

For obtuse angles: $\sin\theta = \sin(180 - \theta)$
$\cos\theta = -\cos(180 - \theta)$
$\tan\theta = -\tan(180 - \theta)$

EDE

Worked example

Solve the equation $\sin\theta = 0.5$, where $0° \leqslant \theta \leqslant 180°$.

TIP

Remember that '$\sin^{-1}(0.5)$' means 'the angle with a sine of 0.5'. It is known as the inverse sine.

Answer

$\sin^{-1}(0.5) = 30°$

But as $\sin\theta = \sin(180 - \theta)$, there are two values of θ that satisfy the equation.

The second solution is $180° - 30° = 150°$.

So $\theta = 30°$ or $150°$

Test yourself

DE

1. Solve the following equations, where $0° \leqslant x \leqslant 180°$. Give your answers to 1 decimal place, where appropriate.

(a) $\cos x = 0$ (b) $\sin x = 0$ (c) $\cos x = -\frac{1}{4}$

(d) $\sin x = \frac{1}{4}$ (e) $\cos x = -0.5$ (f) $\sin x = 0.7$

(g) $\cos x = -\frac{3}{4}$ (h) $\sin x = \frac{3}{4}$

2. Solve the following equations, where $0° \leqslant x \leqslant 180°$. Give your answers to 1 decimal place, where appropriate.

(a) $\tan x = 0.5$ (b) $\tan x = -1$

(c) $\tan x = -\frac{3}{4}$ (d) $\tan x = -3$

Sine and cosine rules

In any triangle, you can find the sizes of angles and lengths of sides using the sine and cosine rules:

sine rule: $\dfrac{a}{\sin A} = \dfrac{b}{\sin B} = \dfrac{c}{\sin C}$ or $\dfrac{\sin A}{a} = \dfrac{\sin B}{b} = \dfrac{\sin C}{c}$

cosine rule: $a^2 = b^2 + c^2 - 2bc \cos A$ or $\cos A = \dfrac{b^2 + c^2 - a^2}{2bc}$

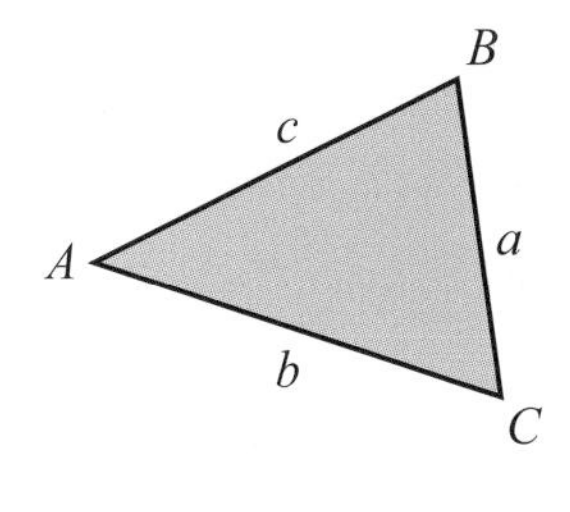

When you know:

- two sides and the included angle (the angle between the two sides), and you need to find the length of the third side, use the cosine rule; you can then use the sine rule to find the size of one of the other angles
- two angles and a side between them, and you need to find the lengths of the other sides, use the sum of angles in a triangle to find the size of the third angle; then use the sine rule to find the lengths of the other sides
- all three sides and need to find the size of the angles, use the cosine rule to find the size of one of the angles; then use the sine rule to find one of the other angles.

Learn both versions of the cosine rule, with a side as the subject and with the cosine as the subject. This is easier than trying to rearrange the formula in an exam.

You can find the area of any triangle using the area sine rule:

area of a triangle $= \frac{1}{2}ab \sin C$

Worked example

1. Find the length x in each of these triangles. Give your answers to 1 decimal place.

(a)

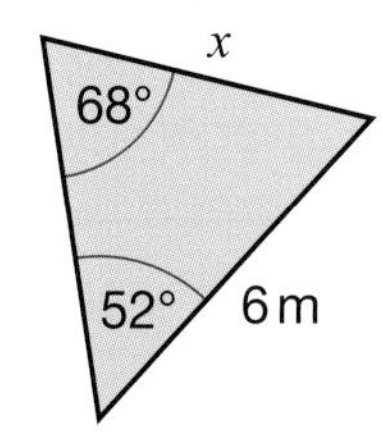

(b)

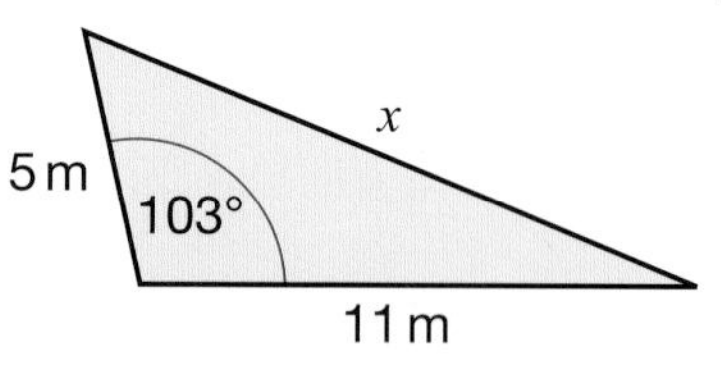

2. Find the angle y in each of these triangles.

(a)

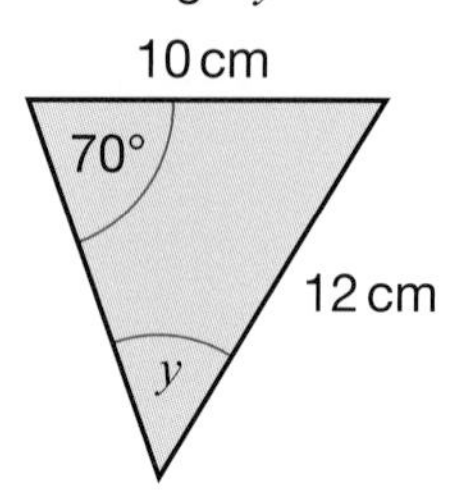

(b)

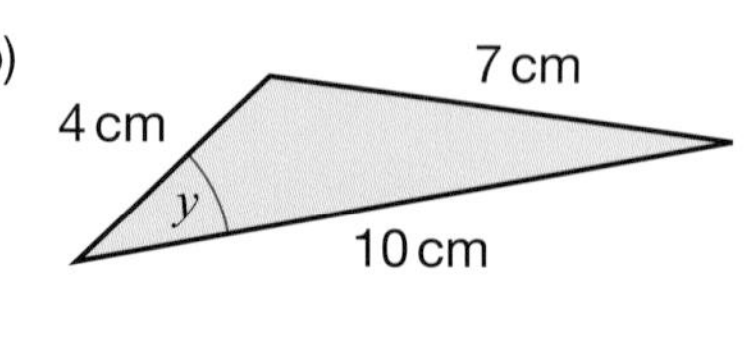

3. Find the area of this triangle:

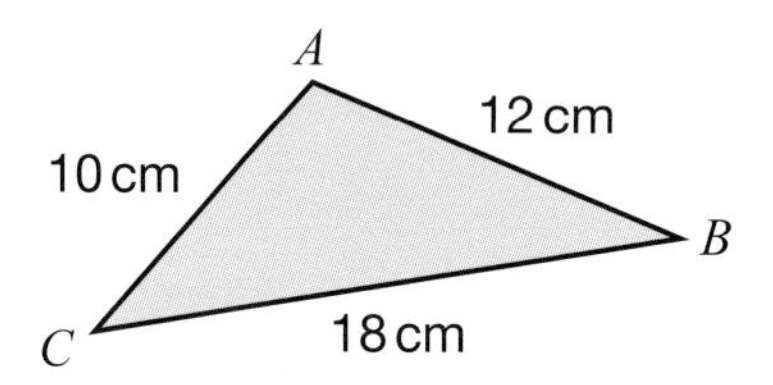

Answer

1. (a) Use the sine rule: $\frac{x}{\sin 52°} = \frac{6}{\sin 68°}$

So $x = \frac{6 \times \sin 52°}{\sin 68°} = \frac{6 \times 0.78801}{0.92718} = 5.1\text{ m}$

(b) Use the cosine rule: $x^2 = 5^2 + 11^2 - 2 \times 5 \times 11 \times \cos 103°$

$= 25 + 121 - (110 \times -0.22495)$

$= 146 + 24.745 = 170.745$

So $x = \sqrt{170.745} = 13.1\text{ m}$

2. (a) Use the sine rule: $\frac{\sin y}{10} = \frac{\sin 70°}{12}$

So $\sin y = \frac{10 \times \sin 70°}{12} = \frac{10 \times 0.93969}{12} = 0.78308$

So $y = \sin^{-1} 0.78308 = 51.5°$

(b) Use the cosine rule: $\cos y = \frac{4^2 + 10^2 - 7^2}{2 \times 4 \times 10} = \frac{16 + 100 - 49}{80} = \frac{67}{80}$

So $y = \cos^{-1} \frac{67}{80} = 33.1°$

3. First find the size of one of the angles using the cosine rule, then use the area sine rule to find the area of the triangle.

Find the size of the angle between the 10 cm and 18 cm sides:

$\cos x = \frac{10^2 + 18^2 - 12^2}{2 \times 10 \times 18} = \frac{100 + 324 - 144}{360} = \frac{280}{360} = \frac{7}{9}$

$x = \cos^{-1} \frac{7}{9} = 38.942°$

$\text{area} = \frac{1}{2}ab \sin C = 0.5 \times 10 \times 18 \times \sin 38.942°$

$= 90 \times 0.62854 = 56.6\text{ cm}^2$

Test yourself

1. Find the length x in each of these triangles.

(a) 15 m, 38°, 32°, x

(b)

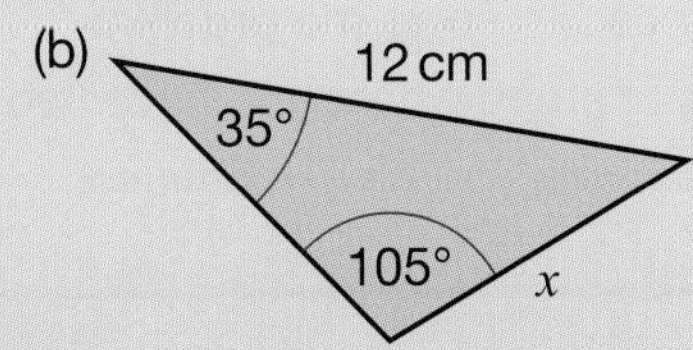

(c)

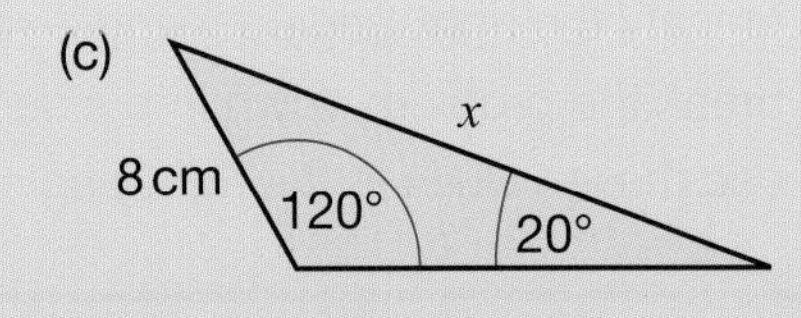

2. Find angle y in each of these triangles.

(a) y, 14 cm, 89°, 10 cm

(b)

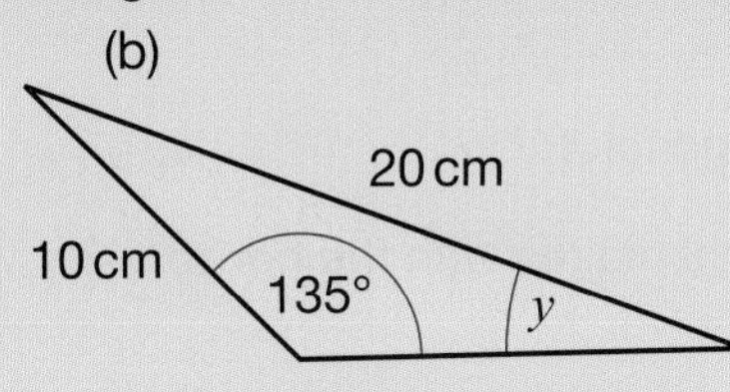

(c)

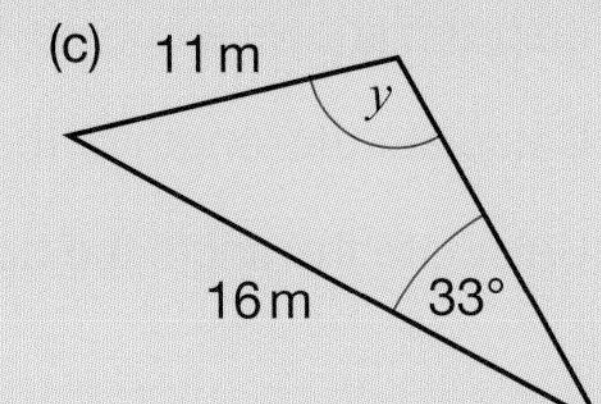

TIP Read the question carefully. Check that you are using or giving the angle that was asked for.

3. Find the length x in each of these triangles.

(a) x, 5 mm, 58°, 12 mm

(b)

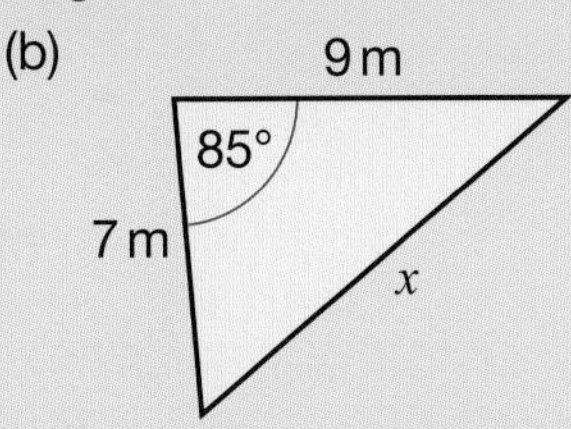

(c)

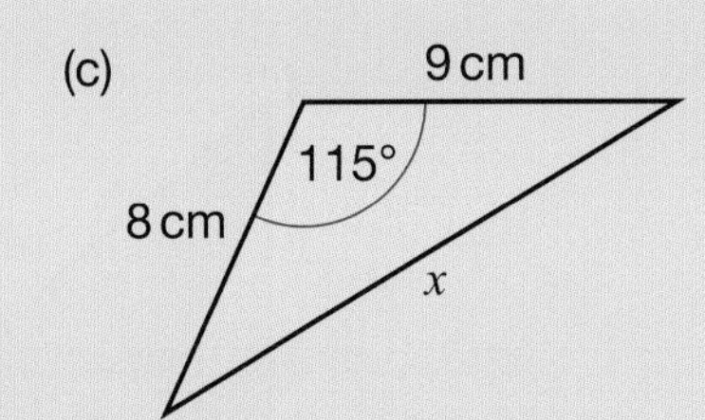

4. Find the angle y in each of these triangles.

(a) 12 cm, y, 6 cm, 8 cm

(b)

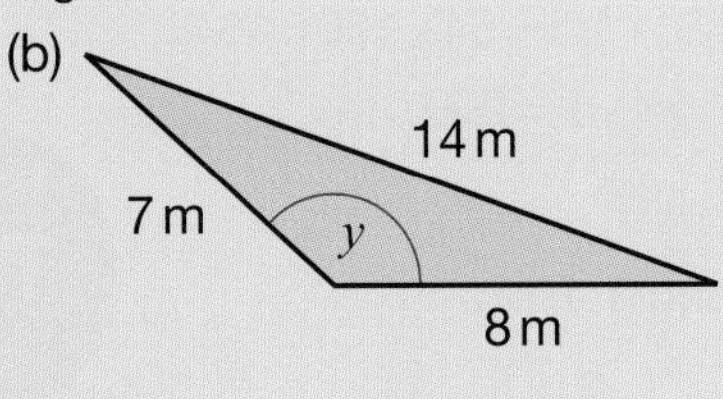

(c)

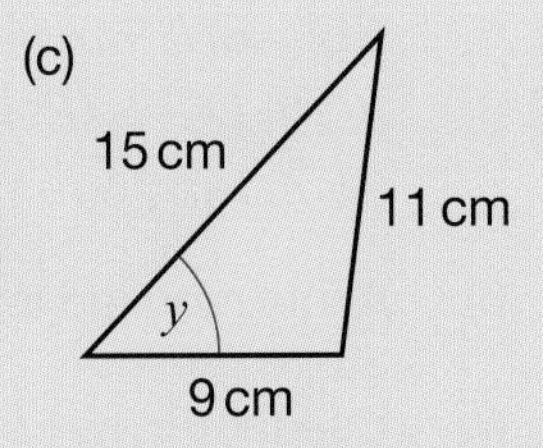

5. Find the area of the following triangles, ABC.

(a) $AB = 7$ cm, $BC = 8$ cm, angle $ABC = 68°$

(b) $AB = 15$ cm, $AC = 10$ cm, angle $BAC = 55°$

(c) $AC = 12$ cm, $BC = 9$ cm, angle $BCA = 103°$

6. The area of a triangle is 123 cm^2. AB is 14 cm and BC is 22 cm. Find the size of angle ABC, which is obtuse.

TIP When a question does not specify the number of decimal places or significant figures to give, use the number of significant figures or decimal places specified on the cover of the exam paper. This is usually 3 significant figures.

3-D problems

When solving problems involving 3-D trigonometry and Pythagoras' theorem:

- identify the right-angled triangle you need to solve the problem
- break the problem down into a series of steps where you have two known values to calculate a third value
- use these values in the right-angled triangle you have identified.

Worked example

The diagram shows a cuboid.

(a) Calculate the length of the diagonal AG.

(b) Calculate the angle the diagonal makes with the horizontal.

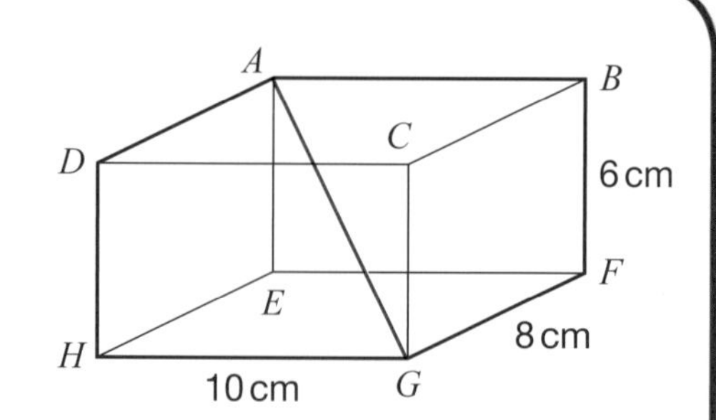

Answer

(a) Identify the right-angled triangle needed for the solution. This is triangle AEG.

The length of AE is given, but you need to find the length EG.

You can find the length EG using the triangle HEG: the lengths of EH and HG are given on the diagram.

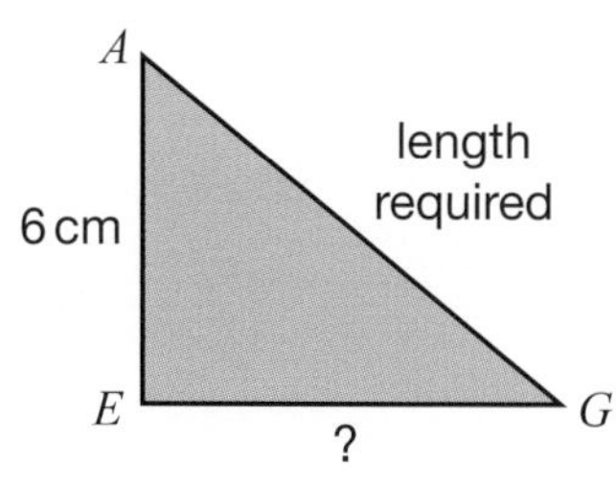

$EG^2 = EH^2 + GH^2 = 8^2 + 10^2 = 64 + 100 = 164$
$AG^2 = EG^2 + AE^2 = 164 + 6^2 = 200$
So $AG = \sqrt{200} = 14.1$ cm

(b) Angle required is angle AGE.

Use $\tan\theta = AE \div EG = \dfrac{6}{\sqrt{164}} = 0.46852$

So angle $= \tan^{-1} 0.46852 = 25.1°$

Always look for the simplest way of calculating something – don't make the calculation more complicated than it needs to be.

Test yourself

1. A flagpole is held up by four ropes. The bases of the ropes form a square of side 8 m.

   The angle of elevation of the top of the flagpole from the corners is 58°.

   (a) Calculate the height of the flagpole.

   (b) Each rope needs 0.5 m at each end to tie the rope off. Calculate the total length of rope needed.

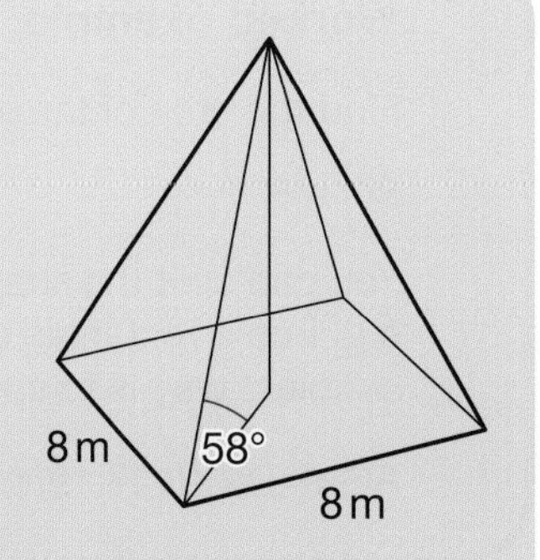

2. A farmer is using a piece of wood 2.5 m long to brace the corner of a fence.

   The corner is a right angle and the piece of wood bisects the corner.

   (a) How far from each fence should the base of the piece of wood be placed?

   (b) What angle does the piece of wood make with the horizontal?

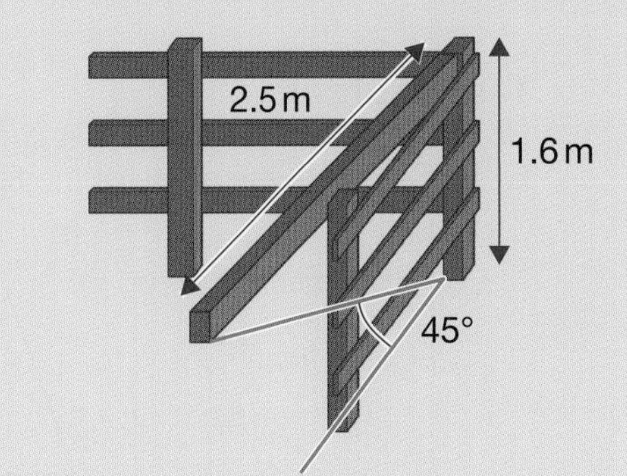

3. $ABCD$ is a vertical rectangle. CDE is a horizontal right-angled triangle.

   (a) Work out the length AE.

   (b) What angle does the line AE make with the horizontal?

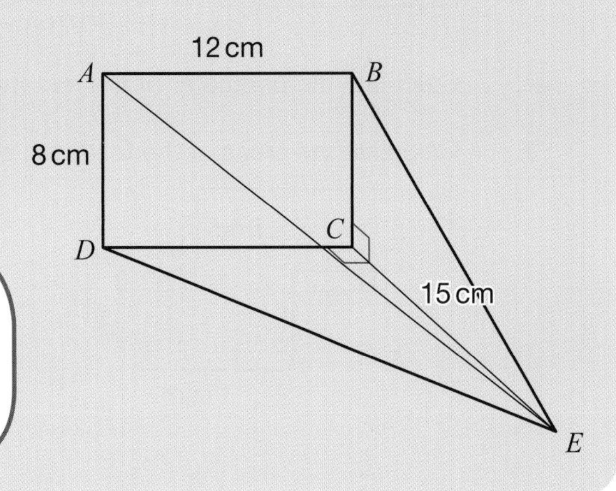

Remember that the memory and answer functions on your calculator can be useful when doing multi-stage calculations. Do not round your answers during a calculation – only do it at the end.

3.6 2-D shapes

Perimeter and area

The perimeter of a shape is the distance around the outside of the shape.

The perimeter of a rectangle is given by the expression $2(l+w)$.

The formulae for calculating the areas of different shapes are:

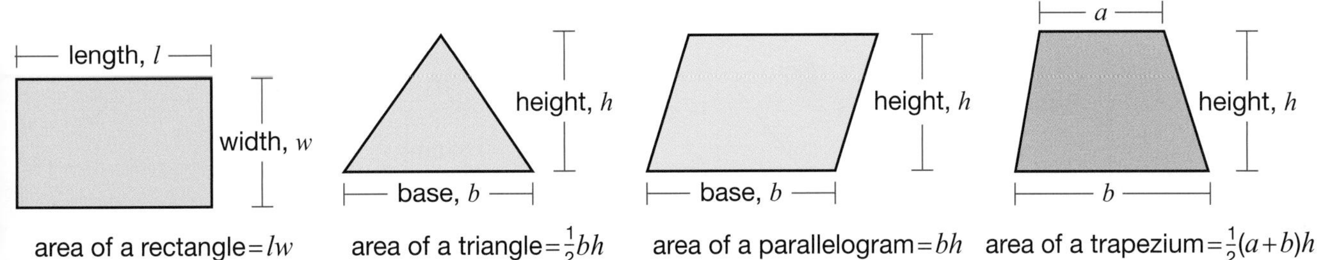

area of a rectangle $= lw$ area of a triangle $= \frac{1}{2}bh$ area of a parallelogram $= bh$ area of a trapezium $= \frac{1}{2}(a+b)h$

Worked example

Find the area of the shape shown in the diagram.

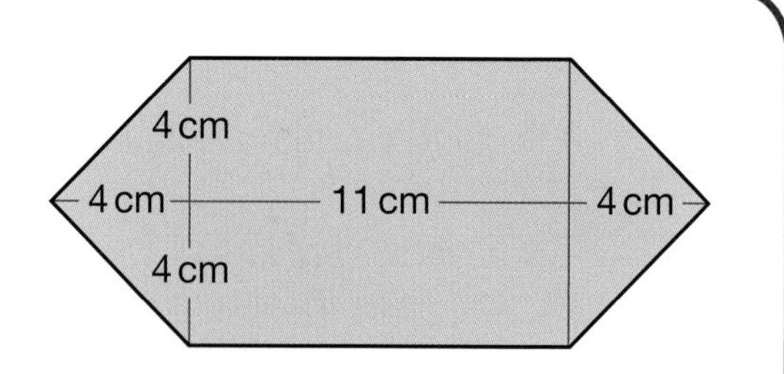

Answer

You can split the shape in several different ways, e.g. into a rectangle and two triangles. But the simplest way is to split it into two identical trapezia.

Area $= 2 \times \frac{1}{2}(11 + 19) \times 4 = 30 \times 4 = 120\,\text{cm}^2$

Test yourself

1. Calculate the areas of the following shapes.

(a)

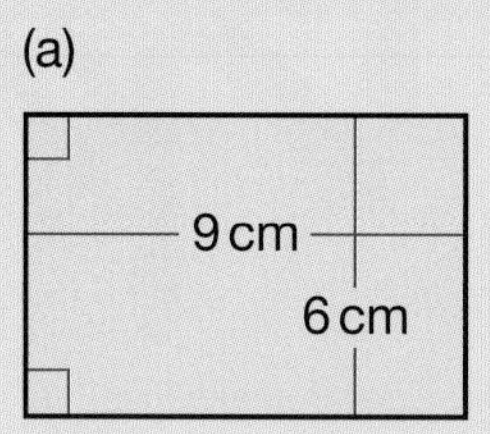

(b)

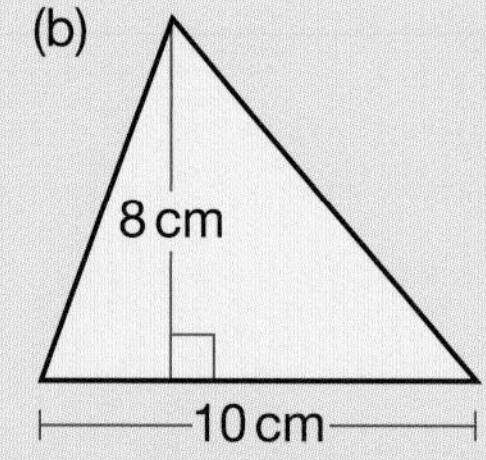

(c)

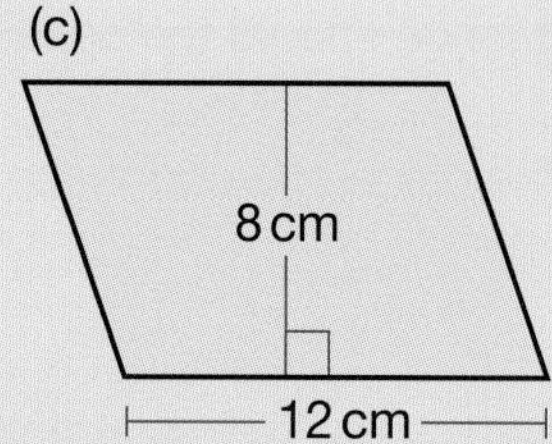

(d)

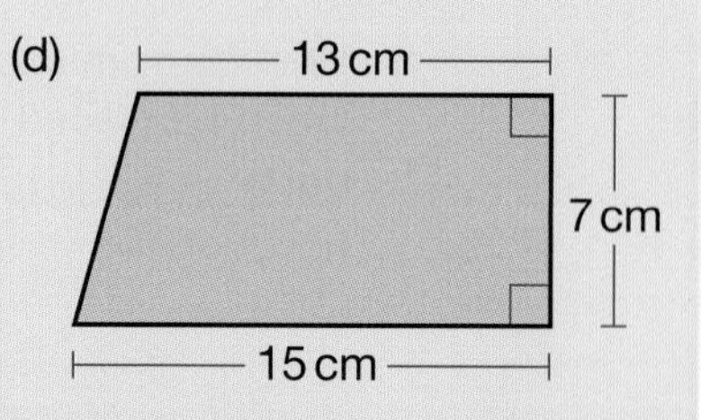

2. Calculate the perimeter of the rectangle in Q1.

3. Calculate the areas of the following compound shapes.

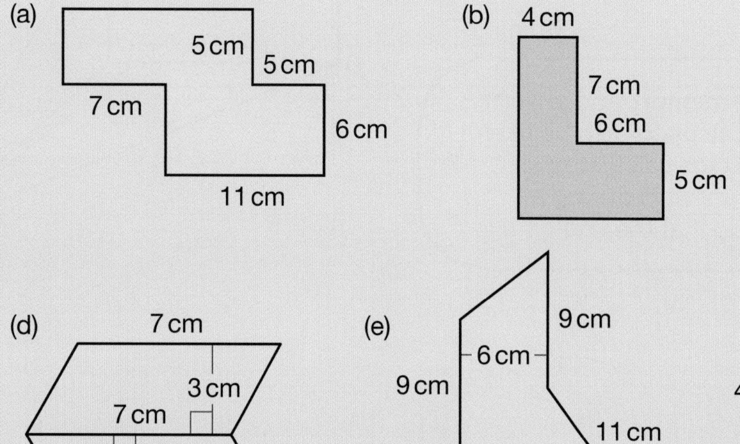

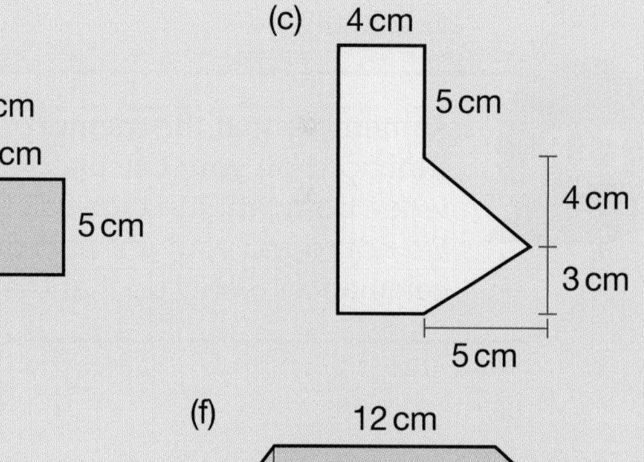

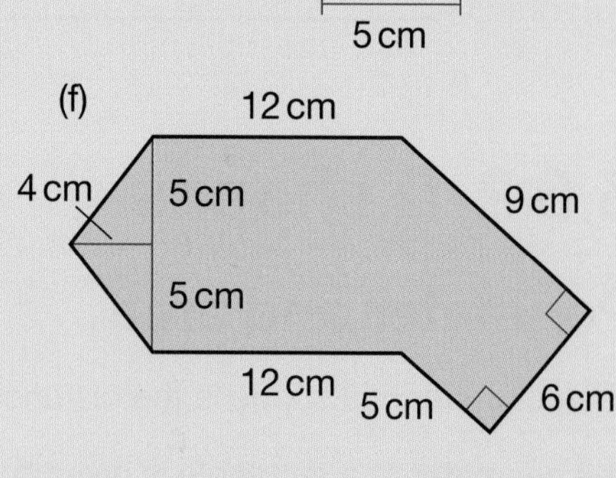

4. Calculate the shaded area of each of the following shapes.

(a)

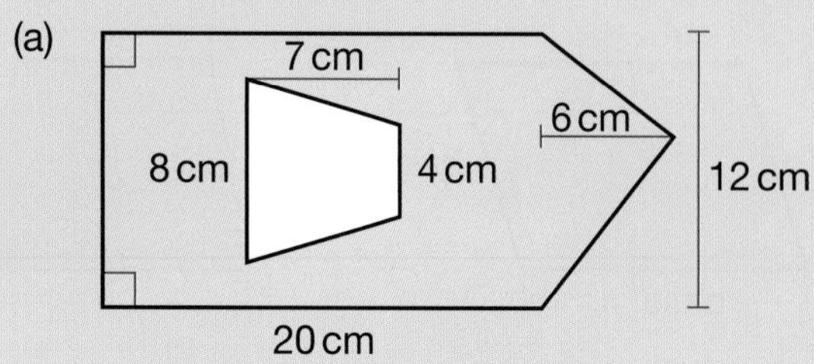

(b)

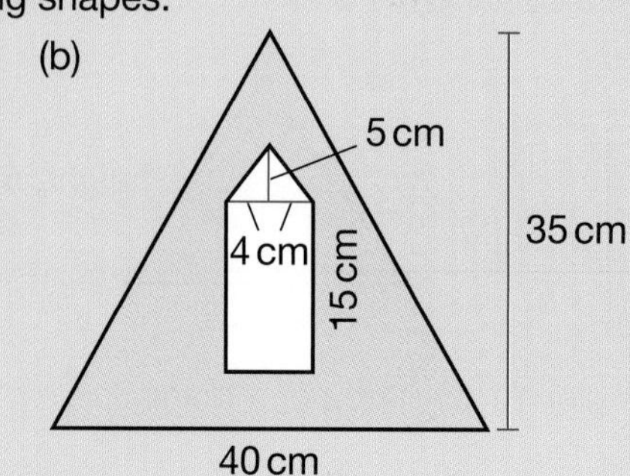

Circles

The circumference, C, of a circle of diameter, d, or radius, r, is given by $C=\pi d$ or $C=2\pi r$.

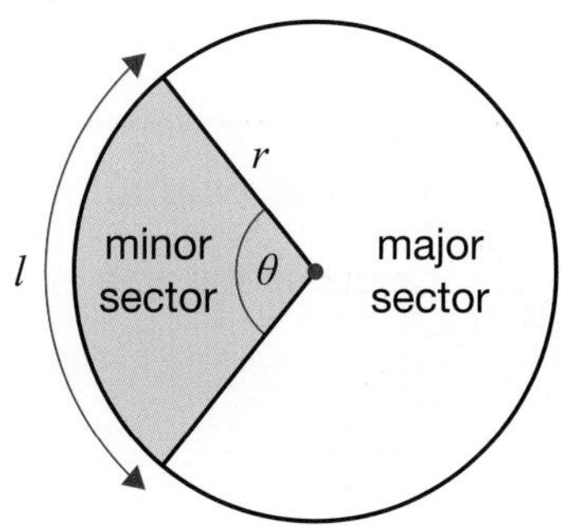

The area, A, of a circle of radius, r, is given by $A=\pi r^2$.

The length of an arc, l, of the circumference of a circle where the angle in the sector is θ is given by $l=\frac{\theta}{360°}\times\pi d$.

The area, A, of a sector where the angle in the sector is θ is given by $A=\frac{\theta}{360°}\times\pi r^2$.

When a circle is divided into two sectors, the smaller sector is called the minor sector and the larger sector is called the major sector.

Worked example

Calculate the arc length and area of the sector shown in the diagram.

Give your answers in terms of π.

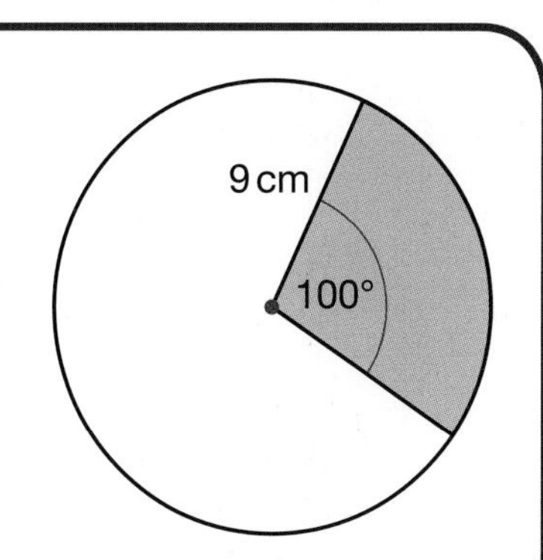

Answer

Arc length, $l=\frac{100°}{360°}\times\pi\times2\times9=\frac{1800\pi}{360}=5\pi$ cm

Area of sector, $A=\frac{100°}{360°}\times\pi\times9^2=\frac{8100\pi}{360}=\frac{45\pi}{2}$ cm^2

Test yourself

1. Calculate the area and circumference of the following circles.
   (a) diameter = 6 cm (b) diameter = 10 cm (c) radius = 6 cm (d) radius = 9 cm

2. Calculate the length of the arc and area of each of the following sectors. Give your answers in terms of π.

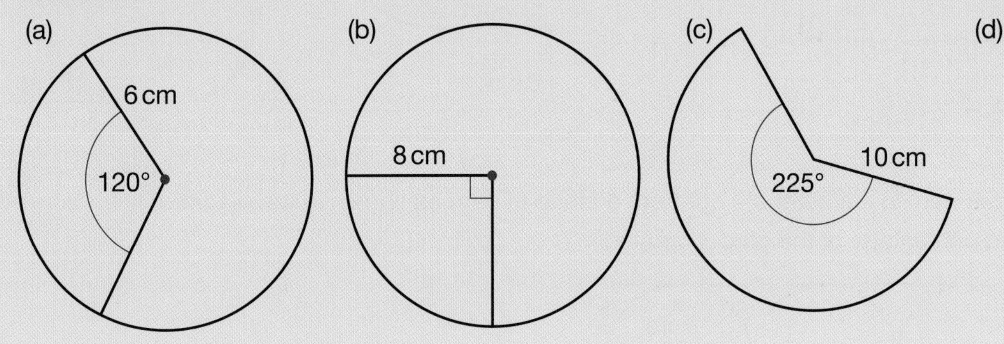

Compound shapes

To calculate the area of a compound shape, break down the shape into simpler shapes that you can calculate the area of.

Worked example

Calculate the area of the shape shown in the diagram.

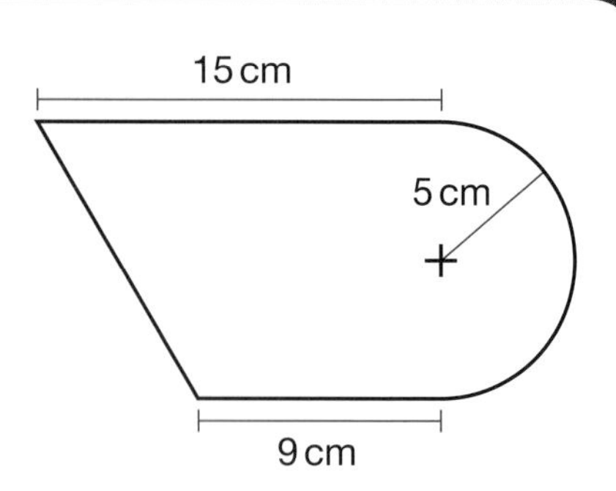

Answer

The shape is made up of a trapezium and a semicircle.

Area = area of trapezium + area of semicircle

$= \frac{1}{2}(9+15)\times 10 + \frac{180^\circ}{360^\circ}\times \pi \times 5^2$

$= 12\times 10 + 0.5\times \pi \times 25 = 120 + 39.27 = 159\,\text{cm}^2$

TIP

Always look for the simplest way of breaking the compound shape into simpler shapes – don't make the calculation more complicated than it needs to be. This shape could be broken down into a triangle, a rectangle and a semicircle, but the example shows a simpler way of breaking it down.

Test yourself

1. Calculate the areas of the following shapes. Give your answers to 3 significant figures.

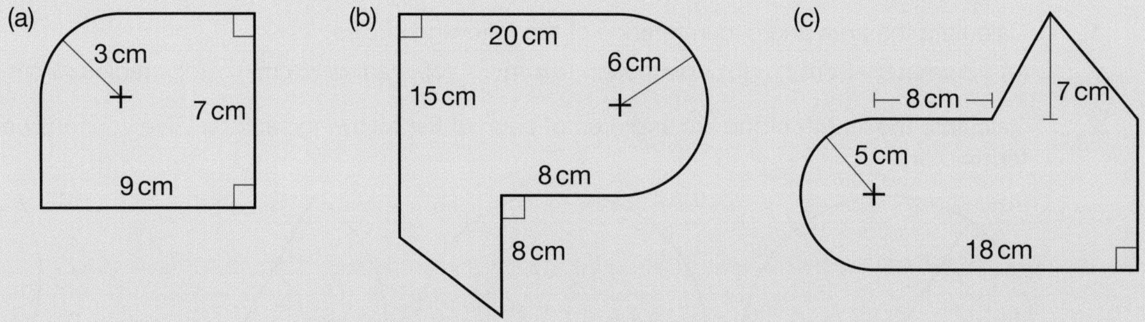

(a) (b) (c)

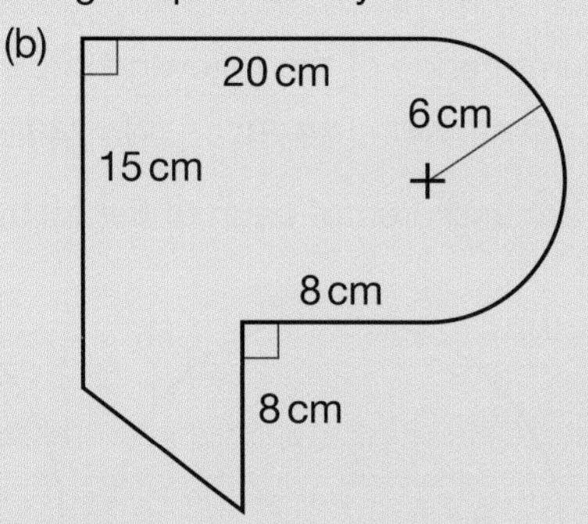

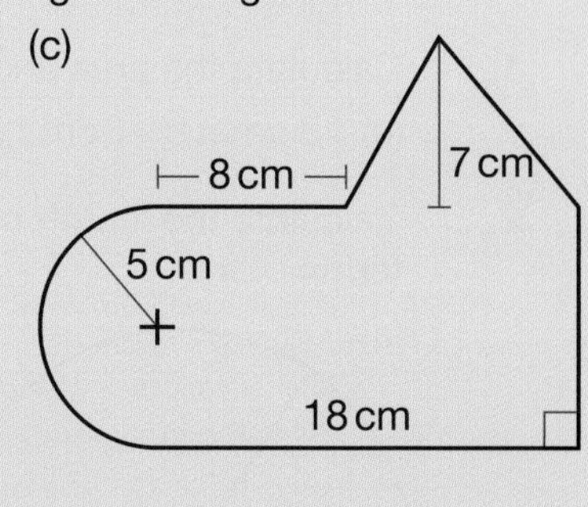

2. Circles 9 cm in diameter are cut from a piece of card as shown in the diagram. What percentage of the card is wasted?

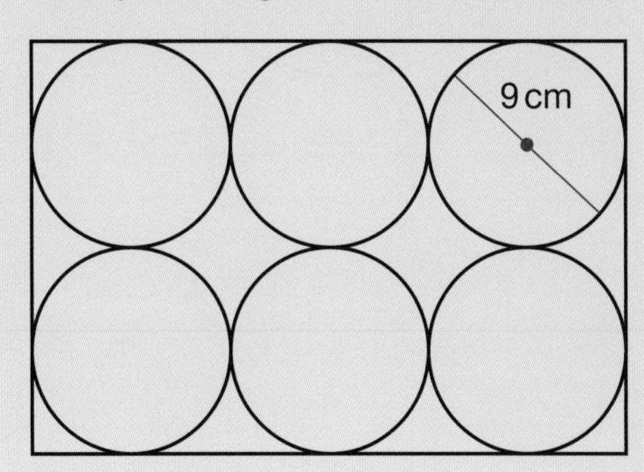

3.7 3-D shapes and volume

Nets

A prism is a three-dimensional shape that has the same cross-section all along its length.

Examples of prisms are:

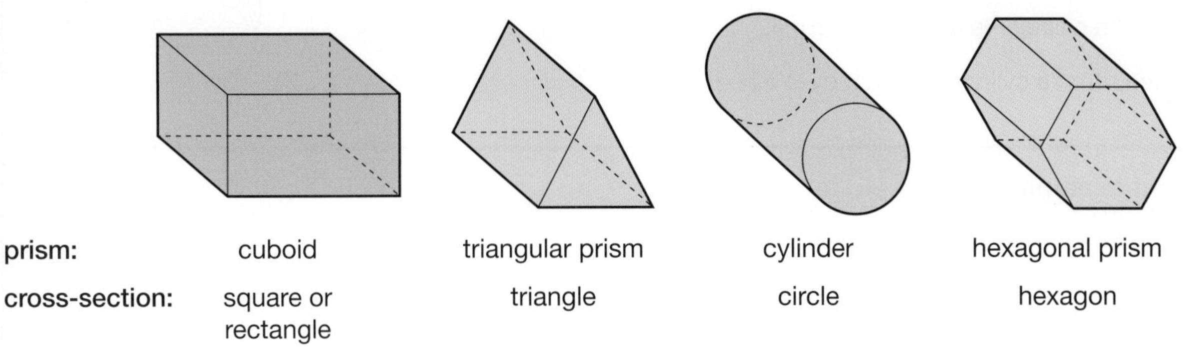

A pyramid has a polygon as a base. The other faces are triangles that meet at one vertex.

Examples of pyramids are:

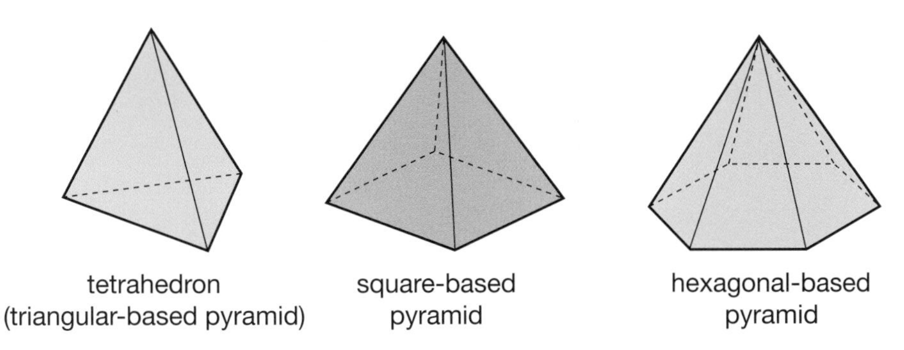

A net of a shape is a two-dimensional representation of a three-dimensional shape. It contains all of the faces of the shape and can be folded to make the solid shape.

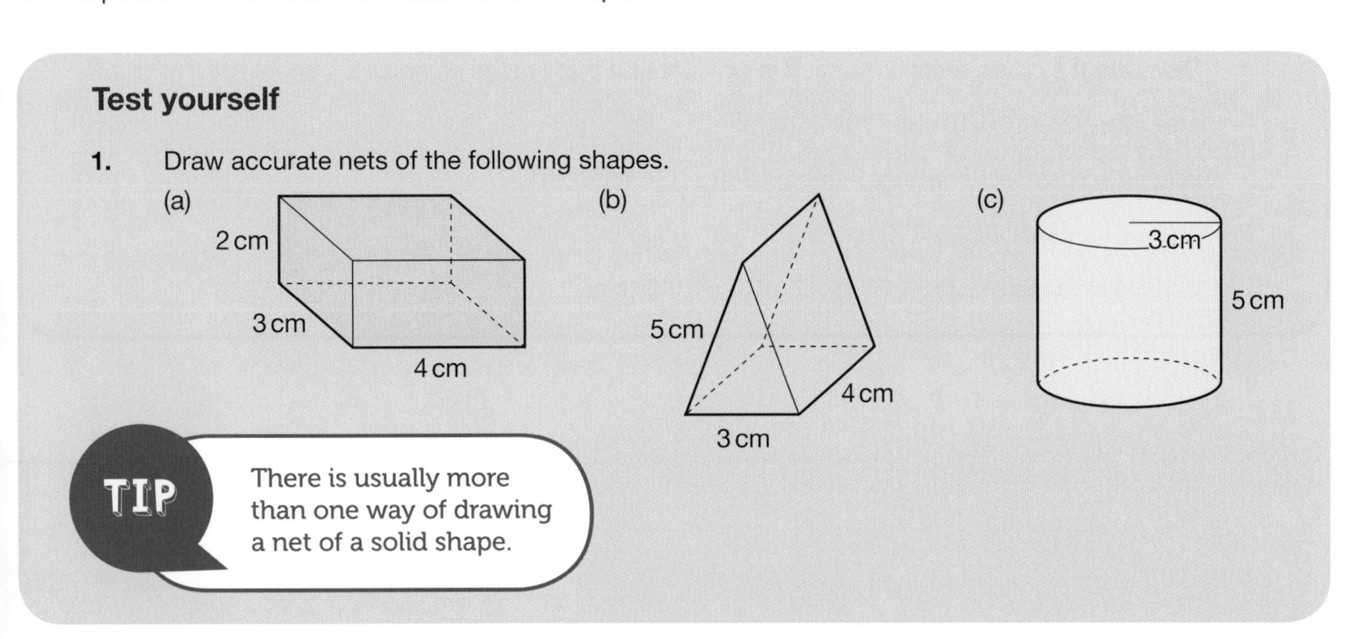

Test yourself

1. Draw accurate nets of the following shapes.

Volume and surface area of prisms

The volume, V, of a prism is given by V = surface area of cross-section × length of prism.

The surface area of a prism is the total of the area of all the faces.

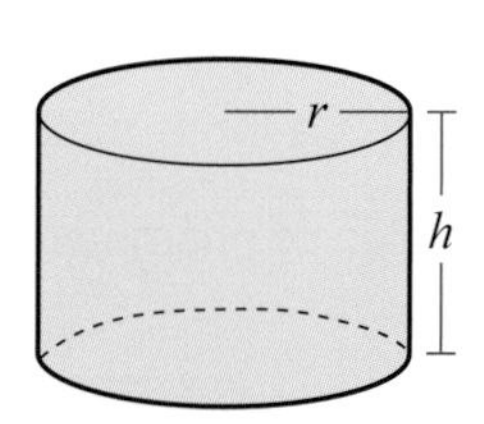

The volume, V, of a cuboid is given by V = length l × width w × height $h = lwh$.

The surface area, A, of a cuboid is given by $A = 2(lw + lh + wh)$.

The volume, V, of a cylinder is given by $V = \pi r^2 h$.

The surface area, A, of a cylinder is given by $A = 2\pi rh + 2\pi r^2$ (or $2\pi r(h + r)$).

Worked example

1. Calculate the volume of this prism.

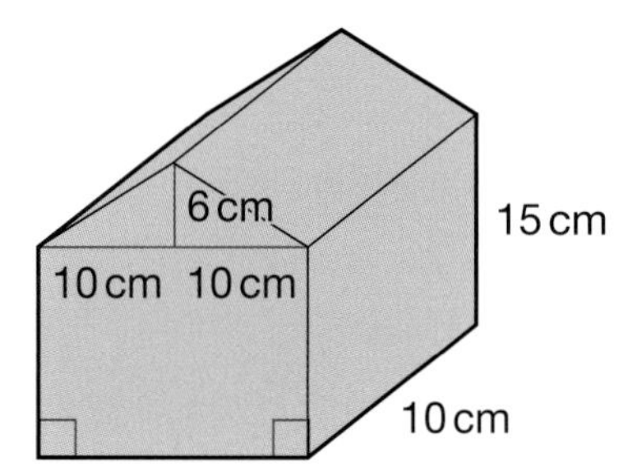

2. Calculate the volume and surface area of this cylinder.

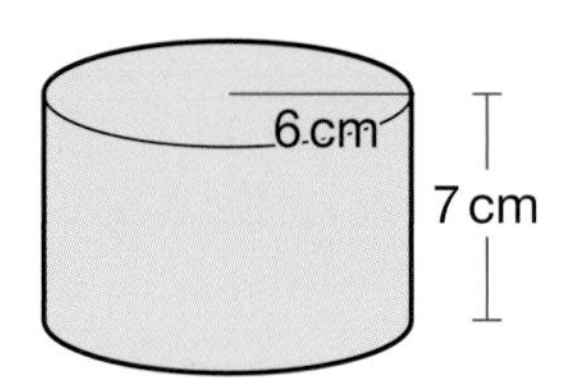

Answer

1. Calculate the cross-sectional area. It is two trapezia that are the same size.

   area $= 2 \times \frac{1}{2}(21 + 15) \times 10 = 36 \times 10 = 360$ cm^2

   volume = cross-sectional area × length $= 360 \times 10 = 3600$ cm^3

2. Volume $= \pi r^2 h = \pi \times 6^2 \times 7 = 792$ cm^3

   Surface area $= 2\pi rh + 2\pi r^2 = 2\pi \times 6 \times 7 + 2\pi \times 6^2 = 490$ cm^2

Test yourself

1. Calculate the volumes and surface areas of the following prisms.

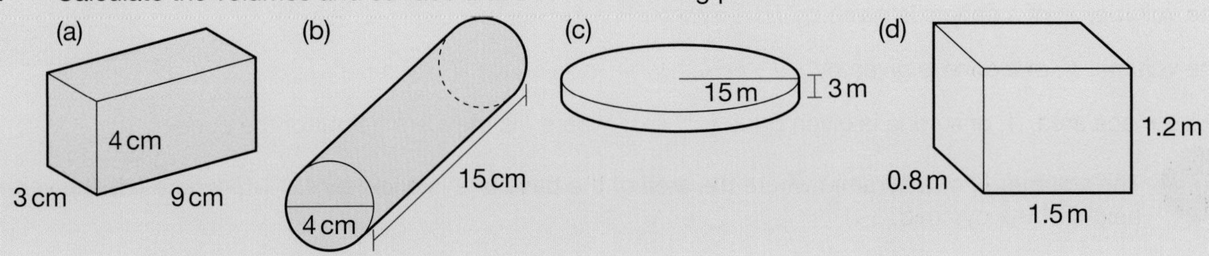

2. Calculate the volumes of the following prisms.

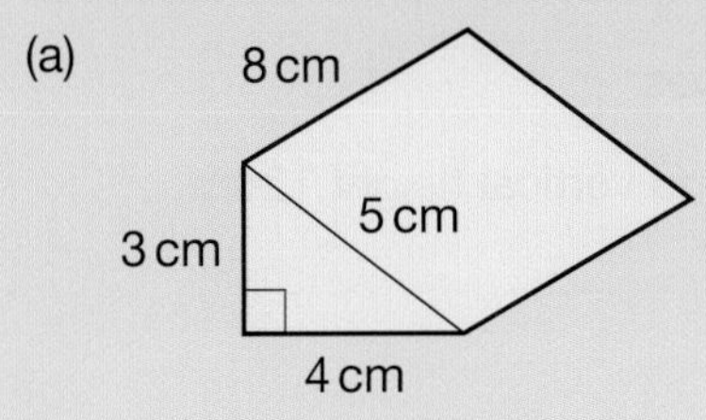

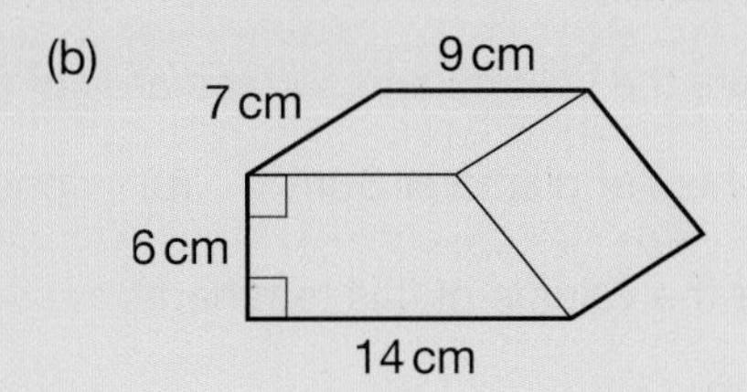

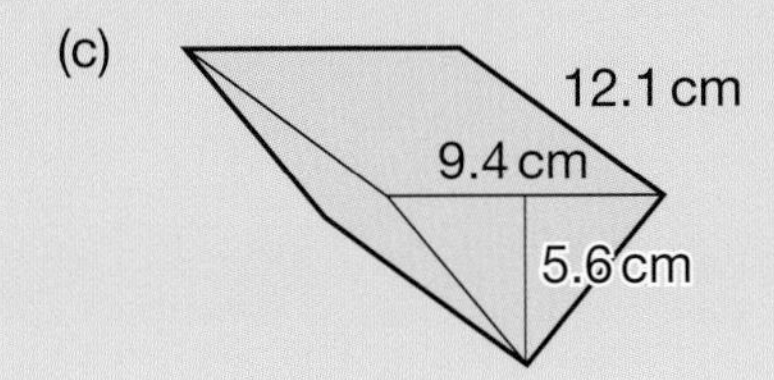

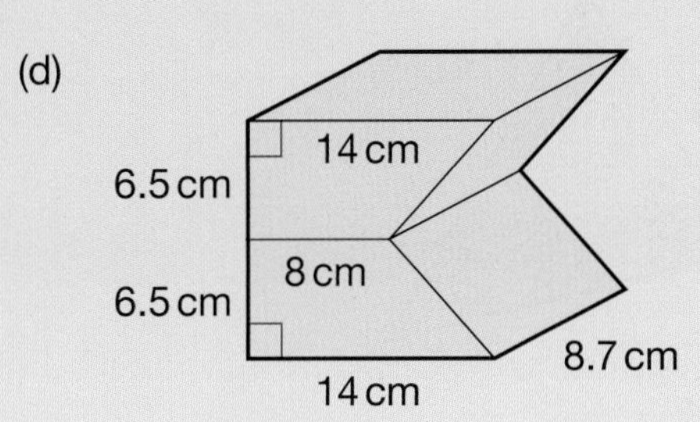

Converting between units

You should know the following relationships between units:

- length: 10 mm = 1 cm, 100 cm = 1 m, 1000 m = 1 km
- mass: 1000 g = 1 kg, 1000 kg = 1 t
- area: 100 mm^2 = 1 cm^2, 10 000 cm^2 = 1 m^2
- volume: 1000 mm^3 = 1 cm^3, 1 000 000 cm^3 = 1 m^3
- capacity: 10 ml = 1 cl, 100 cl = 1 litre = 1000 cm^3, 1 ml = 1 cm^3

Test yourself

1. Convert:

(a) 1857 mm to m	(b) 5.6 m to cm	(c) 23.65 t to kg
(d) 0.25 kg to g	(e) 3740 mm^2 to cm^2	(f) 6500 cm^2 to m^2
(g) 23 m^2 to cm^2	(h) 45 cm^2 to mm^2	(i) 330 ml to mm^3
(j) 330 ml to litres	(k) 6500 mm^3 to cm^3	(l) 0.37 m^3 to cm^3

2. (a) Convert your answers for volume from Q1 (a) and (b) in the Test yourself exercise on Volume and surface area of prisms to mm^3 and m^3. Give your answers in standard form.

(b) Convert your answers for surface area from Q1 (a) and (b) in the Test yourself exercise on Volume and surface area of prisms to mm^2 and m^2. Give your answers in standard form.

Other 3-D shapes

The surface area, A, of a sphere is given by $A = 4\pi r^2$.

The volume, V, of a sphere is given by $V = \frac{4}{3}\pi r^3$.

The volume, V, of a cone is given by $V = \frac{1}{3}\pi r^2 h$.

The surface area, A, of a cone is given by $A = \pi r l + \pi r^2$ where l is the slant height of the cone.

EDE The volume, V, of a pyramid where the area of the base is A is given by $V = \frac{1}{3}Ah$ where h is the vertical height of the pyramid.

Worked example

1. Calculate the volume and surface area of the following shapes:

   (a) sphere of diameter 6 cm (b) cone of radius 5 cm and vertical height 12 cm.

EDE 2. Calculate the volume of this tetrahedron.

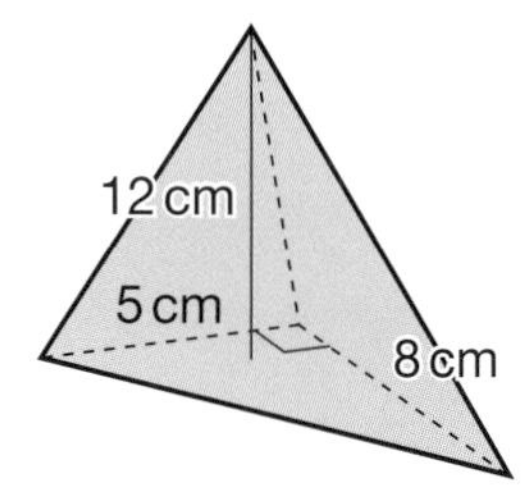

Answer

1. (a) Volume of sphere $= \frac{4}{3}\pi r^3 = \frac{4}{3} \times \pi \times 3^3 = 113\,\text{cm}^3$

   Surface area of sphere $= 4\pi r^2 = 4 \times \pi \times 3^2 = 113\,\text{cm}^2$

   (b) Volume of cone $= \frac{1}{3}\pi r^2 h = \frac{1}{3} \times \pi \times 5^2 \times 12 = 314\,\text{cm}^3$

   Use Pythagoras' theorem to work out the slant height:

   $$l^2 = r^2 + h^2 = 5^2 + 12^2 = 25 + 144 = 169$$

   So $l = 13\,\text{cm}$

   Surface area $= \pi r l + \pi r^2 = \pi \times 5 \times 13 + \pi \times 5^2 = 90\pi = 283\,\text{cm}^2$

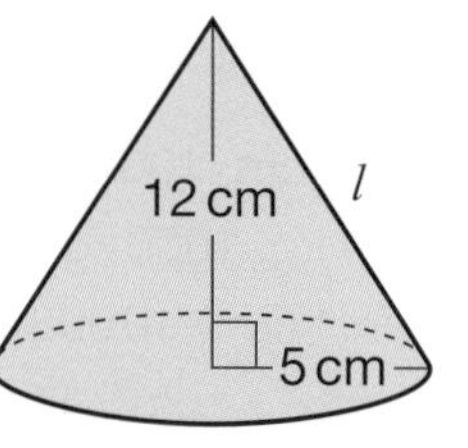

EDE 2. Area of base $= 0.5 \times 5 \times 8 = 20\,\text{cm}^2$

   Volume $= \frac{1}{3}Ah = \frac{1}{3} \times 20 \times 12 = 80\,\text{cm}^3$

Test yourself

1. Find the volume and surface area of each of the following shapes.

(a) sphere of radius 6 cm
(b) sphere of radius 9 cm
(c) sphere of diameter 10 cm
(d) sphere of diameter 20 cm
(e) cone of radius 6 cm and vertical height 8 cm
(f) cone of radius 8 cm and vertical height 10 cm
(g) cone of diameter 8 cm and vertical height 15 cm
(h) cone of diameter 14 cm and vertical height 12 cm

2. Find the volume of each of the following pyramids.

(a)

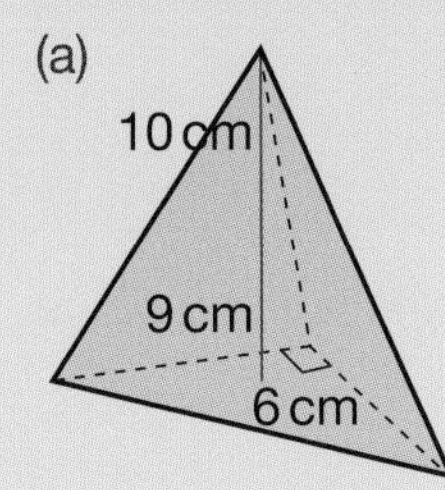

(b)

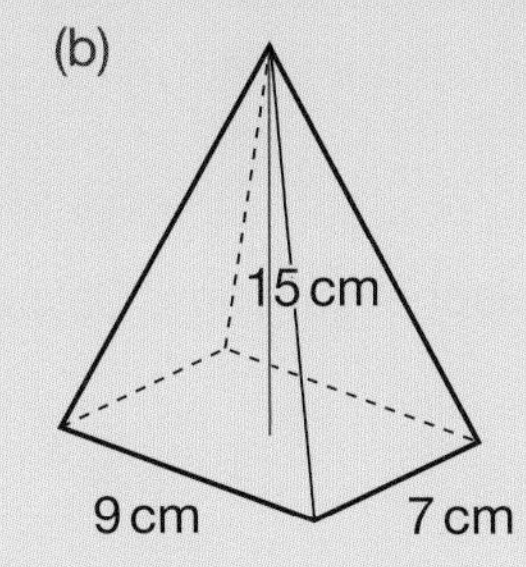

(c)

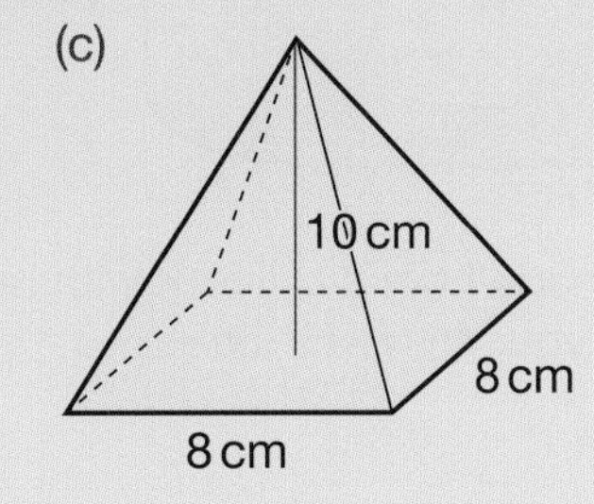

(d)

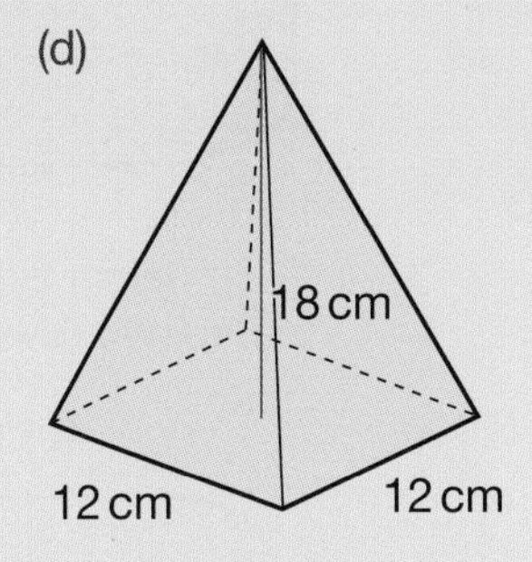

Compound shapes

When working out the volume of compound 3-D shapes, break down the shape into two or more shapes whose volumes you know how to calculate.

Worked example

A toy is made of a cone on top of a hemisphere.

Calculate the volume of the toy.

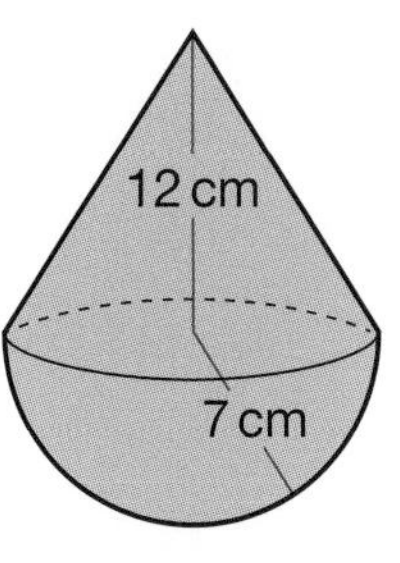

Answer

Volume of toy = volume of cone + volume of hemisphere

$$= \tfrac{1}{3} \times \pi \times 7^2 \times 12 + \tfrac{1}{2} \times \tfrac{4}{3} \times \pi \times 7^3$$

$$= 615.75 + 718.38 = 1334\,\text{cm}^3$$

Always look for the simplest way of breaking the shape down.

Test yourself

1. Calculate the volume of this shape. Give your answer in terms of π.

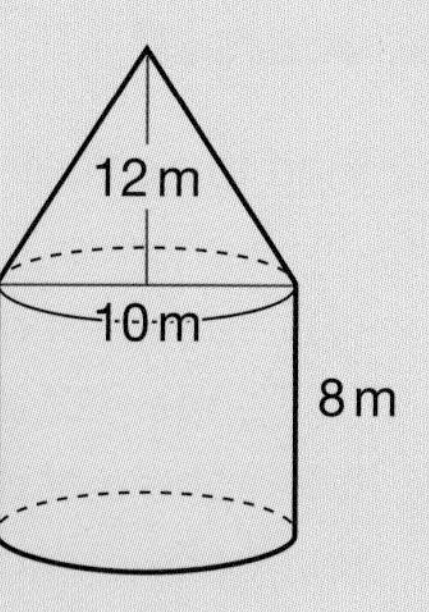

2. A tin is made from a cuboid with semicircular ends. Calculate the volume of the tin.

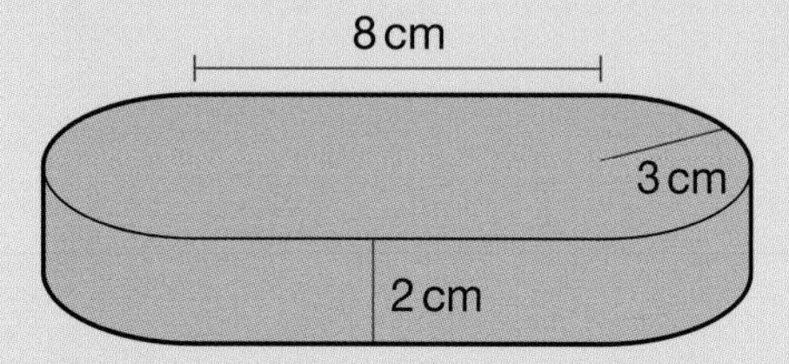

3. A container is made from a cylinder with hemispherical ends. Calculate the volume of the container. Give your answer in litres.

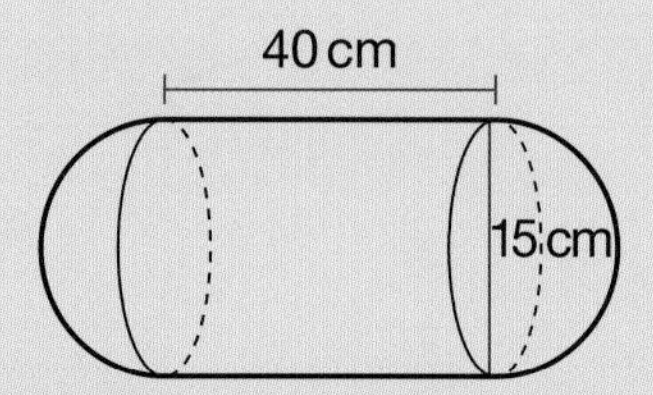

4. A swimming pool is a prism as shown in the diagram. Calculate the volume of the pool.

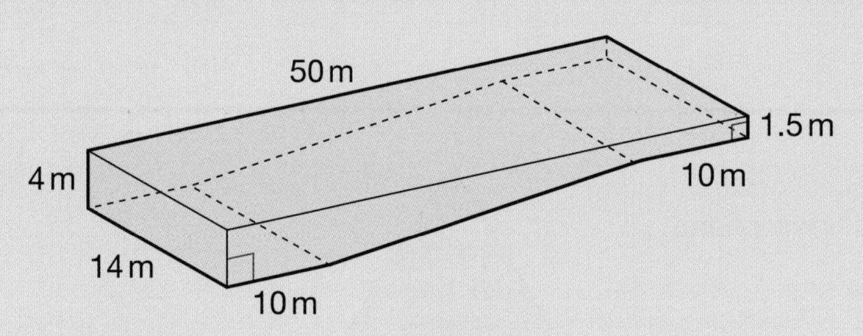

3.8 Symmetry

2-D symmetry

A shape has a line of symmetry when you can draw a line through the shape and the part of the shape on one side of the line is a reflection of the part of the shape on the other side of the line.

The line is also called a mirror line.

A shape has rotational symmetry when it can be rotated through an angle of 180° or less and the shape looks the same.

The order of rotational symmetry is the number of times the shape looks the same when it is rotated through 360°.

Test yourself

1. How many lines of symmetry do the following letters and shapes have?

(a) A (b) E (c) M (d) X (e) D (f) C

(g)  (h)  (i) (j) (k) (l) 

2. What is the order of rotational symmetry of the following letters and shapes?

(a) N (b) 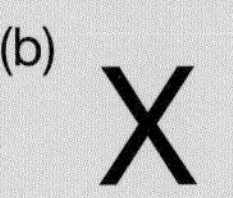 X (c) S (d) 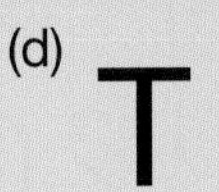 T (e) Z (f) 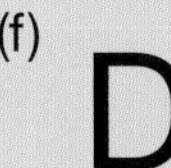 D

(g)  (h) (i) 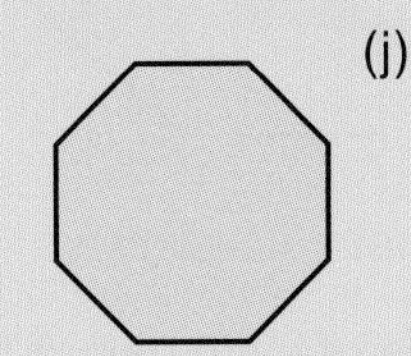 (j)  (k) 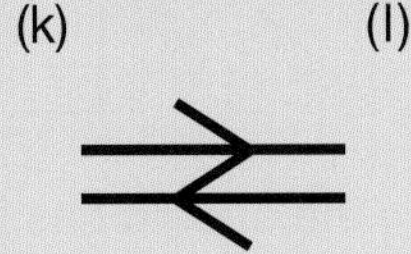 (l) 

3. Fill in squares to give the following shape:

(a) 1 line of symmetry
(b) 2 lines of symmetry
(c) order of rotational symmetry 2
(d) order of rotational symmetry 4.

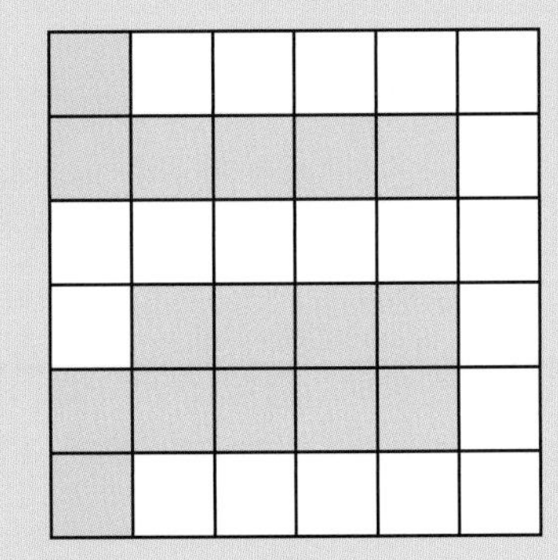

4. Which quadrilateral has 1 line of symmetry and zero order of rotational symmetry?

AM

3-D symmetry

A 3-D shape has a plane of symmetry when you can cut the shape along the plane of symmetry and the two parts of the shape are mirror images of each other.

A 3-D shape has rotational symmetry when you can rotate the shape about an axis of symmetry 180° or less and the shape looks the same.

The order of rotational symmetry is the number of times the shape looks the same when it is rotated through 360°.

Worked example

The cross-section of this cuboid is a square.

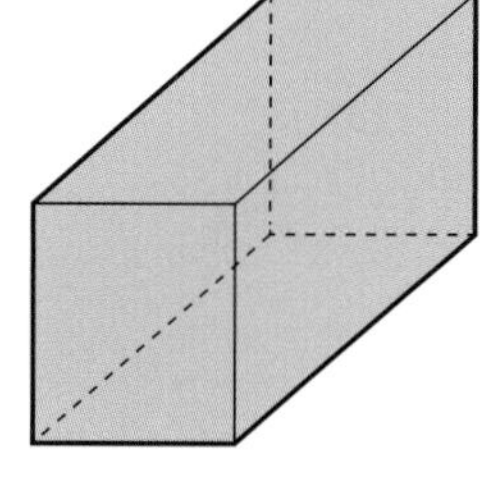

(a) How many planes of symmetry does the cuboid have?

(b) How many axes of symmetry does the cuboid have?

(c) What is the order of rotational symmetry for each axis of symmetry?

Answer

(a) The cuboid has 5 planes of symmetry as shown.

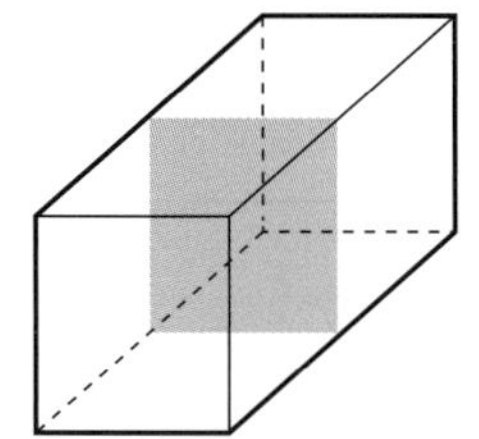
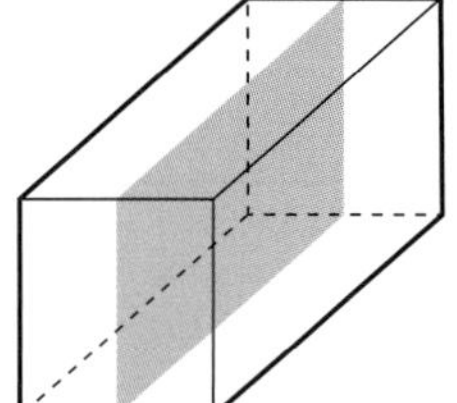
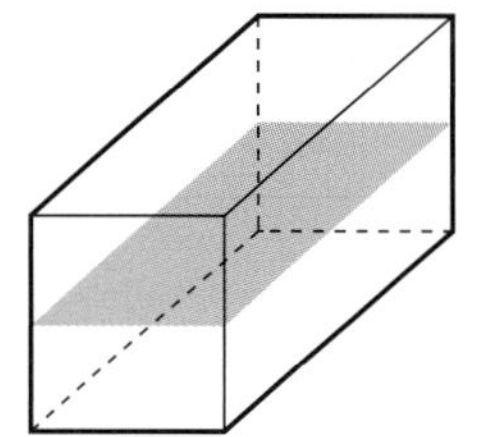
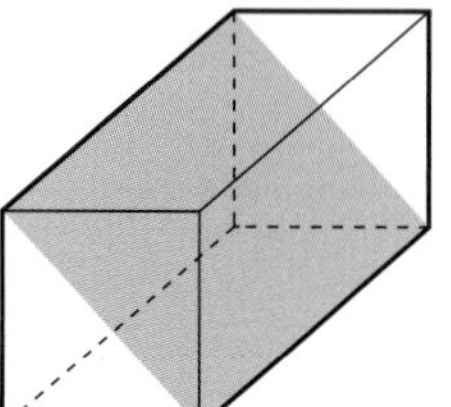
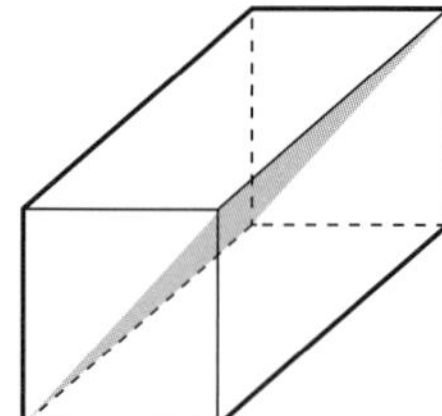

(b) The cuboid has 5 axes of symmetry as shown.

There is one between the middle of each pair of faces, and one between the middle of opposite long edges, and one between the middle of the other opposite long edges.

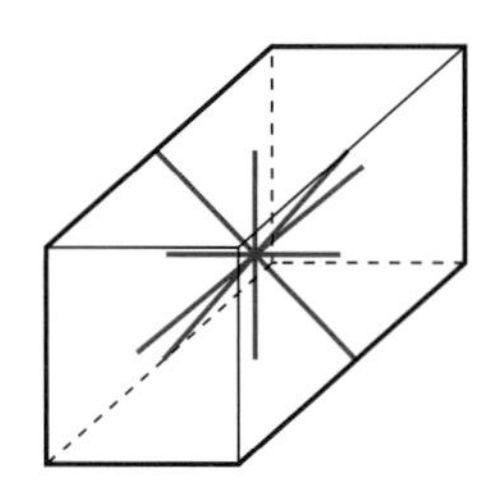

(c) The order of rotational symmetry about each axis of symmetry is 2.

Test yourself

1. For each of the following shapes, write down:
   (i) the number of planes of symmetry and axes of symmetry
   (ii) the order of rotational symmetry about each axis of symmetry.

(a)

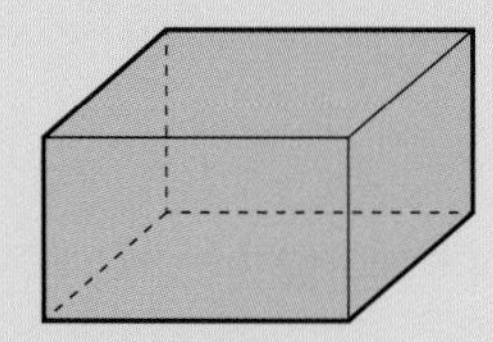

(b)

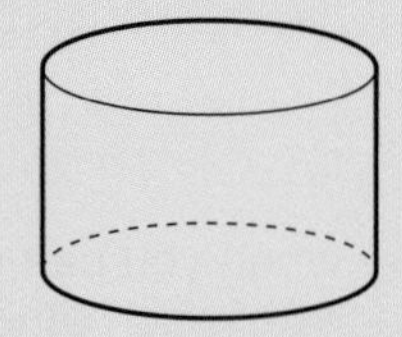

(c)

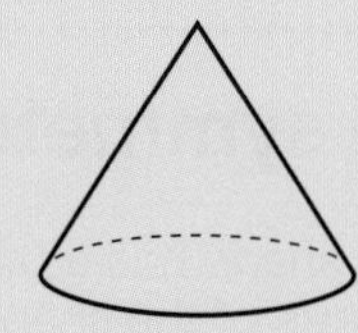

(d)

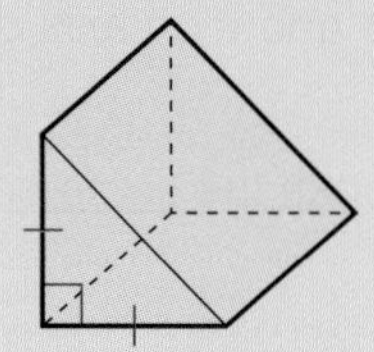

(e)

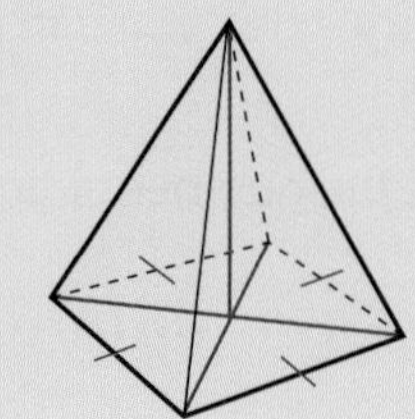

(f)

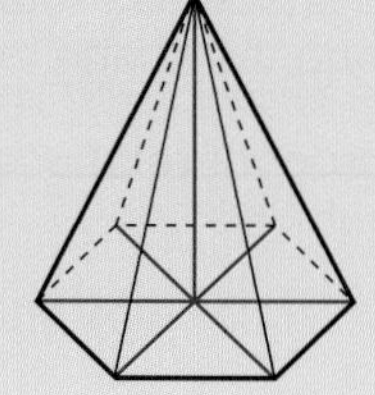

3.9 Similarity

Lengths and areas of similar shapes

Two shapes are similar if each of their corresponding angles are equal.

The lengths of corresponding sides are in the same ratio, $1:n$. n is also known as the linear scale factor.

When the linear scale factor is n, the area scale factor is n^2.

Worked example

1. The two triangles are similar. Find the lengths of x and y.

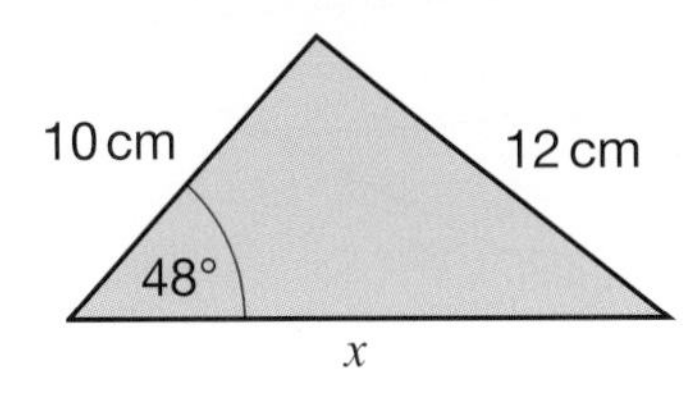

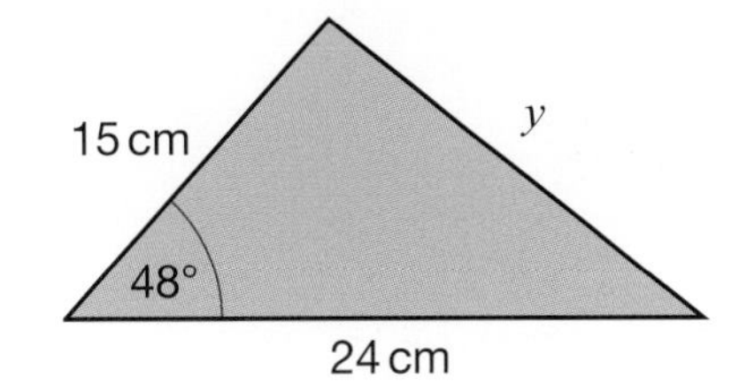

2. The area of the smaller triangle is 67 cm^2. Calculate the area of the larger triangle.

Answer

1. The triangles are similar, so the lengths of the sides will be in the same ratio.

   $\frac{x}{24} = \frac{10}{15}$, so $x = \frac{10 \times 24}{15} = 16\,\text{cm}$

   $\frac{y}{12} = \frac{15}{10}$, so $y = \frac{15 \times 12}{10} = 18\,\text{cm}$

2. Linear scale factor $= 15 \div 10 = 1.5$

   So the area scale factor $= 1.5^2 = 2.25$

   Area of larger triangle $=$ area of smaller triangle $\times$ area scale factor

   $= 67\,\text{cm}^2 \times 2.25$

   $= 150.75\,\text{cm}^2$

Test yourself

1. Each pair of shapes is similar. Find the lengths shown in the diagrams.

(a)

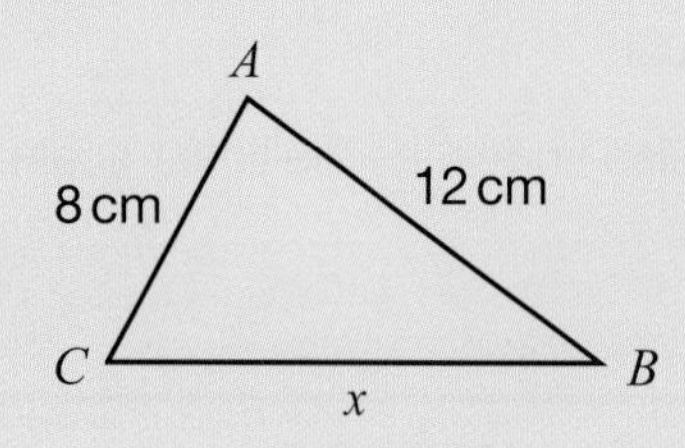

D
y
15 cm
F
E
12 cm

(b)

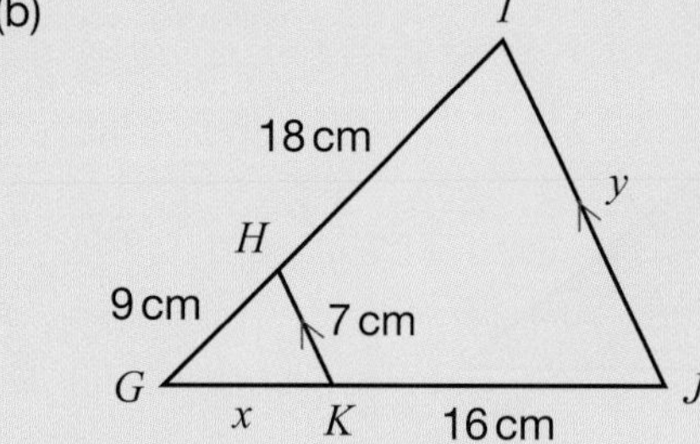

(c)

L
x
M
20 cm
36 cm
22 cm
P
N
30 cm
y
O

(d)

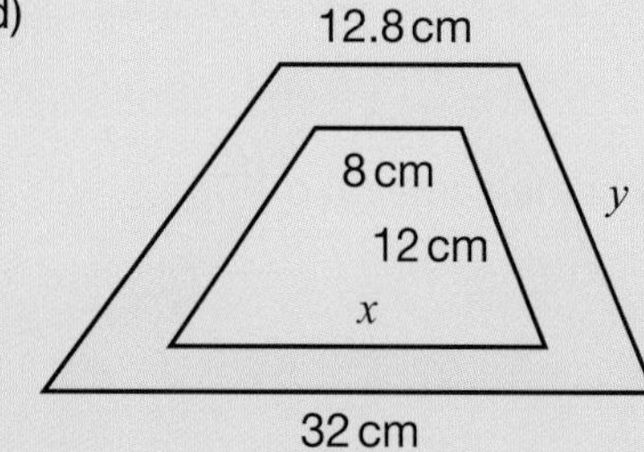

2. In Q1(a), the area of triangle ABC is 38 cm^2. Calculate the area of triangle DEF.

3. In Q1(b), the area of triangle GIJ is 243 cm^2. Calculate the area of triangle GHK.

4. In Q1(c), the area of triangle PNO is 465 cm^2. Calculate the area of trapezium $LMNP$.

TIP

Remember that you don't necessarily get all the marks just for writing down the answer. Often there are marks for showing your working. You should always show your working.

Areas and volumes of similar shapes

In similar 3-D shapes, when the linear scale factor is n:

- the area scale factor for the surface area is n^2
- the volume scale factor is n^3.

Worked example

A cuboid has a volume of 80 cm^3 and a surface area of 132 cm^2. It is 8 cm long.

A similar cuboid is 20 cm long. Calculate the volume and surface area of this cuboid.

Answer

Linear scale factor $= 20 \div 8 = 2.5$

So area scale factor $= 2.5^2 = 6.25$

Volume scale factor $= 2.5^3 = 15.625$

So volume of 20 cm cuboid $= 80\text{ cm}^3 \times 15.625 = 1250\text{ cm}^3$

Surface area of 20 cm cuboid $= 132\text{ cm}^2 \times 6.25 = 825\text{ cm}^2$

Test yourself

1. A ball bearing is a sphere 5 mm in diameter. It has a surface area of 80 mm^2. It is made of solid metal and has a mass of 0.52 g. The mass is proportional to the volume of the ball bearing.
A similar ball bearing is 8 mm in diameter. Calculate its mass and surface area.

2. A cylindrical tin has a volume of 330 cm^3 and is 12 cm high. It has a surface area of 280 cm^2.
A similar tin is 18 cm high. Calculate its volume and surface area.

3. A bottle contains 800 cm^3 and is 15 cm high.
A similar bottle contains 100 cm^3. Work out the height of the bottle.

4. A cereal packet has a volume of 1200 cm^3 and a surface area of 860 cm^2. It is 30 cm high.
A similar packet is 24 cm high. Work out its volume and surface area.

TIP

Remember that areas increase or decrease by the square of the linear scale factor and volumes increase or decrease by the cube of the linear scale factor.

3.10 Vectors

Vectors

A vector is a quantity that has direction as well as size (magnitude).

Vectors can be written as $\overrightarrow{AB}$, **a** or $\begin{pmatrix} x \\ y \end{pmatrix}$.

When vectors are written as $\begin{pmatrix} x \\ y \end{pmatrix}$, the top number gives the distance moved across (in the x-direction) and the bottom number gives the distance moved up or down (in the y-direction).

Vectors can be used to describe a position in relation to the origin as well as a translation (movement) from one point to another.

You can add and subtract vectors and multiply them by a scalar (a number).

The vector –**a** is the reverse of **a**. It has the same magnitude or length but it is in the opposite direction.

Worked example

(a) Write **a** and **b** as column vectors.

(b) Write the position of C as a position vector.

(c) Write $\overrightarrow{AC}$ as a column vector.

(c) Work out 2**a** – **b**.

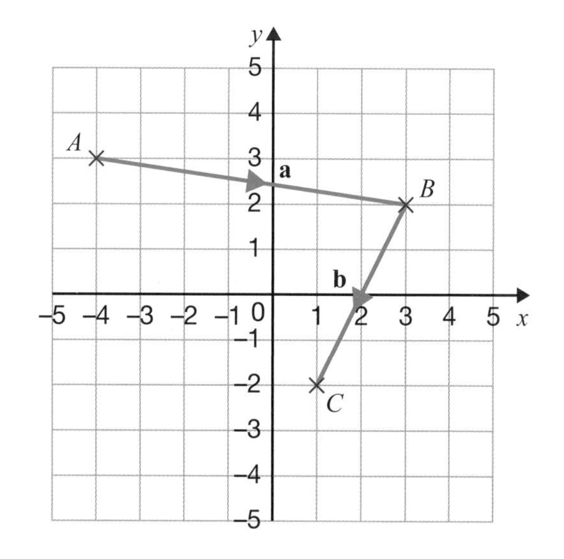

Answer

(a) **a** is 7 squares to the right and 1 square down, so $\mathbf{a} = \begin{pmatrix} 7 \\ -1 \end{pmatrix}$.

b is 2 squares to the left and 4 squares down, so $\mathbf{b} = \begin{pmatrix} -2 \\ -4 \end{pmatrix}$.

(b) The position vector is the coordinates of point $C = \begin{pmatrix} 1 \\ -2 \end{pmatrix}$.

(c) $\overrightarrow{AC} = \begin{pmatrix} 5 \\ -5 \end{pmatrix}$

(d) $2\mathbf{a} - \mathbf{b} = \begin{pmatrix} 2\times7--2 \\ 2\times-1--4 \end{pmatrix} = \begin{pmatrix} 16 \\ 2 \end{pmatrix}$

TIP When writing vectors by hand, underline them or put an arrow over the top to show that they are vectors.

Test yourself

1. Write A, B, C and D as position vectors.

2. Write down the vectors:

   (a) $\overrightarrow{AB}$ (b) $\overrightarrow{BA}$ (c) $\overrightarrow{AD}$ (d) $\overrightarrow{CD}$

3. $\mathbf{a}=\begin{pmatrix}2\\3\end{pmatrix}$, $\mathbf{b}=\begin{pmatrix}-3\\4\end{pmatrix}$, $\mathbf{c}=\begin{pmatrix}5\\-2\end{pmatrix}$

   Work out:

   (a) $\mathbf{a}+\mathbf{b}$

   (b) $\mathbf{b}-\mathbf{a}$

   (c) $2\mathbf{c}+\mathbf{b}$

   (d) $3\mathbf{b}-2\mathbf{c}$

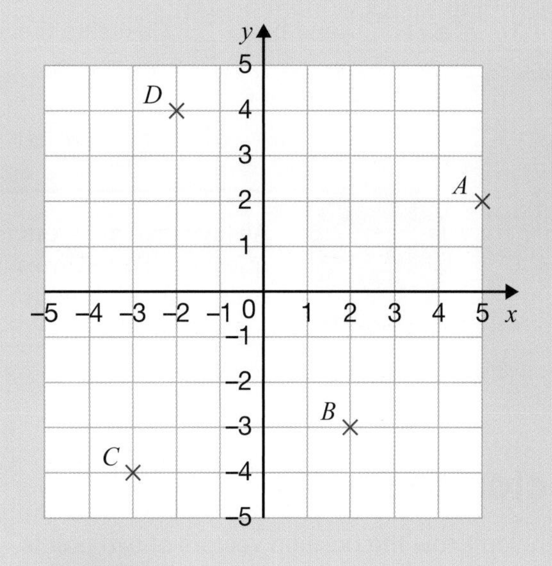

TIP Don't just count the squares – check the scale on the axes first.

Magnitude of a vector

You can calculate the magnitude of a vector using Pythagoras' theorem.

The symbol for magnitude is a vertical line before and after the vector, e.g. $|\overrightarrow{AB}|$ or $|\mathbf{a}|$.

When $\mathbf{a}=\begin{pmatrix}x\\y\end{pmatrix}$, $|\mathbf{a}|=\sqrt{x^2+y^2}$

Worked example

$\mathbf{a}=\begin{pmatrix}2\\-3\end{pmatrix}$ and $\mathbf{b}=\begin{pmatrix}-6\\5\end{pmatrix}$. Find $|\mathbf{a}+2\mathbf{b}|$.

Answer

$\mathbf{a}+2\mathbf{b}=\begin{pmatrix}2+2\times-6\\-3+2\times5\end{pmatrix}=\begin{pmatrix}-10\\7\end{pmatrix}$

$|\mathbf{a}+2\mathbf{b}|=\sqrt{(-10)^2+7^2}=\sqrt{149}=12.2$

Test yourself

1. $\mathbf{a}=\begin{pmatrix}-5\\2\end{pmatrix}$ and $\mathbf{b}=\begin{pmatrix}6\\-8\end{pmatrix}$. Calculate the following. Give your answers to three significant figures, where appropriate.

(a) $|\mathbf{a}|$ (b) $|\mathbf{b}|$ (c) $|\mathbf{a}+\mathbf{b}|$ (d) $|\mathbf{a}-\mathbf{b}|$ (e) $|\mathbf{b}-\mathbf{a}|$ (f) $|\mathbf{b}-2\mathbf{a}|$

Always give answers to the accuracy specified in the question. Sometimes it will be specified on the cover of the exam paper if it is not specified in the question.

Vector geometry

When you know the position vectors of two points, you can use them to specify other vectors in terms of these points.

Worked example

1. $\overrightarrow{OA}$ is the vector **a** and $\overrightarrow{OB}$ is the vector **b**.
   Write down the following in terms of **a** and **b**.

   (a) $\overrightarrow{OH}$ (b) $\overrightarrow{OC}$ (c) $\overrightarrow{OE}$ (d) $\overrightarrow{EM}$

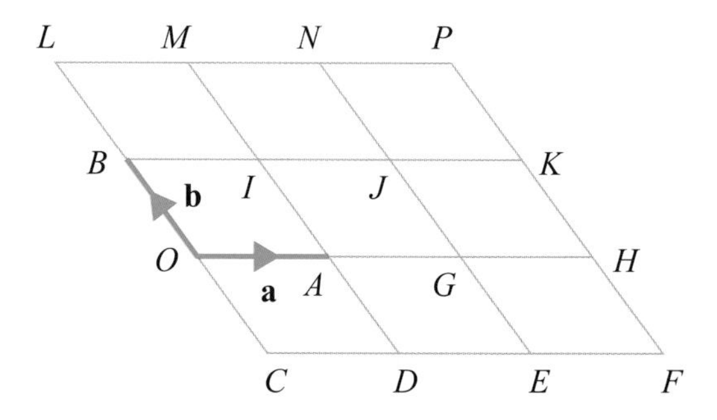

2. In the diagram, $\overrightarrow{OA}=\mathbf{a}$, $\overrightarrow{OB}=\mathbf{b}$, $\overrightarrow{AC}=\frac{1}{3}\overrightarrow{AB}$, $\overrightarrow{OD}=\frac{2}{3}\overrightarrow{OB}$.

   Work out these vectors in terms of **a** and **b**.

   (a) $\overrightarrow{OC}$ (b) $\overrightarrow{OD}$ (c) $\overrightarrow{CD}$

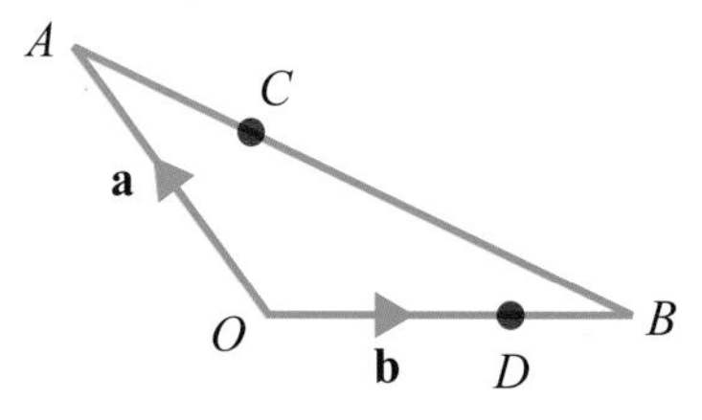

Answer

1. (a) $\overrightarrow{OH}=3\mathbf{a}$ (b) $\overrightarrow{OC}=-\mathbf{b}$

   (c) $\overrightarrow{OE}=2\mathbf{a}-\mathbf{b}$ (d) $\overrightarrow{EM}=3\mathbf{b}-\mathbf{a}$

2. (a) $\overrightarrow{AC}=\frac{1}{3}\overrightarrow{AB}$

   $\overrightarrow{AB}=\mathbf{b}-\mathbf{a}$

   $\overrightarrow{OC}=\overrightarrow{OA}+\frac{1}{3}\overrightarrow{AB}=\mathbf{a}+\frac{1}{3}(\mathbf{b}-\mathbf{a})=\frac{2}{3}\mathbf{a}+\frac{1}{3}\mathbf{b}$

   (b) $\overrightarrow{OD}=\frac{2}{3}\mathbf{b}$

   (c) $\overrightarrow{CD}=\overrightarrow{OC}+\overrightarrow{OD}=\left(\frac{2}{3}\mathbf{a}+\frac{1}{3}\mathbf{b}\right)+\frac{2}{3}\mathbf{b}=\frac{2}{3}\mathbf{a}+\mathbf{b}$

TIP

When writing vectors, first write the vectors down in terms of the points, as shown here. Then put in the actual vectors.

Test yourself

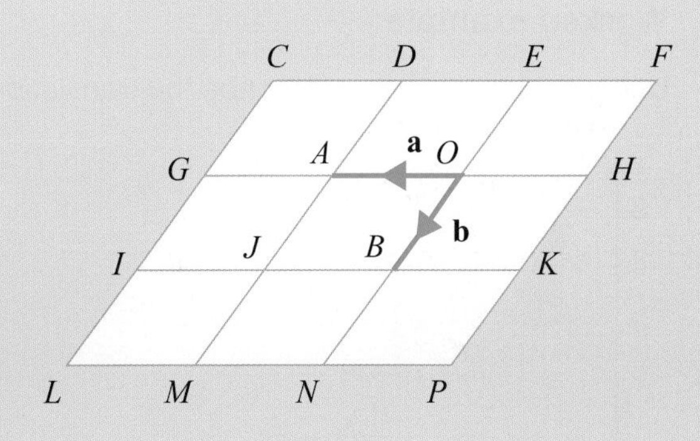

1. $\overrightarrow{OA}$ is the vector **a** and $\overrightarrow{OB}$ is the vector **b**.
   Write down the following in terms of **a** and **b**.
   (a) $\overrightarrow{OE}$ (b) $\overrightarrow{OG}$ (c) $\overrightarrow{OP}$
   (d) $\overrightarrow{NC}$ (e) $\overrightarrow{IE}$ (f) $\overrightarrow{HL}$

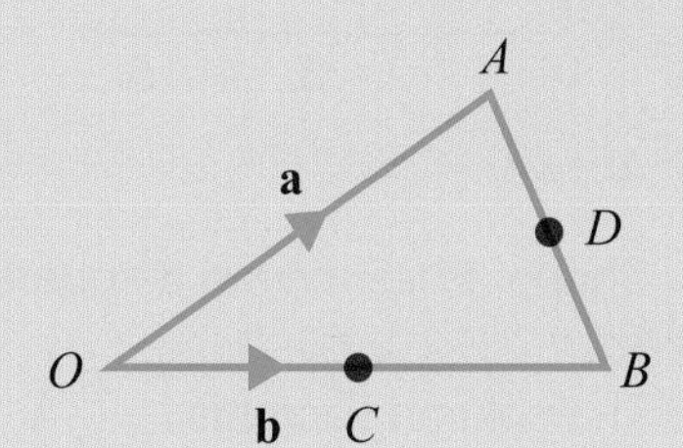

2. In the diagram, $\overrightarrow{OA}=\mathbf{a}$, $\overrightarrow{OB}=\mathbf{b}$, C is the midpoint of $\overrightarrow{OB}$ and D is the midpoint of $\overrightarrow{AB}$.
   (a) Work out these vectors in terms of **a** and **b**.
   (i) $\overrightarrow{OC}$ (ii) $\overrightarrow{OD}$
   (b) Show that $\overrightarrow{CD}$ is parallel to $\overrightarrow{OA}$.

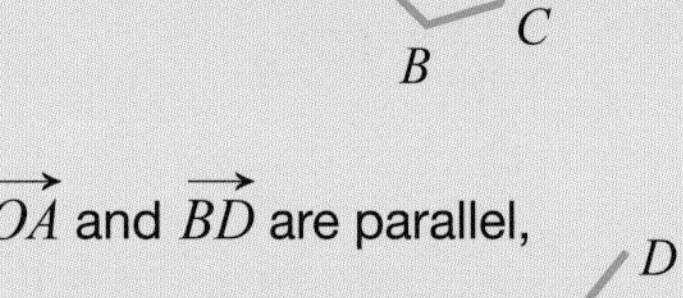

3. In the diagram, $\overrightarrow{OA}=5\mathbf{a}$, $\overrightarrow{OB}=\mathbf{b}$, $\overrightarrow{BC}=\frac{1}{5}\overrightarrow{OA}$ and M is the midpoint of $\overrightarrow{AC}$.
   (a) Work out these vectors in terms of **a** and **b**.
   (i) $\overrightarrow{OC}$ (ii) $\overrightarrow{OM}$
   (b) D is the position vector $2\mathbf{a}+\frac{3}{4}\mathbf{b}$.
   Where on the diagram should it go?

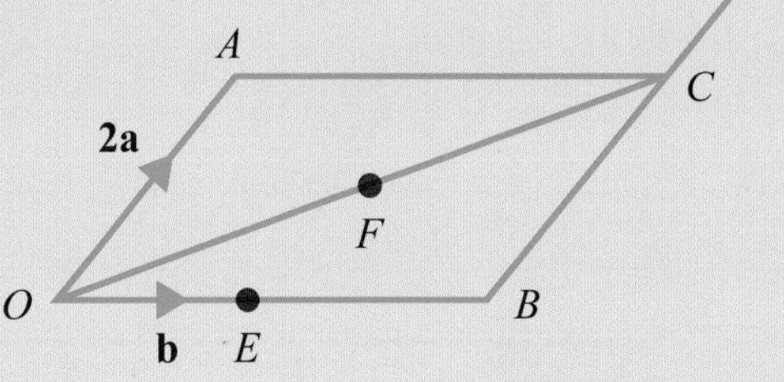

4. In the diagram, $\overrightarrow{OA}=2\mathbf{a}$, $\overrightarrow{OE}=\mathbf{b}$, $\overrightarrow{OB}=4\overrightarrow{OE}$, $\overrightarrow{OB}$ and $\overrightarrow{AC}$ are parallel, $\overrightarrow{OA}$ and $\overrightarrow{BD}$ are parallel, $\overrightarrow{BC}=2\overrightarrow{CD}$ and F is the midpoint of $\overrightarrow{OC}$.
   (a) Work out these vectors in terms of **a** and **b**.
   (i) $\overrightarrow{BC}$ (ii) $\overrightarrow{OF}$ (iii) $\overrightarrow{EF}$
   (b) Show that EFD is a straight line.

When showing that an answer is true, make sure you show every stage in your working. Also check that you have added signs correctly.

3.11 Transformations

Translations

A translation is a movement in the x-direction, a movement in the y-direction or a combination of the two.

Translated shapes are congruent with the original. A translation does not change the shape, size or orientation of an object.

Translations can be given in the form of column vectors, $\begin{pmatrix} x \\ y \end{pmatrix}$.

Worked example

Use a column vector to describe the translation of A to B.

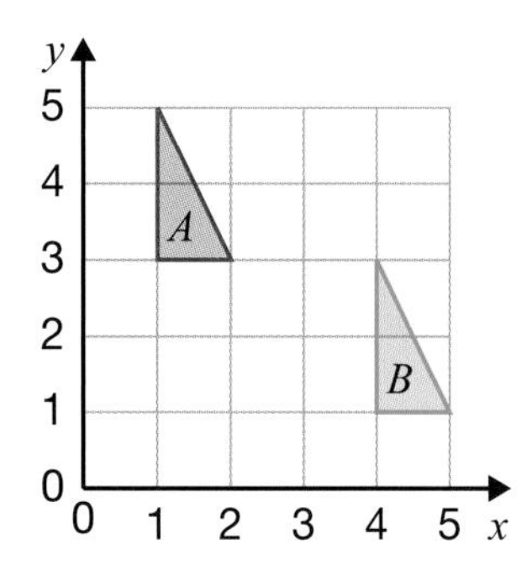

Answer

Shape A has moved 3 squares to the right and 2 squares down.

The column vector is $\begin{pmatrix} 3 \\ -2 \end{pmatrix}$.

Test yourself

1. Use column vectors to describe the following translations.

(a) A to B (b) A to C (c) A to D (d) A to E

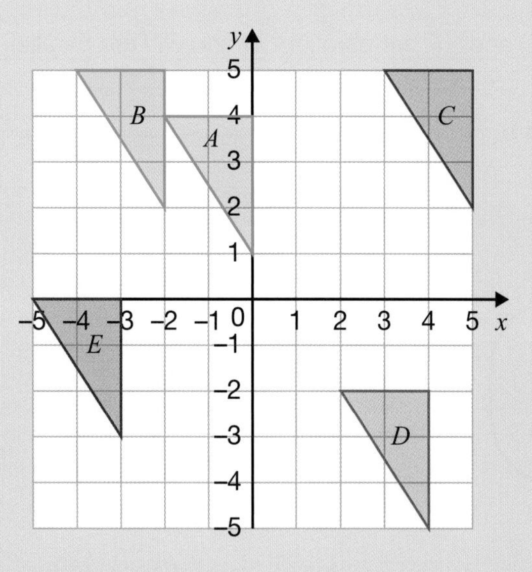

TIP

When asked to give a translation as a position vector, it should only have two entries and the movement in the x-direction always goes first.

2. Draw coordinate axes from –5 to +5 in both directions.
Draw a triangle with coordinates (–1, 2), (2, 2) and (0, –1).
Draw the image after the following translations.

(a) $\begin{pmatrix} 2 \\ 3 \end{pmatrix}$ (b) $\begin{pmatrix} -3 \\ 1 \end{pmatrix}$ (c) $\begin{pmatrix} 3 \\ -4 \end{pmatrix}$ (d) $\begin{pmatrix} -4 \\ -3 \end{pmatrix}$

Reflections

A reflection is a movement where a shape has been reflected in a mirror line.

A reflected image is congruent with the object. A reflection does not change the size or shape but does change the orientation.

Each vertex on the image is the same distance from the mirror line as it is from its corresponding vertex on the object, but on the opposite side of the mirror line.

Worked example

Describe the reflection that maps A onto B.

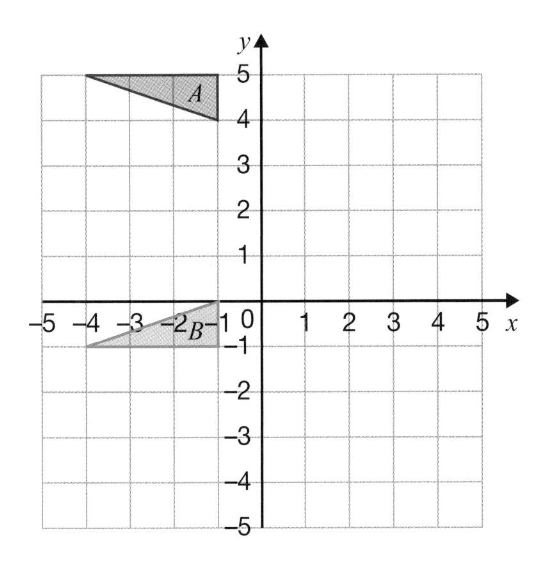

Answer

The image is a reflection in the line $y=2$.

Test yourself

1. Describe the reflections that map the following shapes.
   (a) A onto B (b) A onto C
   (c) A onto D (d) A onto E

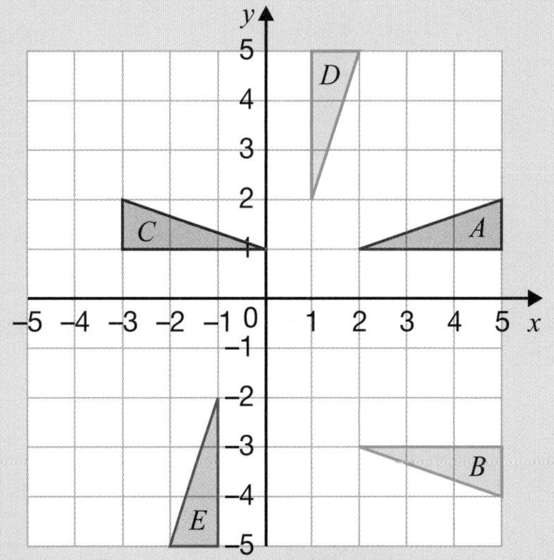

2. Draw coordinate axes from –5 to +5 in both directions.
   Draw a triangle with coordinates $A(2, 1)$, $B(4, 1)$ and $C(2, 4)$.
   Draw the image after reflections in the following mirror lines.
   (a) $y=0$ (b) $x=2$ (c) $y=x$ (d) $y=-x$

Rotations

A rotation is a movement where the shape has been rotated about the centre of rotation.

A clockwise rotation is usually positive and an anticlockwise rotation negative.

A rotation does not change the size or shape of an object, but does change the orientation.

Worked example

Describe the rotation that maps A onto B.

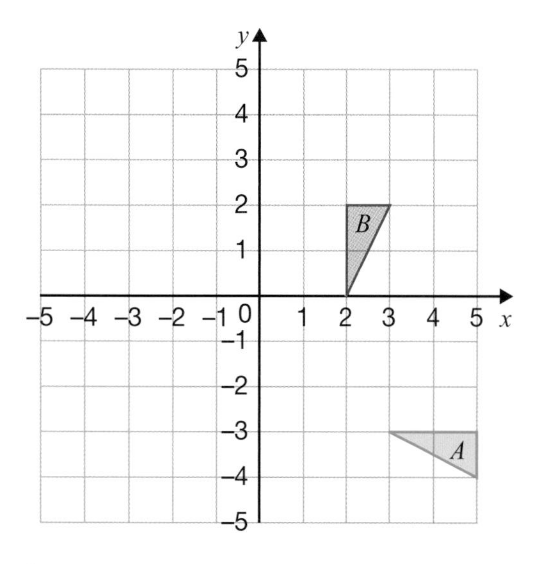

TIP When finding the centre of rotation, look for a point that is equidistant from corresponding vertices on the object and image.

Answer

The image is a rotation of 90° anticlockwise about the point (1, –2).

Test yourself

1. Describe the rotations that map the following shapes.

(a) A onto B (b) A onto C

(c) A onto D (d) A onto E

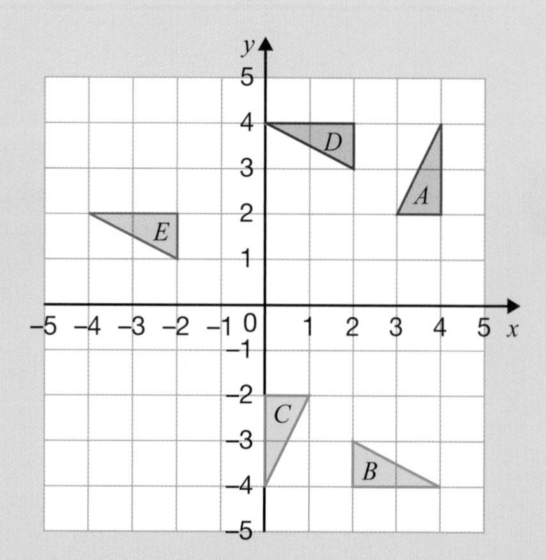

2. Draw coordinate axes from –5 to +5 in both directions.

Draw a triangle with coordinates A(2, 1), B(4, 1) and C(2, 4).

Draw the image after the following rotations.

(a) 90° clockwise about (0, 0)

(b) 180° about (0, 0)

(c) 90° anticlockwise about (1, –1)

(d) 90° clockwise about (0, 2)

TIP Always read questions like this carefully – make sure you are giving the answer the question asks for.

Enlargements

An enlargement changes the size of a shape but not the angles in a shape.

An enlargement has a scale factor and a centre of enlargement.

The length of the side of the image = length of side of object × scale factor.

A fractional enlargement produces an image that is smaller than the object.

A negative enlargement produces an image on the opposite side of the centre of enlargement from the object.

You can use the ray method or coordinate method to construct an enlargement.

In the ray method:

- Draw rays (lines) from the centre of each vertex; extend them beyond the vertex when the scale factor is more than 1.
- Multiply the distance of each vertex from the centre of enlargement by the scale factor.
- Mark the new vertex on each ray and join up the points.

In the coordinate method:

- Measure the distance of each vertex from the centre of enlargement.
- Multiply the distance by the scale factor; the new vertices lie on the same line as the line from the centre of enlargement to the original vertex at this new distance.
- Mark the vertices and join up the points.

You can find the centre of enlargement by drawing rays from each vertex on the image to the corresponding vertex on the object and continuing the lines. The centre of enlargement is where the rays cross.

Worked example

1. Enlarge the shape shown by:

   (a) scale factor 2 about the centre of enlargement (–1, 0)

   (b) scale factor 0.5 about the centre of enlargement (–3, 5)

   (c) scale factor –2 about the centre of enlargement (0, 2).

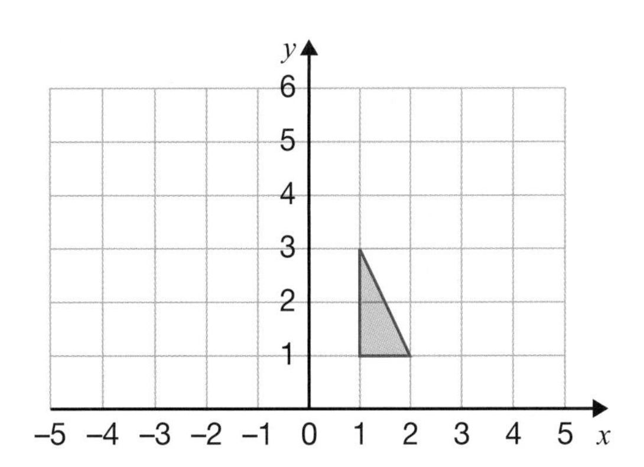

2. Find the centre of enlargement for the object and image.

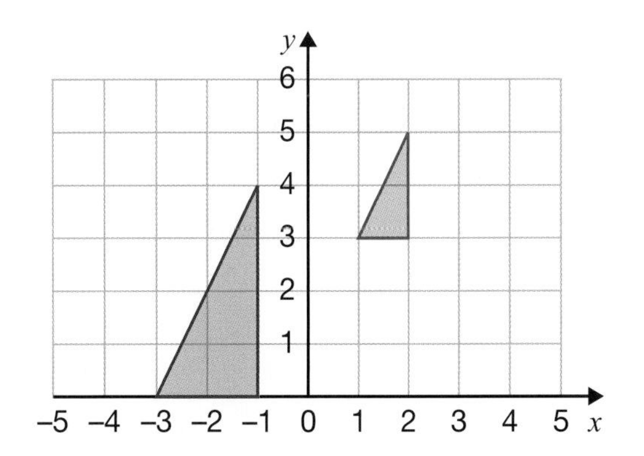

CAM

Answer

1. (a), (b)

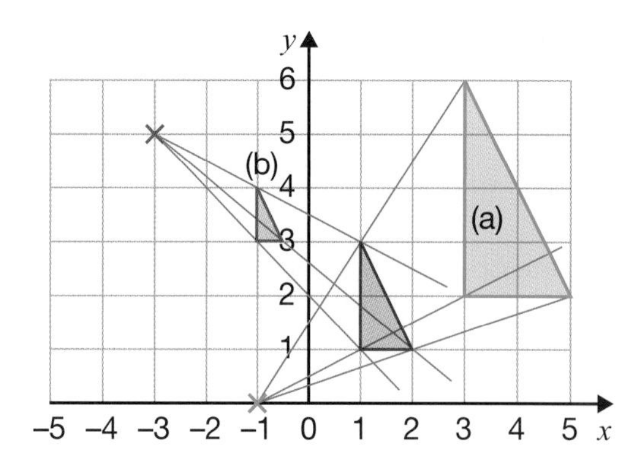

(c)

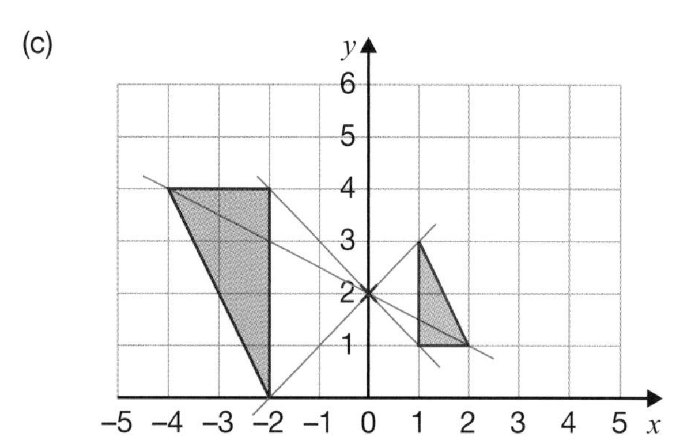

2.

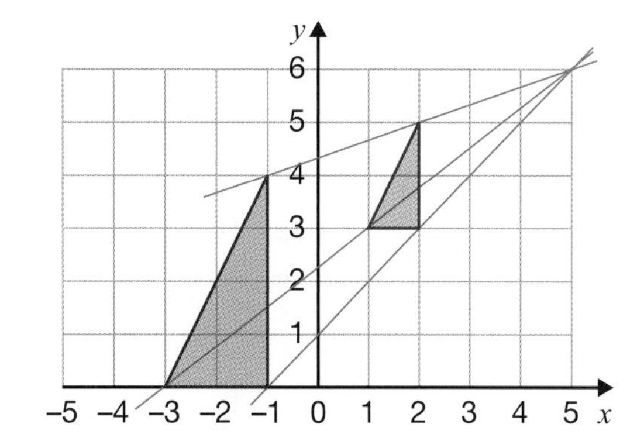

Draw rays connecting corresponding vertices.

Centre of enlargement is where they cross, at (5, 6).

Test yourself

1. Draw coordinate axes from –5 to +5 in both directions.
   Draw a triangle with coordinates (2, 1), (4, 1) and (2, 4).
   (a) Enlarge the triangle by scale factor 2 using a centre of enlargement (4, 5).
   (b) Enlarge the triangle by scale factor 3 using a centre of enlargement (5, 4).

2. Draw coordinate axes from –5 to +5 in both directions.
   Draw a triangle with coordinates (5, 1), (1, 5) and (5, 5).
   (a) Enlarge the triangle by scale factor 0.5 about the centre of enlargement (–3, 3).
   (b) Enlarge the triangle by scale factor 0.25 about the centre of enlargement (–3, –3).

3. Draw coordinate axes from –5 to +5 in both directions.
   Draw a triangle with coordinates (0, 1), (0, –2) and (1, –1). Draw another triangle with coordinates (–4, 2), (–2, –2) and (–4, –4). Find the centre of enlargement.

EXAM 4. Draw coordinate axes from –5 to +5 in both directions.
   Draw a triangle with coordinates (–5, 4), (–3, 3) and (–3, 5).
   (a) Enlarge the triangle by scale factor –2 about the centre of enlargement (–2, 3).
   (b) Enlarge the triangle by scale factor –0.5 about the centre of enlargement (1, 3).

Combined transformations

You can use combinations of transformations.

Worked example

(a) Reflect shape A in line $y=1$. Label the shape B.

(b) Rotate shape B 90° clockwise about the centre of rotation (–1, 1). Label the shape C.

(c) What single transformation would map shape A onto shape C?

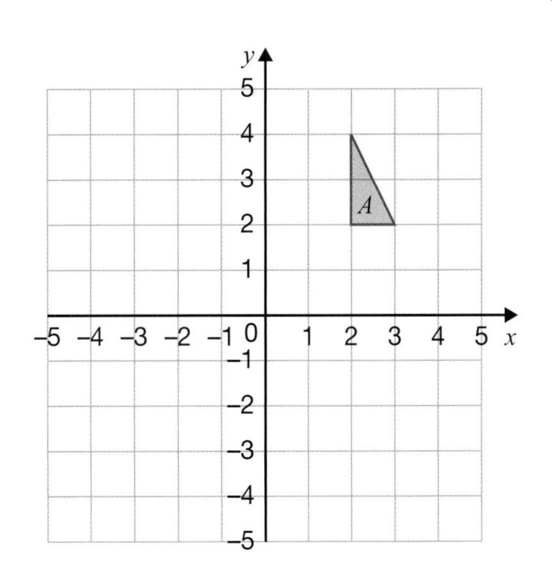

Answer

(a), (b)

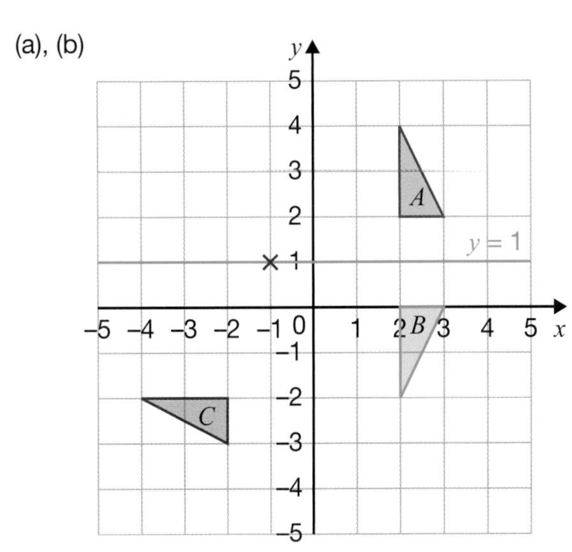

(c) Reflection in the line $y=-x$

Test yourself

1. Draw coordinate axes from –5 to +5 in both directions.
   Draw a triangle with coordinates (3, 1), (3, 3) and (4, 1). Label it A.
   (a) Reflect shape A in the line $x=0$. Label it B.
   (b) Rotate shape B 180° about the centre of rotation (0, 0). Label it C.
   (c) What single transformation would map shape A onto shape C?

2. Draw coordinate axes from –5 to +5 in both directions.
   Draw a triangle with coordinates (1, 1), (1, 2) and (3, 1). Label it A.
   (a) Translate shape A by $\begin{pmatrix} -4 \\ -2 \end{pmatrix}$. Label it B.
   (b) Enlarge shape B by scale factor 2 about the centre of enlargement (–5, 1).
   (c) What single transformation would map shape A onto shape C?

3. Draw coordinate axes from –5 to +5 in both directions.
   Draw a triangle with coordinates (–4, 1), (–3, 1) and (–4, 3). Label it A.
   (a) Rotate shape A 90° anticlockwise about the centre of rotation (1, 1). Label it B.
   (b) Translate shape B by $\begin{pmatrix} -2 \\ 0 \end{pmatrix}$. Label it C.
   (c) What single transformation would map shape A onto shape C?

4. Draw coordinate axes from –5 to +5 in both directions.
   Draw a triangle with coordinates (–3, –2), (–3, –4) and (–4, –4). Label it A.
   (a) Reflect shape A in the line $y=-x$. Label it B.
   (b) Reflect shape B in the line $x=1$. Label it C.
   (c) What single transformation would map shape A onto shape C?

When you are asked to give a single transformation, you probably won't get any marks if you give more than one.

CAM

3.12 Matrices

Matrices

Matrices can be used to store or represent data called elements. They are represented by bold capital letters.

The order of a matrix is the number of rows and columns the matrix has. A matrix of order $N \times P$ has N rows and P columns.

You can add and subtract matrices that have the same order. Add or subtract all the elements that are in the same position in each matrix and write the result in the same position in the resulting matrix.

You can multiply a matrix by a scalar. Multiply each element by the scalar.

You can multiply two matrices when the number of columns in the first matrix is equal to the number of rows in the second matrix. Multiplying a matrix of order $N \times P$ by a matrix of order $P \times M$ gives a matrix of order $N \times M$.

The first element of the resulting matrix is found by taking each element in the first row of the first matrix, multiplying each element by its corresponding element in the first column of the second matrix, and adding all of the products together.

Worked example

$\mathbf{A}=\begin{pmatrix} 2 & 3 \\ 2 & 1 \end{pmatrix}, \mathbf{B}=\begin{pmatrix} 4 & -3 \\ -3 & 2 \end{pmatrix}, \mathbf{C}=\begin{pmatrix} 3 \\ -1 \end{pmatrix}, \mathbf{D}=\begin{pmatrix} 2 \\ 1 \end{pmatrix}$

Work out:

(a) $\mathbf{A}+\mathbf{B}$ (b) $2\mathbf{A}$ (c) $\mathbf{BC}$ (d) $\mathbf{A}+\mathbf{C}$ (e) $\mathbf{CD}$

Answer

(a) **A** and **B** are the same order, 2×2 matrices, so they can be added.

$$\mathbf{A}+\mathbf{B}=\begin{pmatrix} 2+4 & 3+-3 \\ 2+-3 & 1+2 \end{pmatrix}=\begin{pmatrix} 6 & 0 \\ -1 & 3 \end{pmatrix}$$

(b) $$2\mathbf{A}=\begin{pmatrix} 2\times 2 & 3\times 2 \\ 2\times 2 & 1\times 2 \end{pmatrix}=\begin{pmatrix} 4 & 6 \\ 4 & 2 \end{pmatrix}$$

(c) **B** is a 2×2 matrix and **C** is a 2×1 matrix, so you can multiply them together.

$$\mathbf{BC}=\begin{pmatrix} 4 & -3 \\ -3 & 2 \end{pmatrix}\begin{pmatrix} 3 \\ -1 \end{pmatrix}=\begin{pmatrix} 4\times 3+-3\times -1 \\ -3\times 3+2\times -1 \end{pmatrix}=\begin{pmatrix} 12+3 \\ -9-2 \end{pmatrix}=\begin{pmatrix} 15 \\ -11 \end{pmatrix}$$

(d) **A** and **C** are not the same order, so cannot be added.

(e) **C** has one column, but **D** has two rows, so they cannot be multiplied together.

Test yourself

$\mathbf{A}=\begin{pmatrix} 2 & 3 \\ 4 & -2 \\ -1 & 5 \end{pmatrix}, \mathbf{B}=\begin{pmatrix} -3 & 4 \\ 1 & 2 \end{pmatrix}, \mathbf{C}=\begin{pmatrix} 4 \\ 1 \end{pmatrix}, \mathbf{D}=\begin{pmatrix} -3 & 2 \end{pmatrix}, \mathbf{E}=\begin{pmatrix} 5 & -4 \\ 3 & -6 \end{pmatrix}, \mathbf{F}=\begin{pmatrix} 2 & 5 \\ -7 & 3 \end{pmatrix}$

1. Work out:

(a) $\mathbf{B}+\mathbf{E}$ (b) $2\mathbf{F}$ (c) $\mathbf{E}-\mathbf{F}$ (d) $2\mathbf{F}-\mathbf{B}$

(e) $\mathbf{AB}$ (f) $\mathbf{BC}$ (g) $\mathbf{CD}$ (h) $\mathbf{E}^2$

2. Solve the equation $\mathbf{B}\begin{pmatrix} x \\ y \end{pmatrix}=\begin{pmatrix} 17 \\ 1 \end{pmatrix}$

TIP

When a matrix is squared, you multiply the matrix by itself as you would two other matrices.

2×2 matrices

The zero matrix is $\mathbf{Z}=\begin{pmatrix}0&0\\0&0\end{pmatrix}$.

For any 2×2 matrix, $\mathbf{MZ}=\mathbf{Z}$ and $\mathbf{M}+\mathbf{Z}=\mathbf{M}$.

The identity matrix is $\mathbf{I}=\begin{pmatrix}1&0\\0&1\end{pmatrix}$.

For any 2×2 matrix, $\mathbf{MI}=\mathbf{IM}=\mathbf{M}$

The determinant of matrix $\mathbf{M}=\begin{pmatrix}a&b\\c&d\end{pmatrix}$ is $|\mathbf{M}|=ad-bc$.

When $|\mathbf{M}|=0$, a matrix is singular.

When $|\mathbf{M}|\neq0$, a matrix is non-singular and has an inverse.

The inverse of $\mathbf{M}$ is given by $\mathbf{M}^{-1}=\frac{1}{ad-bc}\begin{pmatrix}d&-b\\-c&a\end{pmatrix}$.

Worked example

Find the inverse of the following matrices.

(a) $\mathbf{A}=\begin{pmatrix}2&6\\5&-1\end{pmatrix}$ (b) $\mathbf{B}=\begin{pmatrix}8&4\\6&3\end{pmatrix}$

Answer

(a) $|\mathbf{A}|=2\times-1-5\times6=-32$, so $\mathbf{A}$ is non-singular and has an inverse.

$$\mathbf{A}^{-1}=\frac{1}{-32}\begin{pmatrix}-1&-6\\-5&2\end{pmatrix}=\begin{pmatrix}\frac{1}{32}&\frac{3}{16}\\\frac{5}{32}&-\frac{1}{16}\end{pmatrix}$$

Check your answer by multiplying the matrix and its inverse. The answer should be the identity matrix.

$$\mathbf{AA}^{-1}=\frac{1}{-32}\begin{pmatrix}2&6\\5&-1\end{pmatrix}\begin{pmatrix}-1&-6\\-5&2\end{pmatrix}=\frac{1}{-32}\begin{pmatrix}-2-30&-12+12\\-5+5&-30-2\end{pmatrix}=\frac{1}{-32}\begin{pmatrix}-32&0\\0&-32\end{pmatrix}=\begin{pmatrix}1&0\\0&1\end{pmatrix}$$

(b) $|\mathbf{B}|=8\times3-6\times4=0$, so $\mathbf{B}$ is singular and does not have an inverse.

Test yourself

1. Find the inverses of the following matrices where possible.

(a) $\begin{pmatrix}6&6\\3&4\end{pmatrix}$ (b) $\begin{pmatrix}2&3\\1&1\end{pmatrix}$ (c) $\begin{pmatrix}2&3\\2&3\end{pmatrix}$ (d) $\begin{pmatrix}2&2\\2&4\end{pmatrix}$

2. $\mathbf{P}=\begin{pmatrix}3&2\\2&1\end{pmatrix}$, $\mathbf{Q}=\begin{pmatrix}-1&2\\2&-3\end{pmatrix}$

Show that $\mathbf{P}$ is the inverse of $\mathbf{Q}$.

TIP

When finding the inverse of a matrix, remember that you multiply each term by the determinant of the matrix.

Transformations

You can use matrices to describe transformations. Multiply the matrix describing the transformation by the position vector of each vertex to find the image.

To find the matrix for a transformation, find what it does to the position vectors $\begin{pmatrix} 1 \\ 0 \end{pmatrix}$ and $\begin{pmatrix} 0 \\ 1 \end{pmatrix}$.

The matrix is made up of the image of the two position vectors.

Worked example

1. A triangle has vertices (–2, 3), (–3, 3) and (–3, 1).

   It is transformed by the matrix $\begin{pmatrix} 1 & 0 \\ 0 & -1 \end{pmatrix}$.

   (a) Draw the object and image.

   (b) What transformation does the matrix represent?

2. Find the matrix that represents a rotation of 90° anticlockwise about the origin.

Answer

1. (a) Multiply the matrix by each of the position vectors:

$$\begin{pmatrix} 1 & 0 \\ 0 & -1 \end{pmatrix}\begin{pmatrix} -2 \\ 3 \end{pmatrix} = \begin{pmatrix} 1\times-2+0\times3 \\ 0\times-2+-1\times3 \end{pmatrix} = \begin{pmatrix} -2 \\ -3 \end{pmatrix}$$

Similarly, the images of (–3, 3) and (–3, 1) are (–3, –3) and (–3, –1).

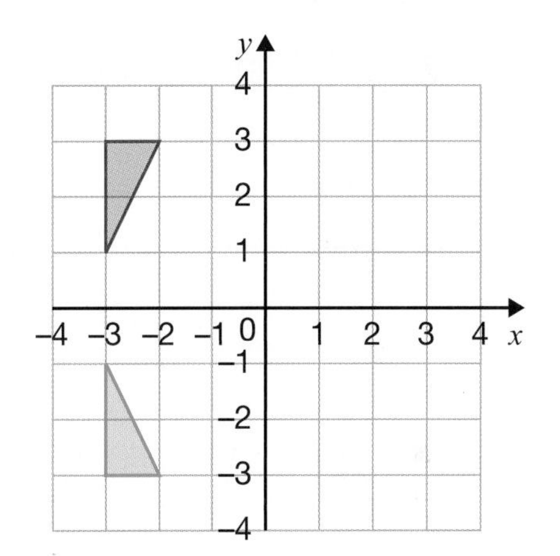

(b) The matrix represents a reflection in the x-axis (or line $y=0$).

2. Look at the position vectors $\begin{pmatrix} 1 \\ 0 \end{pmatrix}$ and $\begin{pmatrix} 0 \\ 1 \end{pmatrix}$ and their images when they have been rotated 90° anticlockwise about the origin.

The image position vectors are $\begin{pmatrix} 0 \\ 1 \end{pmatrix}$ and $\begin{pmatrix} -1 \\ 0 \end{pmatrix}$.

So the matrix representing the transformation is $\begin{pmatrix} 0 & -1 \\ 1 & 0 \end{pmatrix}$.

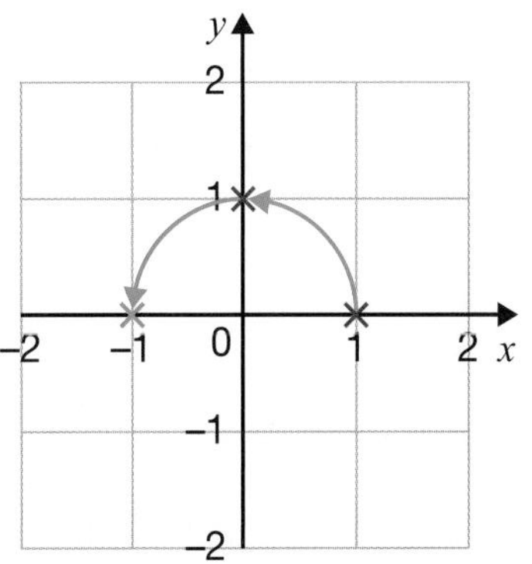

Test yourself

1. Draw coordinate axes from –6 to +6 in both directions.
Draw a triangle with coordinates (1, 1), (1, 2) and (3, 1).

(a) Transform the triangle using these matrices.

(i) $\begin{pmatrix} 0 & 1 \\ -1 & 0 \end{pmatrix}$ (ii) $\begin{pmatrix} 0 & -1 \\ -1 & 0 \end{pmatrix}$ (iii) $\begin{pmatrix} 2 & 0 \\ 0 & 2 \end{pmatrix}$ (iv) $\begin{pmatrix} -0.5 & 0 \\ 0 & -0.5 \end{pmatrix}$

(b) Describe the transformation that each of the matrices represents.

2. Find the matrix that represents the following transformations.

(a) rotation of 180° about the origin
(b) reflection in the y-axis
(c) reflection in the x-axis
(d) enlargement with scale factor 3 about the origin

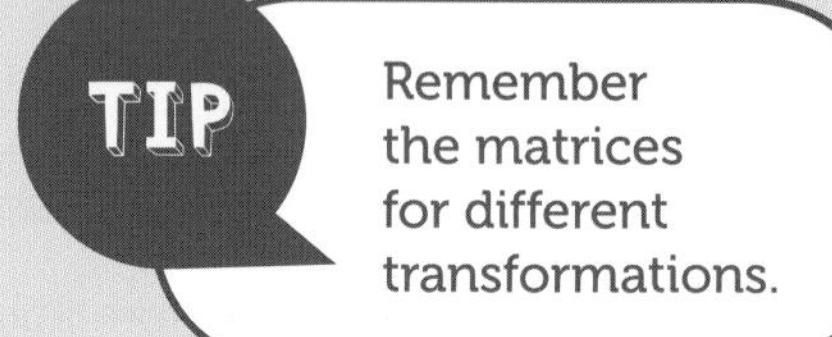

You should now be able to:

- ☆ calculate unknown angles using the properties of angles (see page 110)
- ☆ use the properties of polygons to solve problems (see page 113)
- ☆ construct geometrical shapes using a ruler, protractor and compasses (see page 116)
- CAM ☆ construct loci (see page 121)
- ☆ use the properties of circles and angles in circles (see page 123)
- ☆ use three-figure bearings (see page 128)
- ☆ use trigonometric ratios to solve problems (see page 130)
- ☆ apply Pythagoras' theorem in 3-D problems (see page 136)
- ☆ calculate the perimeter and area of shapes and compound shapes (see page 137)
- ☆ solve problems involving circles (see page 139)
- ☆ calculate the surface area and volume of 3-D shapes (see page 142)
- ☆ use units of mass, length, area, volume and capacity (see page 143)
- ☆ convert between different units (see page 143)
- ☆ know the symmetrical properties of 2-D and 3-D shapes (see page 146)
- ☆ use similarity to solve problems involving triangles, and surface area and volume of 3-D shapes (see page 149)
- ☆ use vectors (see page 152)
- ☆ add and subtract vectors and find their magnitude (see page 153)
- ☆ reflect, rotate, translate and enlarge shapes (see page 155)
- ☆ describe transformations, including combined transformations (see page 161)
-  ☆ add and multiply 2 × 2 matrices (see page 162)
- ☆ find the inverse of a 2 × 2 matrix (see page 164)
- ☆ describe transformations using matrices (see page 165)

Practice questions

When answers are not exact, remember to give your answers to the accuracy specified in the question or on the front of the exam paper.

1. Write the following in order of size, *smallest* first.

$\sin 135°$ $\cos 135°$ $\sin 35°$ $\cos 35°$ **(2)**

2. A circle has a diameter of 80 cm.

(a) Calculate the area of the circle in cm^2. **(2)**

(b) Write your answer to part (a) in m^2. **(1)**

3. A bay window is in the shape of an octagon.

The six unmarked angles are all the same size.

Calculate the size of one of these angles. **(3)**

4. O is the centre of the circle. AB is a tangent to the circle.

Angle $OBA = 28°$.

Find the values of angles a, b and c.

Give reasons for your answers. **(6)**

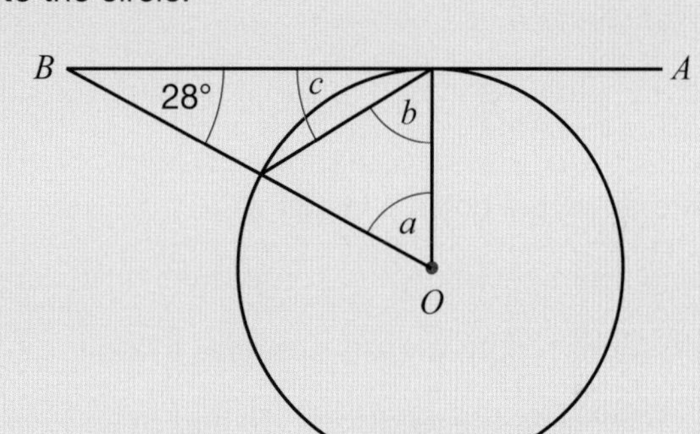

CAM **5.** Work out:

(a) $\begin{pmatrix} 3 & 2 \\ 5 & 3 \end{pmatrix}^{-1}$ **(2)**

(b) $\begin{pmatrix} 3 & 2 \\ 5 & 3 \end{pmatrix}^{2}$ **(2)**

6. A and B have position vectors **a** and 2**b** relative to the origin O.

$\overrightarrow{OB} = 2\overrightarrow{BC}$, $\overrightarrow{OA} = 3\overrightarrow{AE}$, $\overrightarrow{CD} = 2\overrightarrow{DA}$

(a) Find, in terms of **a** and **b** in their simplest form:

(i) the position vector D **(2)**

(ii) the vector $\overrightarrow{BD}$. **(2)**

(b) Show that BDE is a straight line. **(3)**

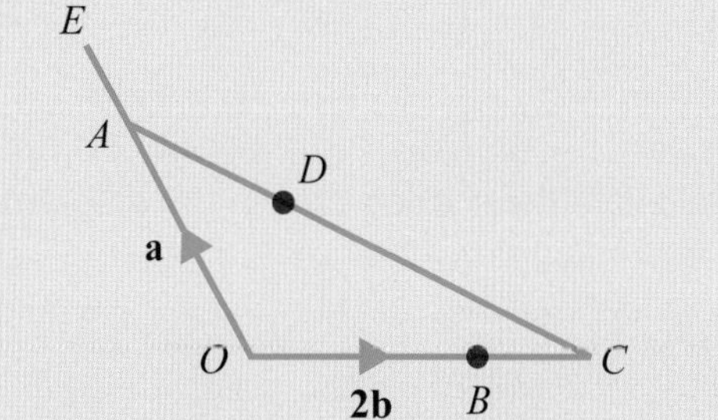

CAM **7.** $\begin{pmatrix} 4 & 0 \\ 1 & -2 \end{pmatrix}\begin{pmatrix} x \\ y \end{pmatrix} = \begin{pmatrix} -8 \\ -8 \end{pmatrix}$

Find the values of x and y. **(3)**

8. O is the centre of the circle.

(a) Calculate angle OBA. **(2)**

(b) A is due north of O and C.

Calculate the bearing of B from A. **(2)**

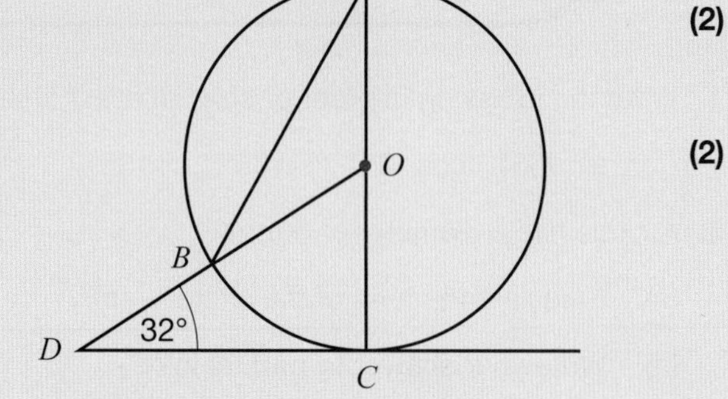

9. Two points are $A(2, 5)$ and $B(6, 3)$.

(a) Write down the column vector $\overrightarrow{AB}$. **(1)**

(b) Draw coordinate axes from 0 to 6 in both directions. Plot these points.

Using a straight edge and compasses only, draw the perpendicular bisector of the points A and B. **(2)**

10. Draw coordinate axes from 0 to 6 in both directions. Plot the points $A(0, 5)$, $B(2, 1)$ and $C(6, 3)$. Draw lines AB and BC.

(a) Write down the column vector $\overrightarrow{AC}$. **(1)**

(b) Using a straight edge and compasses only, draw the bisector of angle ABC. **(2)**

(c) ABC forms a right-angled isosceles triangle.

(i) Calculate the lengths of AB and BC. **(2)**

(ii) Calculate the area of the triangle. **(2)**

11. A cone with base radius r and height $2r$ fits exactly inside a cube of side $2r$.

Calculate the percentage of the cube occupied by the cone. **(3)**

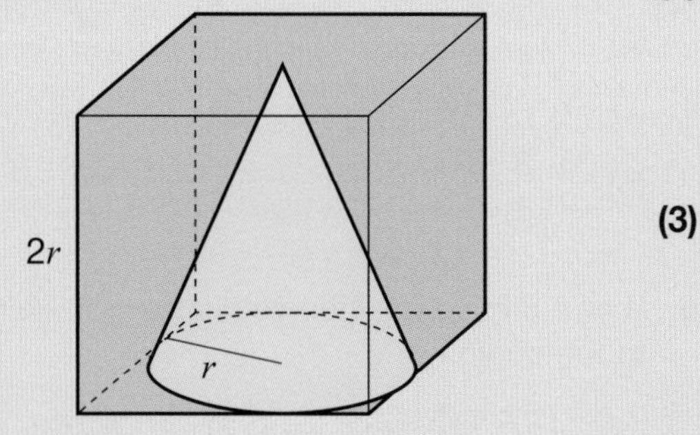

12. Calculate the shaded area in the diagram. **(4)**

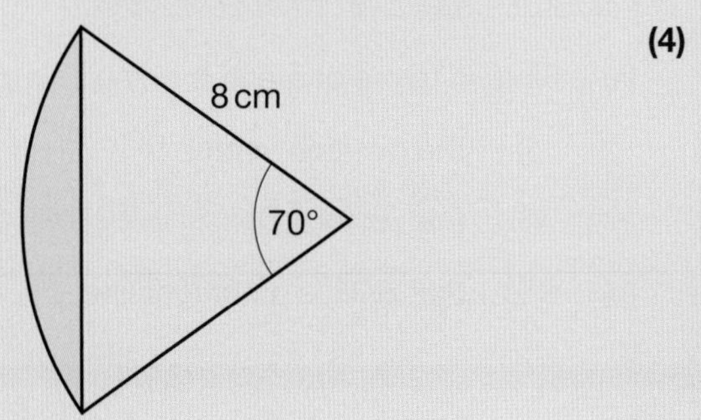

13. The diagram shows the distances between three places.

(a) Calculate angle ABC. Show your working. **(4)**

(b) The bearing of C from B is 222°.
Calculate the bearing of A from B. **(1)**

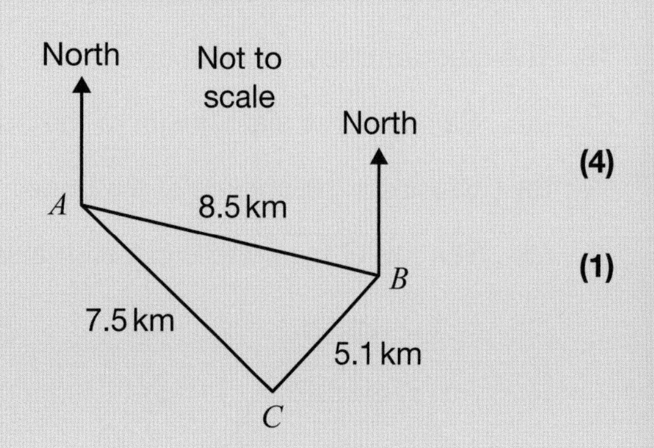

14. A, B, C and D lie on a circle.

(a) Give a reason why angle BCE is equal to angle ADE. **(1)**

(b) Calculate the length of CE. **(2)**

(c) The area of triangle ADE is 22.4 cm^2.

Calculate the area of triangle BEC. **(2)**

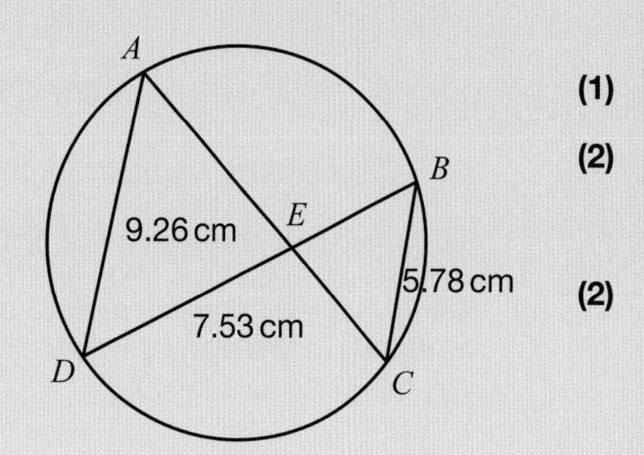

15. (a) Write down the position vector of M. **(1)**

(b) Write down the following column vectors.

(i) $\overrightarrow{MN}$ (ii) $\overrightarrow{LN}$ **(2)**

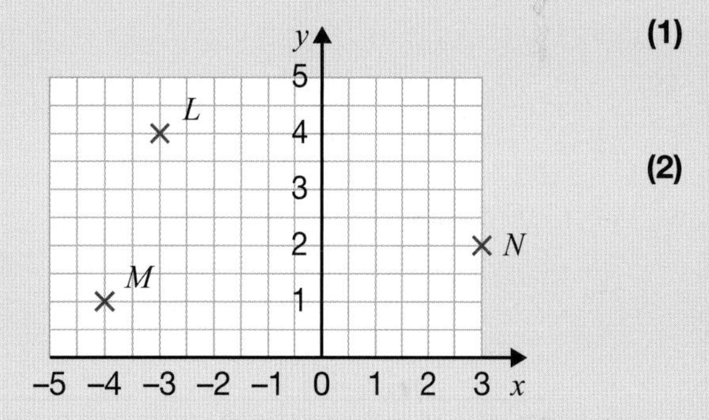

16. In the diagram, $\overrightarrow{OP} = \mathbf{p}$ and $\overrightarrow{OQ} = \mathbf{q}$.

$\overrightarrow{OR} = \frac{1}{4}\overrightarrow{OQ}$ and $\overrightarrow{PS} = \frac{1}{3}\overrightarrow{PQ}$. M is the midpoint of RS.

Find the following in terms of $\mathbf{p}$ and $\mathbf{q}$, giving your answers in their simplest form.

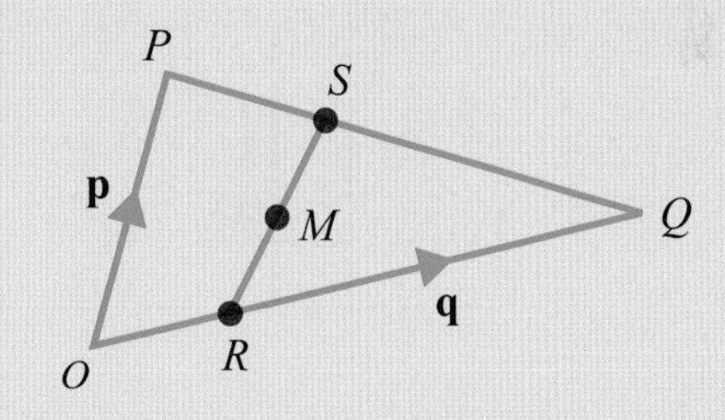

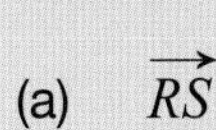

(a) $\overrightarrow{RS}$ **(4)**

(b) $\overrightarrow{OM}$ **(2)**

17. The diagram shows a triangular prism.

(a) Calculate the length of CE. **(3)**

(b) Calculate the angle of elevation of E from C. **(2)**

(c) Calculate angle BCF. **(2)**

(d) G is on CF such that angle $BGF = 60°$.
Calculate the length BG. **(3)**

(e) Calculate the volume of the prism. **(2)**

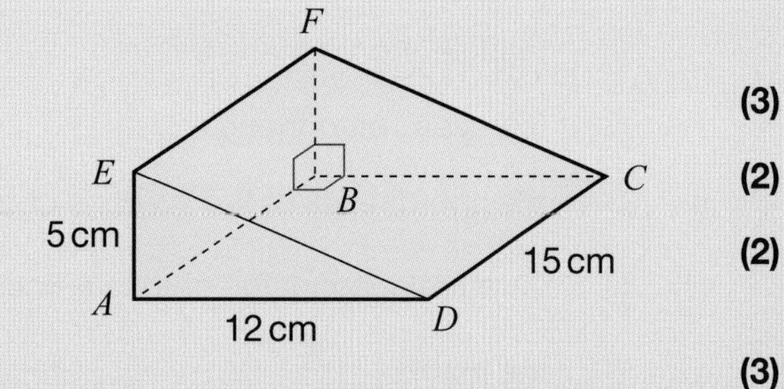

18. The diagram shows a solid cone.

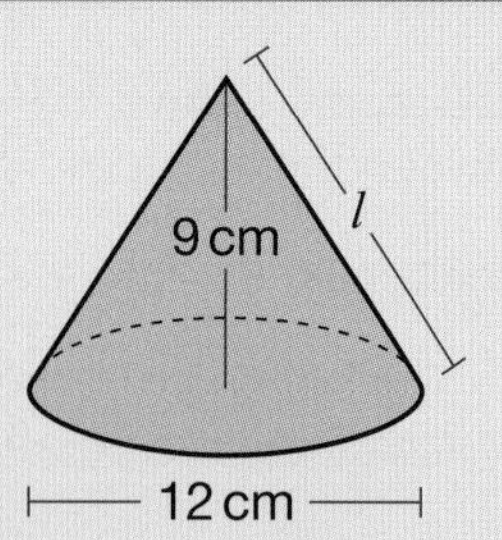

(a) Calculate the slant height of the cone. **(2)**

(b) Calculate the volume of the cone. **(2)**

(c) The top of the cone is cut off making a smaller similar cone.

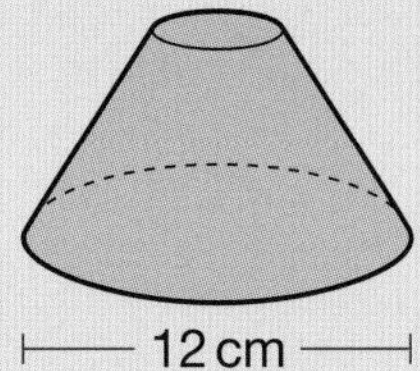

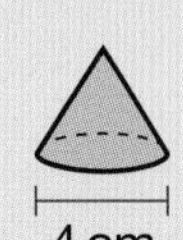

(i) Calculate the vertical height of this cone. **(2)**

(ii) Calculate the volume of this small cone. **(2)**

(d) The truncated cone is joined to a solid cylinder as shown in the diagram. Calculate the total volume of the whole solid. **(4)**

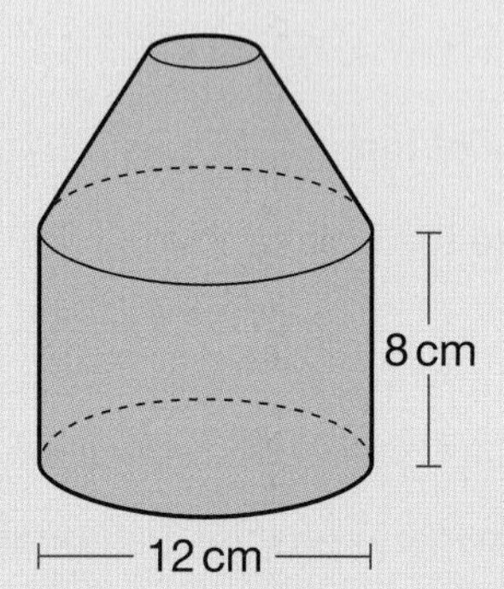

19.

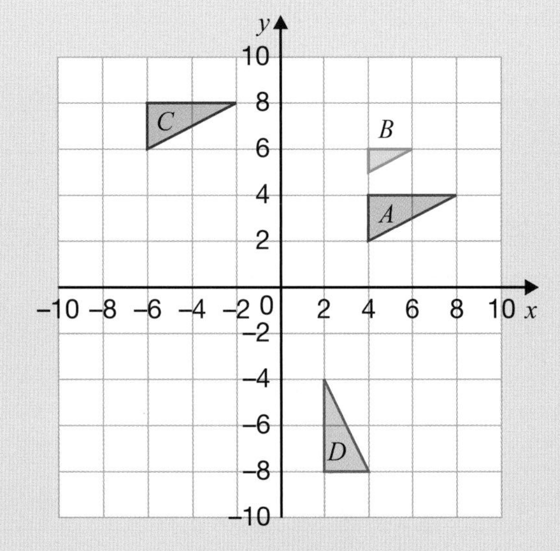

(a) Describe fully the **single** transformation that maps:

(i) triangle A onto triangle B **(3)**

(ii) triangle A onto triangle C **(2)**

(iii) triangle C onto triangle D. **(3)**

(b) Give the coordinates of the vertices of triangle C after reflection in the line $y = -x$. **(3)**

CAM (c) (i) Give the coordinates of the vertices of triangle D after transformation by the matrix $\begin{pmatrix} 0 & 1 \\ -1 & 0 \end{pmatrix}$. **(3)**

(ii) Describe fully the single transformation represented by this matrix. **(3)**

20. This shape is made from a rectangle and a semicircle.

Work out the area of the shape. Give your answer correct to three significant figures. **(4)**

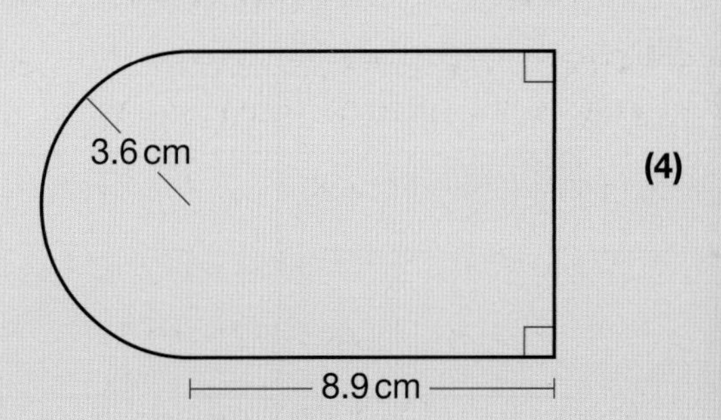

21. (a) Calculate the area of the trapezium. **(2)**

(b) Calculate the length of BC. **(4)**

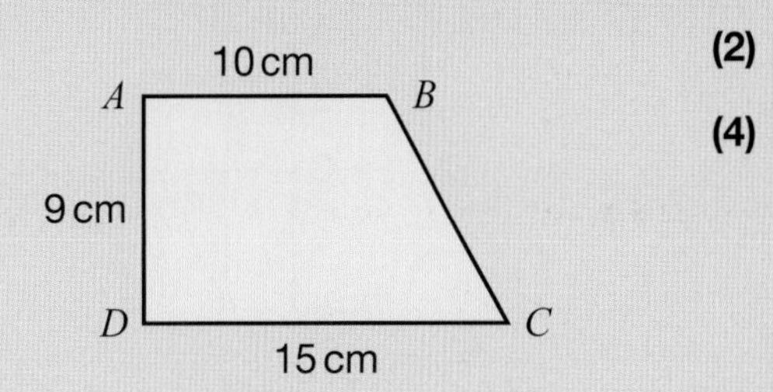

22. O is the centre of the circle.

(a) (i) Calculate the size of angle BCD. **(1)**

(ii) Give a reason for your answer. **(2)**

(b) Calculate the size of angle OBD. **(2)**

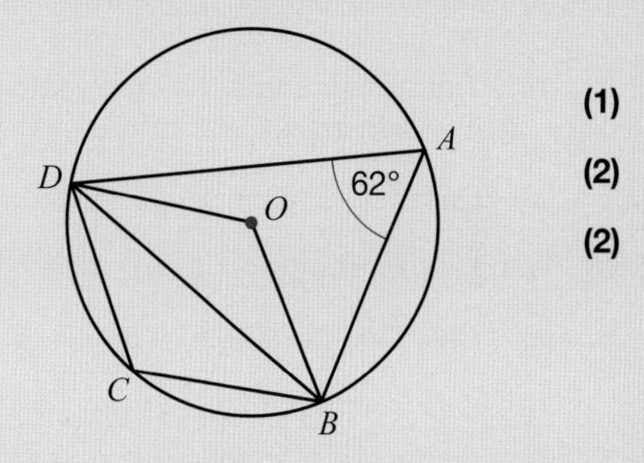

23. Three tennis balls fit exactly inside a hollow cylinder. The radius of each tennis ball is r cm. The height of the cylinder is $6r$ cm.

The volume of space inside the cylinder not occupied by the tennis balls is 54π cm^3.

Calculate the value of r. **(5)**

24. B, C, D and E are points on a circle.

(a) Calculate the length of AB. **(3)**

(b) Calculate the length of BC. **(3)**

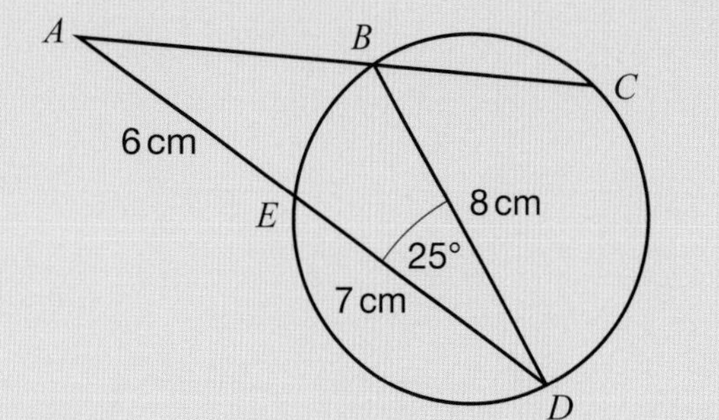

25.

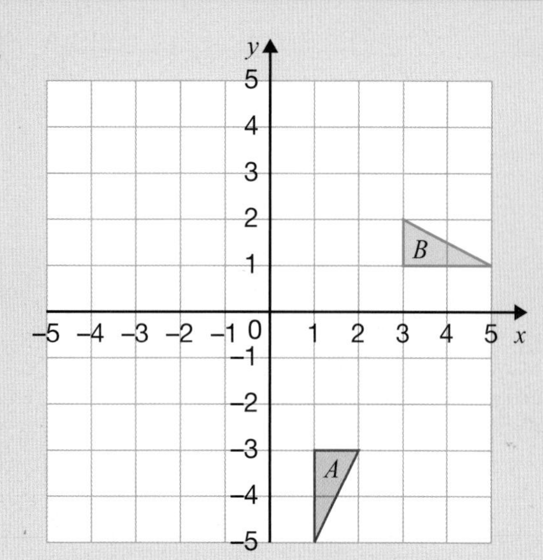

(a) Describe fully the single transformation that maps triangle A onto triangle B. **(3)**

(b) Translate triangle B by the vector $\begin{pmatrix} -4 \\ 2 \end{pmatrix}$. Write down the vertices of the new triangle. Call it triangle C. **(3)**

(c) Describe fully the single transformation that maps triangle A onto triangle C. **(3)**

26. The diagram shows a cuboid.

(a) Calculate the length of the diagonal CE. **(4)**

(b) Calculate the angle between the diagonal CE and the plane $ABCD$. **(3)**

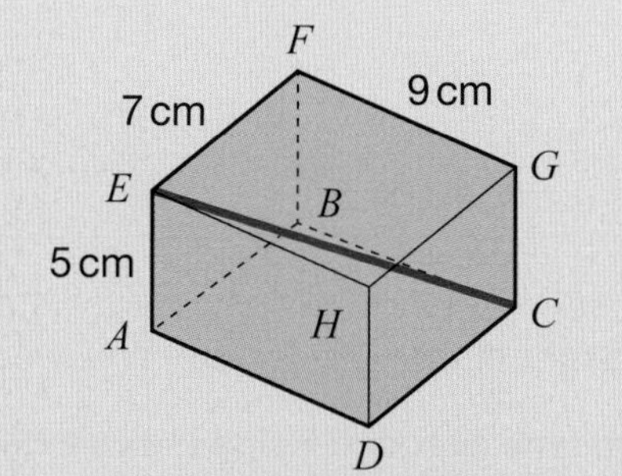

Section Four

4 Statistics and probability

You will be expected to:

- ☆ use bar charts, pie charts, pictograms, histograms and cumulative frequency diagrams
- ☆ calculate averages and find the median, quartiles, percentiles and the interquartile range
- ☆ understand probability.

4.1 Representing data

Collecting data

You can record data in a frequency table.

When there is a wide range of values, the data are recorded in groups called classes or class intervals.

Test yourself

1. Record the following data in frequency tables.

(a) Number of children in a family for students in class 11J

2 1 2 3 4 2 1 2 1 3 4 4 2 6 5
3 2 2 1 2 3 2 2 4 1 3 2 2 5 1

(b) Number of days absent in one term

1 5 1 2 2 3 0 3 0 1 2 1 0 1 0 3 4 1
1 5 6 0 0 5 1 2 1 1 1 1 0 0 4 2 0 5

2. Draw up a grouped frequency table with suitable class intervals and put the data in the table for the following sets of data.

(a) Marks obtained in a test by a class of students

47 26 32 45 47 49 72 58 44 62 67 29 58 53 63 55 61 49
46 36 39 44 55 58 68 57 47 39 46 53 63 47 52 74 59 55

(a) Heights of a group of 15-year-old boys

167 191 152 165 167 169 172 178 164 182 187 149 178 173
183 175 181 169 166 156 159 164 175 178 188 177 167 159
166 173 183 167 172 174 179 175

Pictograms, pie charts and bar charts

A pictogram displays data in a frequency table where the data are represented by a symbol that is repeated. A pictogram should have a key to show what quantity each symbol represents.

A bar chart displays data as a series of bars that are the same width. The length of the bar represents the frequency. The bars can be horizontal or vertical.

Bar charts are used to represent data that are in categories (e.g. colour) or data that cannot have any value between the values given (e.g. number of children in a family).

There is a gap between the bars.

Dual bar charts can be used to compare two sets of data.

A pie chart shows data as sectors of a circle. The whole circle represents the total frequency and the angle of each sector is proportional to the frequency it represents.

Worked example

Draw a pie chart to show the following data.

How 30 students get to school

Method of transport	Walk	Car	Bus	Cycle	Tram
Frequency	12	5	8	3	2

Answer

Find the angle for each sector on the pie chart. Add all the frequencies to find the total frequency.

Method of transport	**Frequency**	**Calculation**	**Angle of sector**
Walk	12	$\frac{12}{30} \times 360° = 144°$	144°
Car	5	$\frac{5}{30} \times 360° = 60°$	60°
Bus	8	$\frac{8}{30} \times 360° = 96°$	96°
Cycle	3	$\frac{3}{30} \times 360° = 36°$	36°
Tram	2	$\frac{2}{30} \times 360° = 24°$	24°
Total	30		360°

Draw the pie chart using the angles calculated for each sector. Label each sector, but you do not have to show the frequencies. Add a title to the pie chart.

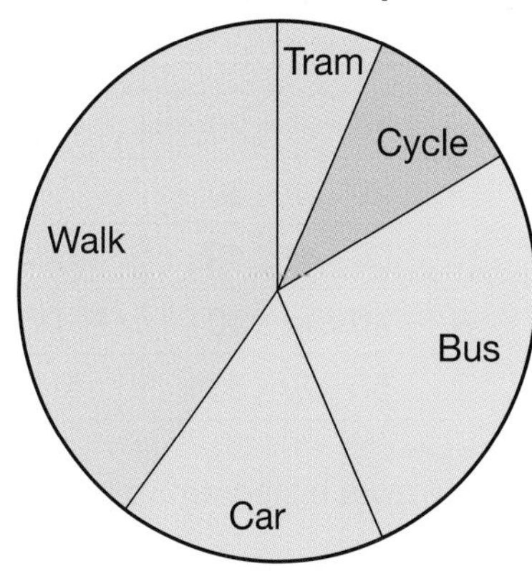

Test yourself

1. Represent the data from Q1 of the preceding exercise as a pictogram, bar chart and pie chart.

2. The table shows the average temperature in two different places for each month. Draw a dual bar chart to represent the data.

Average daily high temperature (°C)

City	Month					
	Apr	May	Jun	Jul	Aug	Sep
Edinburgh	12	15	17	19	19	17
Rome	18	23	27	30	31	27

Histograms and cumulative frequency diagrams

A histogram is used to represent grouped data that can take any value (e.g. height of a person). The area of each bar represents the frequency in each class.

Sometimes, class intervals are not of equal width. In this case the scale on the vertical axis is frequency density:

frequency density = frequency of class interval ÷ width of class interval

To find the frequency, multiply the frequency density by the class interval.

The width of each bar corresponds to the class width.

The horizontal axis has a continuous scale and the bars are drawn touching each other, unlike bar charts.

A cumulative frequency diagram shows the frequency up to and including the current value. The value is on the horizontal axis and cumulative frequency on the vertical axis.

You find the sum of the preceding frequencies to find the cumulative frequency. The points are plotted with the top value of each group against the cumulative frequency for the group. The last point is the total frequency.

The points are joined with a smooth curve.

Worked example

1. The grouped frequency table shows the marks gained by students in a Maths test.

Marks	Frequency
$0 < m \leqslant 10$	0
$10 < m \leqslant 20$	4
$20 < m \leqslant 30$	12
$30 < m \leqslant 40$	18
$40 < m \leqslant 50$	13
$50 < m \leqslant 60$	7

Draw a histogram to represent these data.

2. The grouped frequency table shows the heights of a group of 15-year-old girls.

Height, h (cm)	Frequency
$130 < h \leqslant 140$	4
$140 < h \leqslant 150$	12
$150 < h \leqslant 155$	9
$155 < h \leqslant 160$	10
$160 < h \leqslant 170$	15
$170 < h \leqslant 190$	10

(a) Draw a histogram to represent these data.

(b) Draw a cumulative frequency diagram to represent these data.

Answer

1.

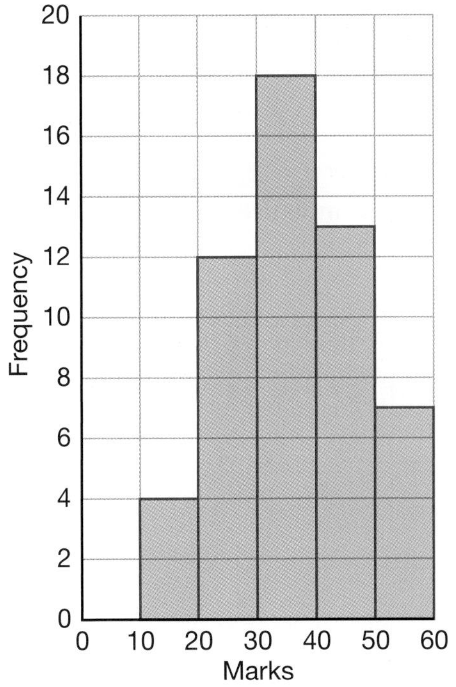

2. (a) The class intervals are unequal, so calculate frequency density.

Height, h (cm)	Frequency	Frequency density
$130 < h \leqslant 140$	4	$4 \div 10 = 0.4$
$140 < h \leqslant 150$	12	$12 \div 10 = 1.2$
$150 < h \leqslant 155$	9	$9 \div 5 = 1.8$
$155 < h \leqslant 160$	10	$10 \div 5 = 2$
$160 < h \leqslant 170$	15	$15 \div 10 = 1.5$
$170 < h \leqslant 190$	10	$10 \div 20 = 0.5$

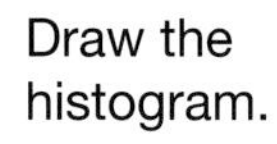
Draw the histogram.

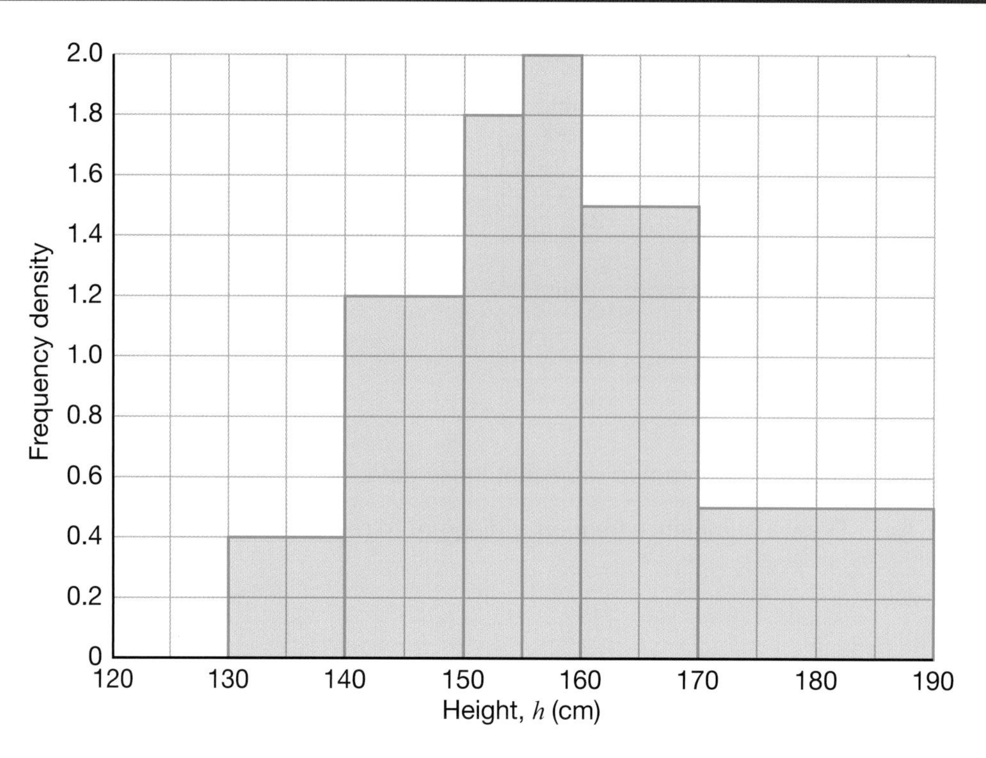

(b) Calculate the cumulative frequency.

Height, h (cm)	Frequency	Cumulative frequency
$130 < h \leqslant 140$	4	4
$140 < h \leqslant 150$	12	16
$150 < h \leqslant 155$	9	25
$155 < h \leqslant 160$	10	35
$160 < h \leqslant 170$	15	50
$170 < h \leqslant 190$	10	60

Draw the cumulative frequency diagram.

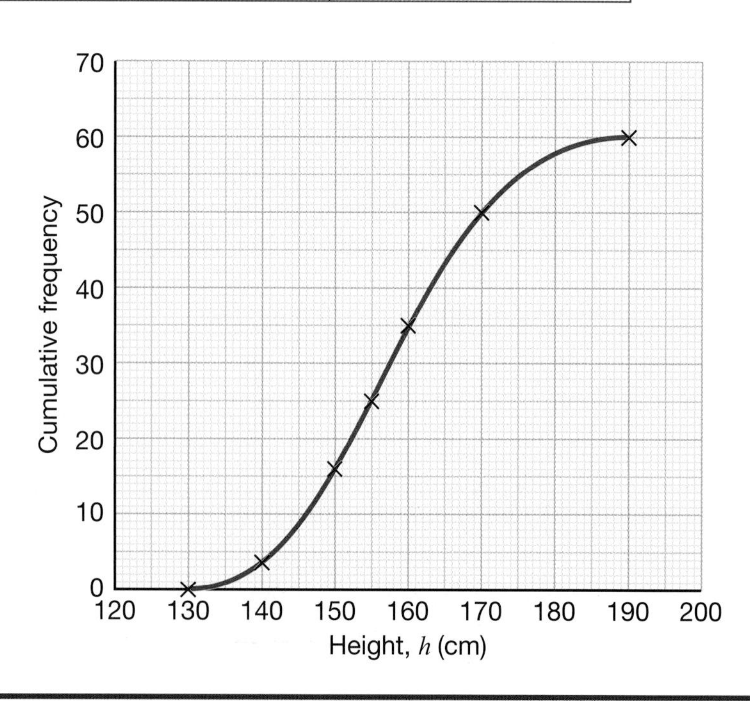

Test yourself

1. Draw histograms and cumulative frequency diagrams for the grouped frequency tables you drew up for Q2 in the first Test yourself in this chapter (page 174).

2. Draw histograms and cumulative frequency diagrams for these grouped data.

(a) Time customers had to wait on a telephone help line before their call was answered

Time taken, t (minutes)	Frequency
$0 < t \leqslant 2$	10
$2 < t \leqslant 3$	15
$3 < t \leqslant 4$	10
$4 < t \leqslant 5$	8
$5 < t \leqslant 7$	8
$7 < t \leqslant 10$	9

TIP Remember that the cumulative frequency is plotted at the top of the class interval.

(b) Time taken to travel to work

Time taken, t (minutes)	Frequency
$0 < t \leqslant 10$	6
$10 < t \leqslant 15$	7
$15 < t \leqslant 20$	8
$20 < t \leqslant 30$	12
$30 < t \leqslant 40$	11
$40 < t \leqslant 50$	8
$50 < t \leqslant 70$	8

3. The histogram shows the amount of time people had to wait in a queue at a supermarket checkout.

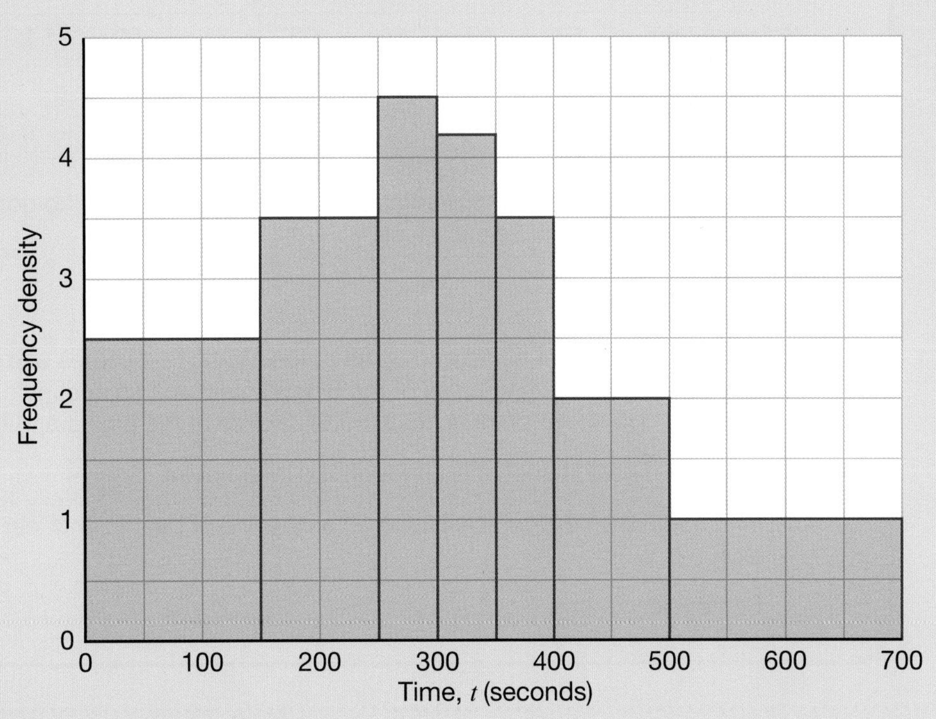

(a) Write down the grouped frequency table.

(b) The manager of the supermarket says the data shows that the supermarket is beating its target of serving 50% of customers in less than 300 seconds and 80% in less than 400 seconds. Is the manager correct?

Scatter diagrams

You can compare two variables using a scatter diagram. They are used to see if there is any correlation between variables.

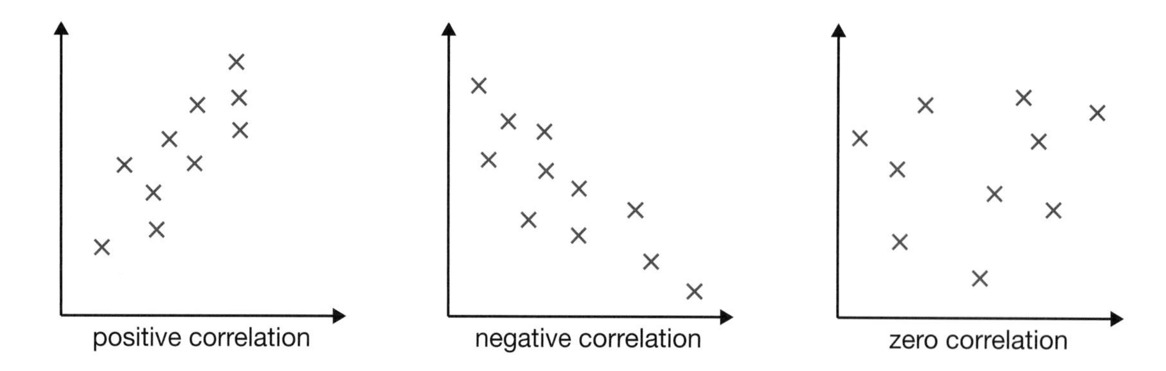

A line of best fit can be drawn through data points when there is correlation. The line should be drawn through the mean point, which is the average of all points on the graph.

There should be equal numbers of points on each side of the line of best fit.

Worked example

The table shows the marks obtained in a Maths test and a Science test by a group of students.

Student	1	2	3	4	5	6	7	8	9	10
Maths test	52	48	62	72	41	43	58	67	75	64
Science test	63	49	69	68	38	50	54	67	78	60

(a) Plot these points on a scatter graph.

(b) Draw a line of best fit.

(c) Use your line of best fit to predict the score that a student who got 55 marks in the Maths test would get in the Science test.

Answer

(a) Find the mean point by adding up all of the Maths test scores and dividing by the number of students, and adding up all of the Science test scores and dividing by the number of students. The mean point is (58.2, 59.6). Plot all of the points and the mean point.

(b) The line of best fit should go through the mean point.

(c) Find 55 on the horizontal axis. Go up to the line of best fit and then across to the vertical axis.

Score = 56

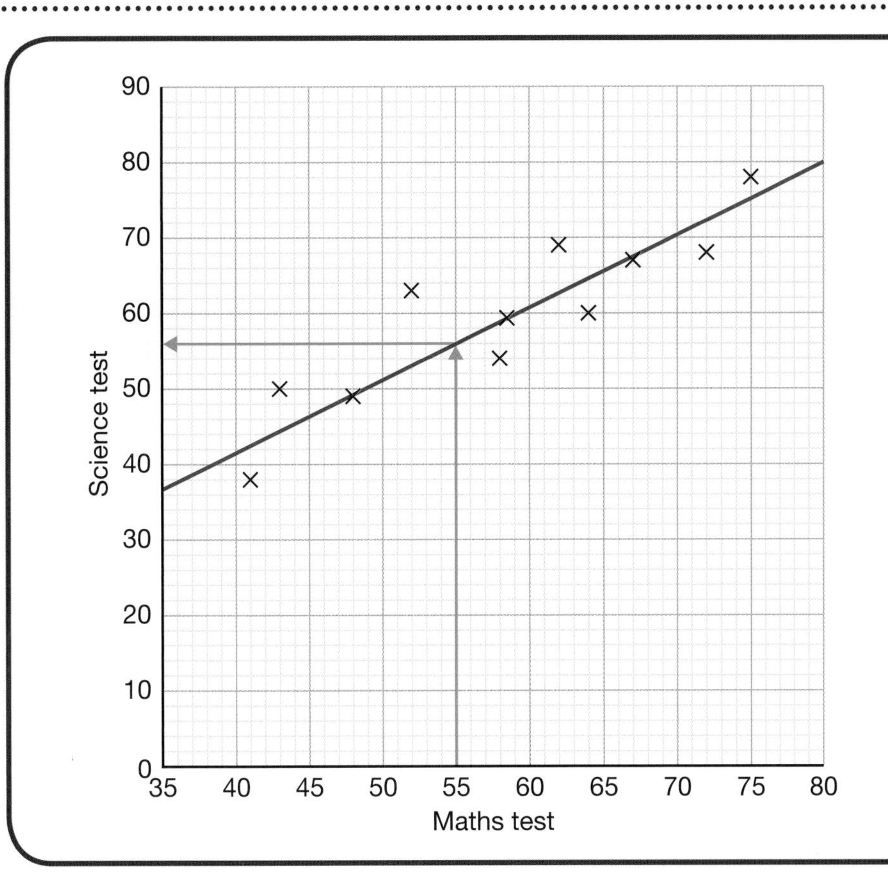

Test yourself

1. The table shows the engine capacity of cars with different size engines and their fuel consumption.

(a) Plot these points on a scatter graph.

(b) Draw a line of best fit.

(c) Use your line of best fit to predict the fuel consumption of a 2.5 litre engine.

Car	Engine capacity (litres)	Fuel consumption (litres/100 km)
A	2	6.3
B	1.2	5
C	1.4	5.7
D	3	7.1
E	1.1	5
F	1.6	6.5
G	1	4.6
H	2.9	9.1

2. The table shows the age of different cars and their values.

(a) Plot these points on a scatter graph.

(b) Draw a line of best fit.

(c) Use your line of best fit to predict the price of a 5-year-old car.

Car	Age of car (years)	Value (£)
A	2	9000
B	1	10 500
C	4	6000
D	6	2900
E	7	2000
F	8	1300
G	4	4200
H	6	1400
I	2	6800
J	3	7000

TIP

When drawing a line of best fit, the line should go through the mean point and should have equal numbers of points on each side.

4.2 Averages

Averages

Averages are used to compare sets of data. The mode, median and mean are all averages.

The mode is the most common value in a set of data.

The median is the middle value when all the values are arranged in ascending order.

When there are n values, the median is the $\frac{n+1}{2}$th value. When n is even, the median is halfway between the $\frac{n}{2}$th and $\left(\frac{n}{2}+1\right)$th values.

The mean is the sum of all the values divided by the number of values.

The range is the difference between the highest value and the lowest value.

The characteristics of the three averages are given in the table.

Average	Use	Advantages	Disadvantages
mean	Data with values that are spread evenly.	Uses all the data. Can be used to calculate a total for a given number of values.	Affected by extreme values.
median	Data with extreme values.	Not affected by extreme values.	Does not use all the values.
mode	Non-numerical data; finding the most likely value.	Easy to find. Can be used for any type of data. Not affected by extreme values.	Not all data sets have a mode and some may have more than one mode. Does not use all the values.

EDE The quartiles and interquartile range are often used as measures of spread, or how spread out the data are. They are used because they are less affected by extreme values.

Worked example

The ages of the members of a football team are:

20 35 21 22 24 25 30 24 29 21 24

1. Find: (a) the mean age (b) the median age (c) the modal age.
2. Work out the range.

Answer

1. (a) Add all the ages together and divide by the number of team members (11).

   Sum $=275$
   Mean $=275 \div 11=25$

   (b) Put the ages in ascending order:

   20 21 21 22 24 24 24 25 29 30 35

   There are 11 values, so the median is the $\frac{11+1}{2}$th $=$ 6th value.

   The 6th value is 24.

   (c) The mode is the most common value, which is 24.

2. The range is $35-20=15$.

Test yourself

1. Find the mean, median, mode and range of the following sets of data.

(a) 24 28 29 30 35 32 31 39 25 30 33 32 28 29 27 37 40 36 28 39

(b) –1 2 4 5 –6 –1 0 2 5 –3 –2 1 2 –3 –4 3 –1 2 –5 6

2. Find the mean, median, mode and range of the following sets of data.

(a) Number of children in families in Class 11J

Number of children	Frequency
1	6
2	14
3	6
4	4
5	2
6	1

TIP Check that your answer makes sense – a mean can't be smaller than the lowest value or higher than the highest value.

(b) Number of days students were absent from school

Number of days absent	Frequency
0	9
1	12
2	5
3	3
4	2
5	4
6	1

Mean of grouped data

When data is grouped in a frequency table you can calculate an estimate of the mean.

Take the midpoint of each class interval and multiply it by the frequency. Add all of these class interval totals together and divide by the total number of values.

Worked example

(a) Find the mean of the data in this grouped frequency table.

(b) Give the modal class.

Height, h (cm)	Frequency
$130 < h \leqslant 140$	4
$140 < h \leqslant 150$	12
$150 < h \leqslant 155$	8
$155 < h \leqslant 160$	10
$160 < h \leqslant 170$	13
$170 < h \leqslant 190$	9

Answer

(a) Add a column with the midpoints.

Add a column with the product of the midpoint and the frequency of each class interval.

Height, h (cm)	Frequency	Midpoint	Midpoint × frequency
$130 < h \leqslant 140$	4	135	$135 \times 4 = 540$
$140 < h \leqslant 150$	12	145	$145 \times 12 = 1740$
$150 < h \leqslant 155$	8	152.5	$152.5 \times 8 = 1220$
$155 < h \leqslant 160$	10	157.5	$157.5 \times 10 = 1575$
$160 < h \leqslant 170$	13	165	$165 \times 13 = 2145$
$170 < h \leqslant 190$	9	180	$180 \times 9 = 1620$
Total	56		8840

Find the total of these products and divide by the total frequency:

$8840 \div 56 = 158\,\text{cm}$

(b) The modal class is $160 \leqslant h < 170$.

Remember that you don't necessarily get all the marks just for writing down the answer. Often there are marks for showing your working. You should always show your working.

Test yourself

1. Estimate the mean of the data in each of these grouped frequency tables.

(a)

Marks, m	**Frequency**
$20 < m \leqslant 30$	2
$30 < m \leqslant 40$	4
$40 < m \leqslant 50$	11
$50 < m \leqslant 60$	11
$60 < m \leqslant 70$	6
$70 < m \leqslant 80$	2

(b)

Height, h (cm)	**Frequency**
$140 < h \leqslant 150$	1
$150 < h \leqslant 160$	4
$160 < h \leqslant 170$	11
$170 < h \leqslant 180$	13
$180 < h \leqslant 190$	6
$190 < h \leqslant 200$	1

(c)

Time taken, t (minutes)	**Frequency**
$0 < t \leqslant 2$	10
$2 < t \leqslant 3$	15
$3 < t \leqslant 4$	10
$4 < t \leqslant 5$	8
$5 < t \leqslant 7$	8
$7 < t \leqslant 10$	9

(d)

Time taken, t (minutes)	**Frequency**
$0 < t \leqslant 10$	6
$10 < t \leqslant 15$	7
$15 < t \leqslant 20$	8
$20 < t \leqslant 30$	12
$30 < t \leqslant 40$	11
$40 < t \leqslant 50$	8
$50 < t \leqslant 70$	8

2. Give the modal class in each grouped frequency table.

TIP

Remember to use the halfway values when estimating a value for the grouped mean.

Using cumulative frequency diagrams

You can find the median from a cumulative frequency diagram by finding the middle value on the vertical axis, reading across to the curve and then down to the value on the horizontal axis.

The quartiles are the values at one quarter and three quarters on the cumulative frequency axis.

The interquartile range is the different between the upper and lower quartiles.

Percentiles are the data divided into 100 equal groups.

The 25th percentile is the lower quartile, the 50th percentile is the median and the 75th percentile is the upper quartile.

Worked example

The cumulative frequency diagram shows the heights of a group of 15-year-old girls.

(a) Use the graph to find the median, upper and lower quartiles and interquartile range.

(b) Use the graph to find the 90th percentile.

Answer

(a) Read the values off the cumulative frequency diagram:

median = 30th value = 157.5 cm

upper quartile = 45th value = 166 cm

lower quartile = 15th value = 149.5 cm

interquartile range = upper quartile − lower quartile = 166 − 149.5 = 16.5 cm

(b) The 90th percentile is the 60 × 90% = 54th value.

Read it off the cumulative frequency diagram:

90th percentile = 174

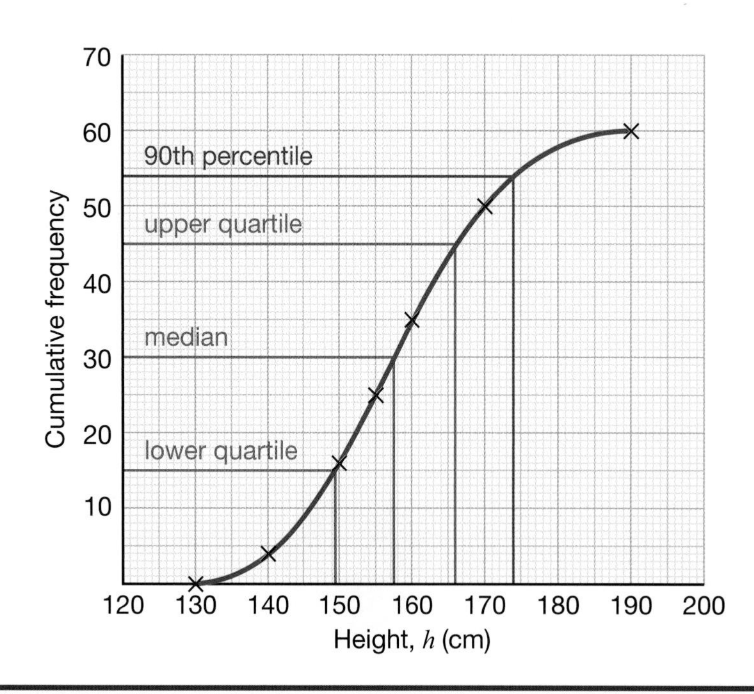

Test yourself

1. For each of these cumulative frequency diagrams, find:

(i) the median, upper and lower quartiles and interquartile range

(ii) the 10th and 80th percentiles.

(a)

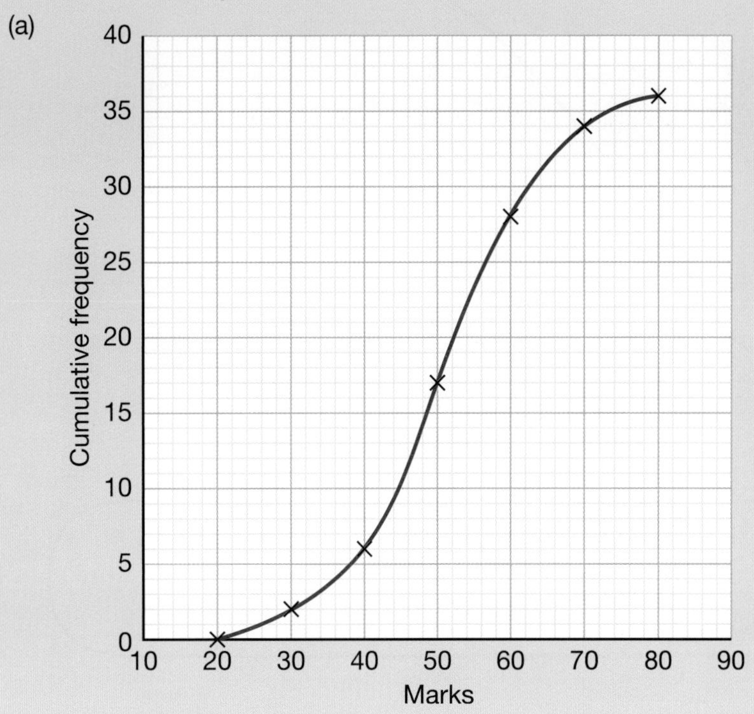

(b)

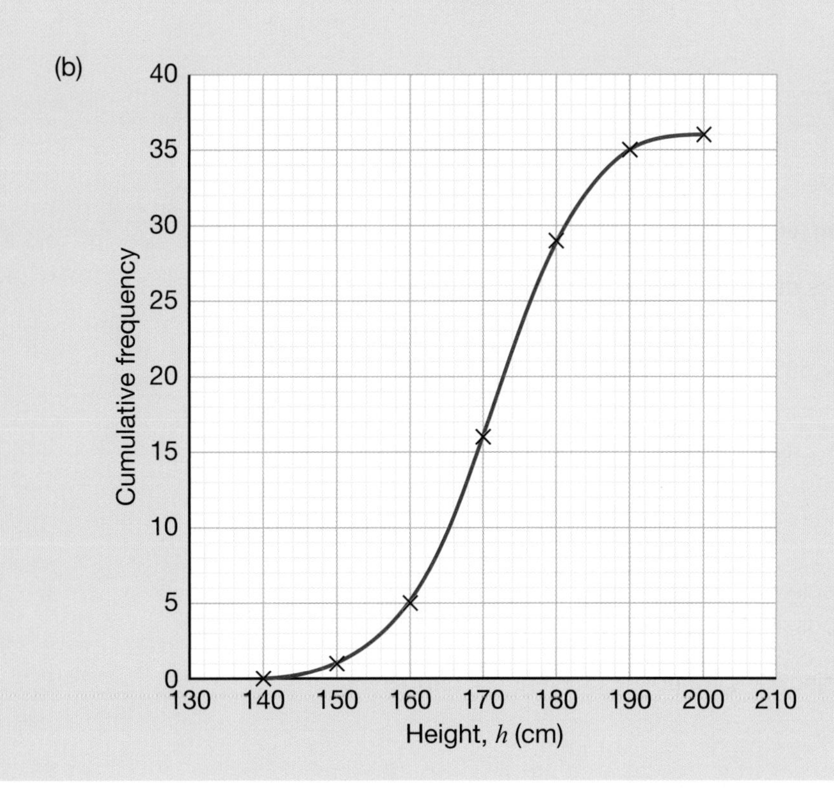

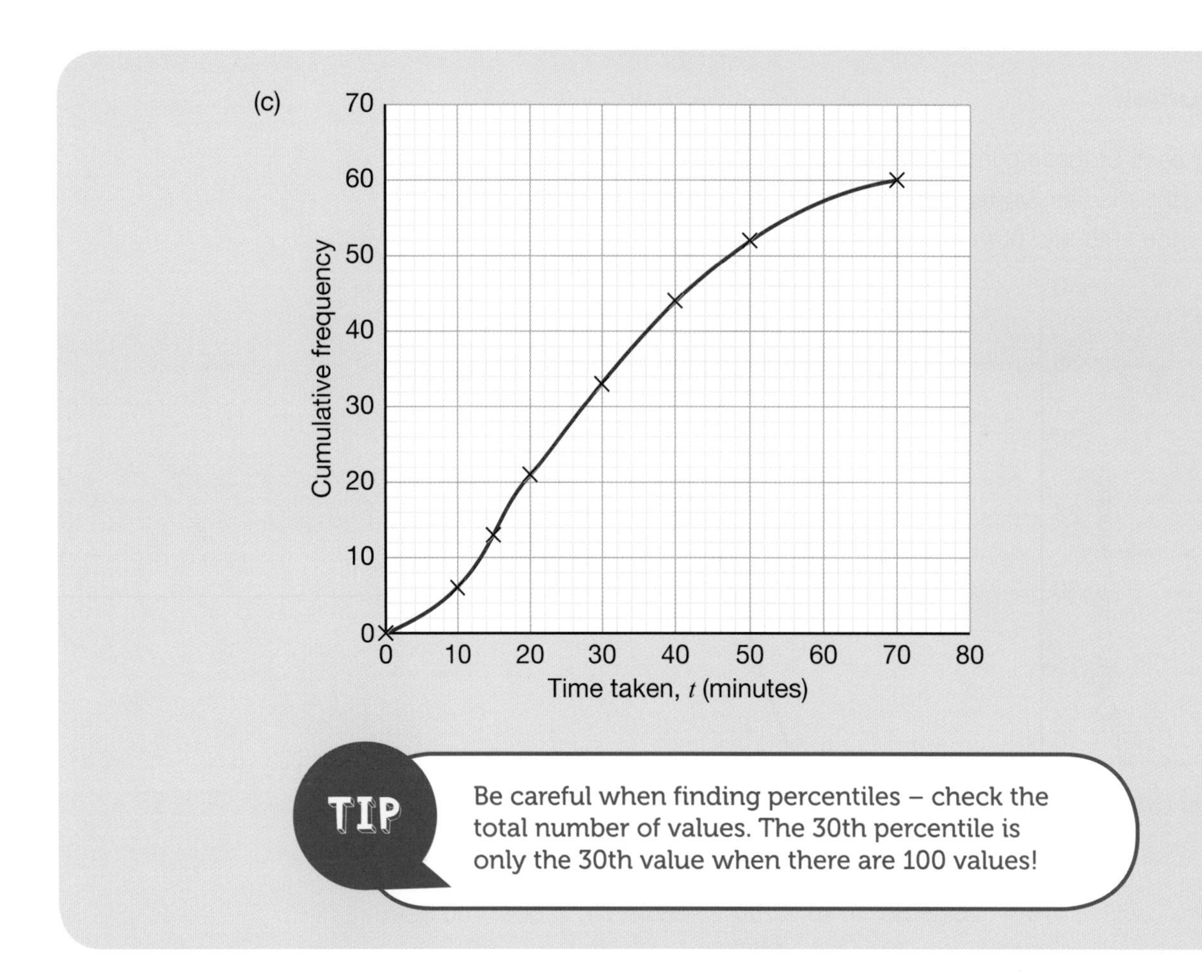

4.3 Probability

Probability

The probability scale goes from 0 to 1.

Probability can be expressed as decimals, fractions or percentages.

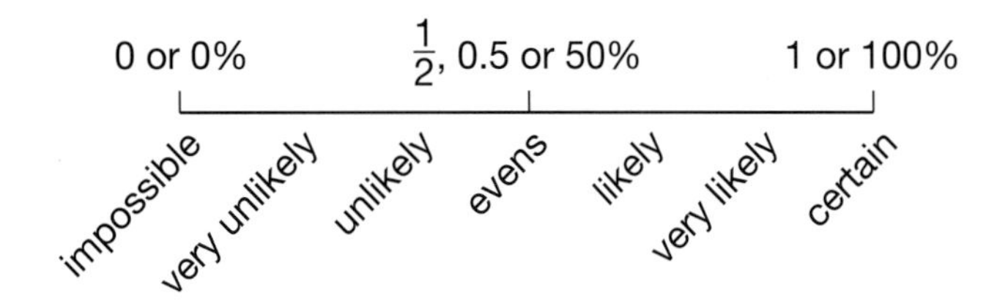

$$\text{Probability} = \frac{\text{number of times selected outcome can occur}}{\text{total number of possible outcomes of event}}$$

Probability of an event happening = 1 − probability of event not happening

Worked example

Megan rolls a six-sided die with the numbers 1 to 6 on its faces.

What is the probability that she:

(a) rolls a 2 (b) does not roll a 2 (c) rolls a number greater than 2?

Give your answers as fractions, decimals and percentages.

Answer

(a) There are 6 possible outcomes and rolling a 2 is one of them. So $P(2) = \frac{1}{6} = 0.167 = 16.7\%$

(b) $P(\text{not rolling a 2}) = 1 - P(\text{rolling a 2}) = 1 - \frac{1}{6} = \frac{5}{6} = 0.833 = 83.3\%$

(c) The possible outcomes are 3, 4, 5 and 6.

$P(\text{rolling a number greater than 2}) = \frac{4}{6} = \frac{2}{3} = 0.667 = 66.7\%$

Test yourself

1. The following letters are put into a bag:

P O S S I B L E O U T C O M E S

Hannah take a letter at random from the bag. What is the probability that she:

(a) takes a letter B (b) takes a letter S

(c) does not take a letter S (d) takes a letter A?

Give your answers as fractions, decimals and percentages.

2. The table shows the number of children in a family in Class 11J.

Number of children	Frequency
1	6
2	14
3	5
4	3
5	1
6	1

Calculate the probability that the number of children in a family is:

(a) 4 (b) not 4 (c) 1 or 2

(d) 3 or more (e) between 0 and 7.

TIP

Remember that probability can never be less than 0 or greater than 1.

Relative frequency

Relative frequency is also known as experimental probability. It is the probability of an event happening that you find from carrying out a sequence of trials.

$$\text{Relative frequency or experimental probability} = \frac{\text{frequency of selected outcome}}{\text{total number of trials}}$$

The relative frequency gets closer to the true probability as the number of trials increases.

Worked example

Raj has an eight-sided spinner with the sides numbered 1 to 8. He records the number of times the spinner lands on 7 after various numbers of spins. The table shows his results.

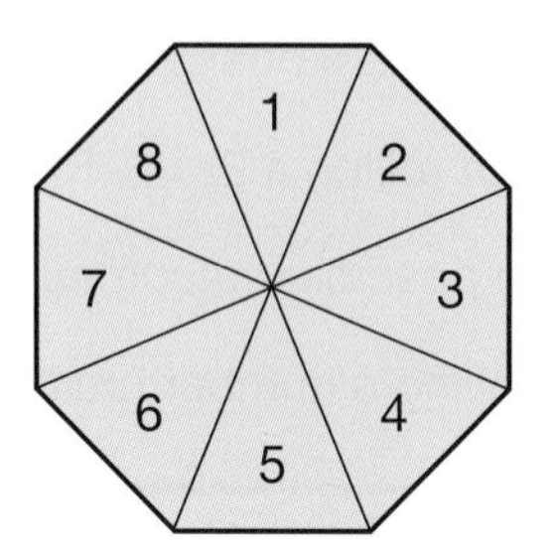

Number of spins	10	20	50	100	200	300
Number of times spinner landed on 7	2	3	5	14	27	36

(a) What is the theoretical probability of the spinner landing on 7? Give your answer as a decimal.

(b) Calculate the experimental probability for each of the numbers of throws shown in the table. Give your answers as decimals.

(c) What happens to the experimental probability as the number of spins increases?

(d) If Raj spinned the spinner 5000 times, how many times would you expect the spinner to land on 7?

Answer

(a) 0.125

(b) 0.2, 0.15, 0.1, 0.14, 0.135, 0.12

(c) It gets closer to the theoretical probability.

(d) 625

Test yourself

1. Sadie rolls a fair four-sided die with sides numbered 1 to 4. She records the number of times the die lands on each number. Her results are shown in the table.

Number	1	2	3	4
Number of times	24	27	26	23

(a) Work out the experimental probability of each number. Give your answers as decimals.

(b) How many times would you expect the die to land on each number?

2. Ben thinks that a six-sided die which has sides numbered 1 to 6 is biased. He records the number of times that the die lands on 2. His results are shown in the table.

Number of rolls	10	20	50	100	200	300
Number of 2s	1	1	3	9	19	32

(a) Work out the experimental probability for each number of throws. Give your answers as decimals.

(b) What is the theoretical probability of a fair six-sided die landing on 2?

(c) Explain why Ben thinks the die is not fair.

Combined events and tree diagrams

Independent events have no effect on each other.
When A and B are independent events, the probability of A and B happening is $P(A) \times P(B)$.

Events that cannot happen together are mutually exclusive. For example, the Sun shining and the Sun not shining are two mutually exclusive events.

When A and B are mutually exclusive events, the probability of A or B happening is $P(A) + P(B)$.

All of the possible outcomes can be shown in a possibility diagram or sample space diagram.

Tree diagrams can be used to show the outcomes of combined events. The outcomes are independent events.

Worked example

1. Alex rolls a six-sided die with sides numbered 1 to 6.

   What is the probability that he rolls a 3 or a 4?

2. Tom rolls a six-sided die with sides numbered 1 to 6 and a four-sided die with sides numbered 1 to 4 and records the total score on the two dice.

   (a) Record the possible outcomes on a possibility diagram or sample space diagram.

   (b) Which scores are most likely?

   (c) Which scores are least likely?

3. There are two red balls and five blue balls in a bag. A ball is taken at random and then put back. A second ball is taken at random.

   (a) Draw a tree diagram to show the possible outcomes.

   (b) Calculate the probability of taking a red ball and a blue ball from the bag.

Answer

1. $P(3 \text{ or } 4) = P(3) + P(4) = \frac{1}{6} + \frac{1}{6} = \frac{2}{6} = \frac{1}{3}$

2. (a)

Score on four-sided die (rows) / **Score on six-sided die** (columns)

	1	**2**	**3**	**4**	**5**	**6**
4	5	6	7	8	9	10
3	4	5	6	7	8	9
2	3	4	5	6	7	8
1	2	3	4	5	6	7

   (b) 5, 6 and 7

   (c) 2 and 10

3. (a)

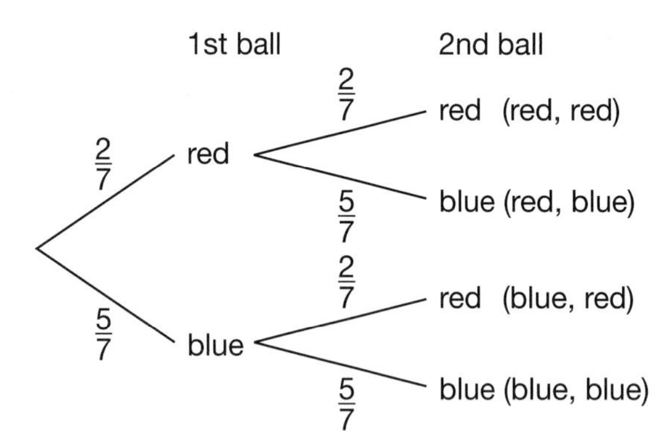

   (b) The possible outcomes are P(red, blue) and P(blue, red).

   Work out the probabilities and add them together.

   $P(\text{red, blue}) = \frac{2}{7} \times \frac{5}{7} = \frac{10}{49} = P(\text{blue, red})$

   Probability of taking a red ball and a blue ball $= \frac{10}{49} + \frac{10}{49} = \frac{20}{49}$

Test yourself

1. A coin is thrown and an eight-sided die is rolled.
   (a) Draw a possibility diagram or sample space diagram for the outcomes.
   (b) What is the probability of throwing a head and rolling a 6?

2. Two eight-sided dice with sides numbered 1 to 8 are rolled and the scores added together.
   (a) Draw a possibility diagram or sample space diagram for the outcomes.
   (b) What is the most likely score? Calculate its probability.
   (c) What are the least likely scores? Calculate the probability of scoring either of them.
   (d) Calculate the probability of scoring 4 or 13.

3. One in every 200 eggs has a double yolk.
   Sam has two boxes of eggs. Sam takes two eggs.
   (a) Draw a tree diagram to show the possible outcomes.
   (b) Calculate the probability that:
      (i) both eggs have double yolks
      (ii) only one egg has a double yolk.

4. A market trader has a bag that contains 160 potatoes. 8 potatoes are rotten.
   He takes a potato from the bag and replaces it. He then takes a second potato from the bag.
   (a) Draw a tree diagram to show the possible outcomes.
   (b) Calculate the probability that the trader takes:
      (i) two good potatoes
      (ii) one rotten potato and one good potato
      (iii) at least one good potato.

Conditional probability

When an event depends on another event, there is conditional probability.

For example, you take a ball from a bag of balls, and then take another ball from the bag without replacing the first ball.

Worked example

There are two red balls and five blue balls in a bag. A ball is taken at random and not put back. A second ball is taken at random.

(a) Draw a tree diagram to show the possible outcomes.

(b) Calculate the probability of taking a red ball and a blue ball from the bag.

Answer

(a) When the second ball is taken, the number of balls to choose from has decreased by one.

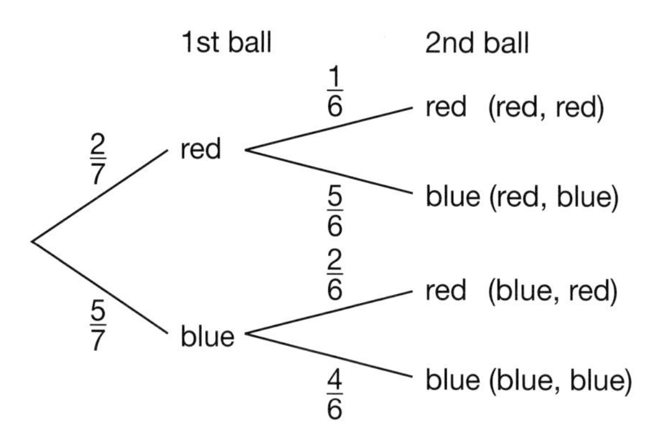

TIP When calculating probability and items are not replaced, remember that the denominator in the fraction does not stay the same.

(b) The possible outcomes are P(red, blue) and P(blue, red).

Work out the probabilities and add them together.

P(red, blue) $= \frac{2}{7} \times \frac{5}{6} = \frac{10}{42}$

P(blue, red) $= \frac{5}{7} \times \frac{2}{6} = \frac{10}{42}$

Probability of taking a red ball and a blue ball $= \frac{10}{42} + \frac{10}{42} = \frac{20}{42} = \frac{10}{21}$

Test yourself

1. A bag contains four white counters and six black counters.
Two counters are taken at random without replacement.
(a) Draw a tree diagram to show the possible outcomes.
(b) Calculate the probability that:
(i) only one of the counters is white (ii) both counters are black.

2. A market trader has a bag that contains 160 potatoes. 8 potatoes are rotten.
He takes a potato from the bag and does not replace it. He then takes a second potato from the bag.
(a) Draw a tree diagram to show the possible outcomes.
(b) Calculate the probability that the trader takes:
(i) two good potatoes
(ii) only one rotten potato
(iii) at least one good potato.

You should now be able to:

- ★ construct and read bar charts, pie charts, pictograms, histograms and cumulative frequency diagrams (see pages 175–79)
- ★ draw scatter diagrams and use correlation (see page 180)
- ★ calculate and use averages (see page 182)
- ★ calculate estimates of the mean for grouped data (see page 184)
- ★ use cumulative frequency diagrams to find the median, quartiles, percentiles and interquartile range (see page 186)
- ★ use fractions, decimals and percentages for probabilities (see page 188)
- ★ calculate the probability of events (see page 190)
- ★ calculate the probability of combined events (see page 191)
- ★ use tree diagrams and possibility diagrams or sample space diagrams (see page 191)
- ★ use simple conditional probability (see page 193).

TIP

When answers are not exact, remember to give your answers to the accuracy specified in the question or on the front of the exam paper.

Practice questions

1. The times taken for 200 athletes to run 1500 m are shown in the table.

Time, t (minutes)	$0 < t \leqslant 5$	$5 < t \leqslant 6$	$6 < t \leqslant 7$	$7 < t \leqslant 10$
Frequency	18	64	76	42

(a) Write down the class interval that contains the median. **(1)**

(b) Calculate an estimate of the mean. Show your working. **(4)**

(c) Draw up a cumulative frequency table. **(2)**

(d) Draw a cumulative frequency diagram. **(3)**

(e) Use your diagram to find the median, upper quartile and interquartile range. **(3)**

2. Two bags contain the following letters:

Bag 1: A D D I T I O N
Bag 2: D I V I S I O N

(a) One letter is taken at random from bag 1 and replaced.

(i) Write down the probability that the letter taken is a D. **(1)**

(ii) A letter is taken at random from bag 1 and replaced 500 times.

Write down the expected number of times the letter taken would be a D. **(1)**

(b) One letter is taken at random from bag 1 and one letter is taken at random from bag 2.

Calculate the probability that both letters are I. **(2)**

(c) Two letters are taken at random from bag 2 and not replaced. Find the probability that both letters are I. **(2)**

3. In Toronto, the mid-day temperatures, in °C, are recorded during a week in December.
The temperatures are:

2 0 –3 –2 –1 –3 –4

(a) Calculate the range. **(1)**

(b) Calculate the mean temperature. **(2)**

(c) Write down the mode. **(1)**

4. The brands of mobile phones owned by 90 people are recorded in the table.

Brand A	Brand B	Brand C	Brand D
36	42	5	7

(a) Write down the mode. **(1)**

(b) Ellie drew a pie chart to illustrate the data.

Calculate the angle of the sector for brand B. **(2)**

(c) Calculate the probability that a person chosen at random will own a brand A phone.
Write your answer as a fraction in its simplest form. **(2)**

5. The table shows the numbers of text messages sent by 60 teenagers in one day.

Number of text messages	Number of teenagers
0 to 4	8
5 to 9	19
10 to 14	23
15 to 19	10

(a) Work out an estimate for the mean number of text messages sent by the 60 teenagers. **(4)**

(b) Explain why your answer is an estimate. **(1)**

6. The histogram shows information about the times, in minutes, that a group of people took to complete a puzzle.

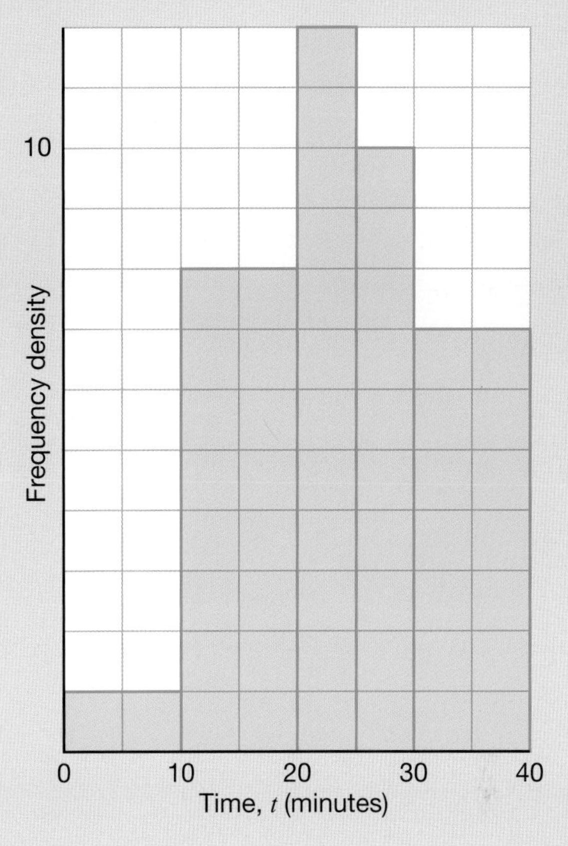

(a) Use the histogram to complete the frequency table. **(4)**

Time, t (minutes)	$0 < t \leqslant 10$	$10 < t \leqslant 20$	$20 < t \leqslant 25$	$25 < t \leqslant 30$	$30 < t \leqslant 40$
Frequency					14

(b) Calculate the percentage of people who took more than 25 minutes to complete the puzzle. **(3)**

(c) Calculate an estimate of the number of people who took between 15 and 30 minutes to complete the puzzle. **(2)**

7. Max travels from London to Crete.
Max changes planes in Athens.

The probability that his plane is on time arriving in Athens is 0.7.

The probability that his connecting plane is on time arriving in Crete is 0.9.

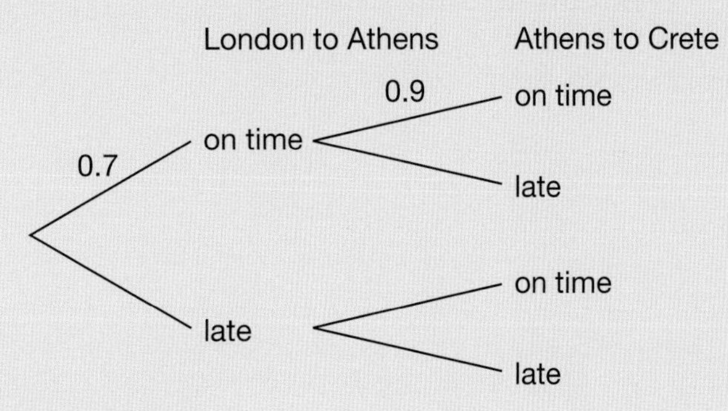

(a) Calculate the probability that both planes are on time. **(2)**

(b) Calculate the probability that one of the planes is late. **(3)**

8. Eight numbers have a mean of 9. Seven of the numbers are:

6 8 12 9 11 7 6

The other number is x. Work out the value of x. **(3)**

Answers

1 Number

1.1 Basic number

Numbers

1. (a) rational (b) rational (c) rational
   (d) irrational (e) irrational (f) irrational
2. (a) $2^2 \times 7$ (b) $2^3 \times 5$ (c) 3^4
   (d) 24×3^2 (e) 5^3 (f) $2^2 \times 3^2 \times 5$

Order of operations

1. (a) $2 \times (8-5) = 6$ (b) $(10+2) \div 3 = 4$
   (c) $(15-10) \times 3 = 15$

Directed numbers

1. (a) (i) 15 °C (ii) 19.5 °C (iii) 16.5 °C
   (b) (i) Rio de Janeiro and Yellowknife
   (ii) 48.5 °C
2. (a) 100 m (b) 69 m (c) 189 m

1.2 Fractions

Fraction problems

1. (a) $\frac{3}{10}, \frac{2}{5}, \frac{1}{2}, \frac{11}{20}, \frac{7}{10}$ (b) $\frac{7}{12}, \frac{2}{3}, \frac{3}{4}, \frac{5}{6}, \frac{7}{8}$ (c) $\frac{1}{7}, \frac{5}{14}, \frac{3}{5}, \frac{9}{14}, \frac{7}{10}$
2. (a) £4 (b) 36 kg (c) 21 cm
   (d) 99 litres

Adding and subtracting fractions

1. (a) $1\frac{29}{30}$ (b) $1\frac{11}{24}$ (c) $7\frac{2}{5}$
   (d) $\frac{5}{8}$ (e) $1\frac{13}{16}$ (f) $4\frac{2}{3}$

Multiplying and dividing fractions

1. (a) $\frac{1}{4}$ (b) $\frac{2}{7}$ (c) $3\frac{11}{28}$
   (d) 9 (e) $1\frac{2}{7}$ (f) $1\frac{1}{10}$
   (g) $1\frac{1}{4}$ (h) $1\frac{19}{21}$

Converting fractions to decimals and percentages

1. (a) 0.4, 40% (b) 0.3, 30%
   (c) 0.9, 90% (d) 0.35, 35%
   (e) 0.625, 62.5% (f) 0.6875, 68.75%

1.3 Decimals

Decimals, fractions and percentages

1. (a) $\frac{4}{5}$, 80% (b) $\frac{3}{20}$, 15% (c) $\frac{7}{25}$, 28%
   (d) $\frac{43}{50}$, 86% (e) $\frac{17}{40}$, 42.5% (f) $\frac{98}{125}$, 78.4%
2. (a) 0.0022, 0.02, 0.022, 0.2, 0.22
   (b) 0.0036, 0.035, 0.036, 0.35, 0.38

Recurring decimals

1. (a) $\frac{5}{9}$ (b) $\frac{8}{11}$ (c) $\frac{5}{11}$
   (d) $\frac{78}{111}$ (e) $\frac{8}{15}$ (f) $\frac{7}{30}$

1.4 Percentages

Percentages

1. (a) 0.6, $\frac{3}{5}$ (b) 0.25, $\frac{1}{4}$ (c) 0.65, $\frac{13}{20}$
   (d) 0.76, $\frac{19}{25}$ (e) 0.875, $\frac{7}{8}$ (f) 0.9375, $\frac{15}{16}$
2. (a) £29.90 (b) 61.05 kg (c) 42.7 litres
   (d) 202.5 g (e) 205.9 cm (f) £116.82
3. (a) £29.75 (b) 36 litres (c) 65.6 g
   (d) 77.5 kg (e) 99 m (f) £26.95
4. (a) 84.4% (b) 76.9% (c) 85.7%
   (d) 33.6% (e) 19.5% (f) 4.5%
5. (a) 322 (b) 819 (c) 438.84
   (d) 426.56 (e) 34.56 (f) 161.28

Reverse percentages

1. (a) 150 g (b) £55 (c) 68 litres
   (d) 25 cm (e) 130 mm (f) £120
2. (a) 64 cm (b) 128 mm (c) £150
   (d) 225 g (e) 320 litres (f) £444

Interest

1. £419.20
2. (a) £1680 (b) £1688.26
3. 4 years
4. £69.97
5. (a) compound (b) 3.5%
6. (a) 2.7% simple interest (interest earned = £145.80 against £138.40 in compound interest account)
   (b) 2.5% compound interest (interest earned = £393.13 against £388.80 in simple interest account)

Compound interest problems

1. £4973
2. £144 000
3. £18 500
4. (a) (i) 40 074 167 (ii) 31 881 702
   (b) 2023
5. 9.6%
6. (a) 1 (b) 5 120 000

1.5 Powers, roots and indices

Square numbers and cube numbers

1. (a) 2.56 (b) 15.625 (c) 0.9
   (d) 1.2 (e) 0.8 (f) 1.5

Indices

1. (a) 32 (b) $\frac{1}{216}$ (c) $\frac{1}{12}$
   (d) $\frac{1}{27}$ (e) 9 (f) 216
2. (a) 3 (b) 2 (c) 0.04
   (d) 4 (e) 0.177 (f) 3.674

HCF and LCM

1. (a) 42 (b) 24 (c) 22
   (d) 18 (e) 15 (f) 21
2. (a) 252 (b) 576 (c) 462
   (d) 810 (e) 600 (f) 924

Standard form

1. (a) 3.65×10^5 (b) 4.6×10^7 (c) 7.82×10^6
   (d) 3.4×10^{-4} (e) 5.6×10^{-3} (f) 1.94×10^{-6}
2. (a) 1.25×10^8 (b) 5.84×10^6 (c) 2.48×10^9
   (d) 2.7×10^{10} (e) 1.71×10^9 (f) 2.361×10^8
3. (a) Canada (b) New Zealand
   (c) New Zealand (d) Finland

Surds

1. (a) $4\sqrt{2}$ (b) $5\sqrt{3}$ (c) $3\sqrt{7}$
   (d) $5\sqrt{5}$ (e) $10\sqrt{6}$ (f) $4\sqrt{3}$
2. (a) $6\sqrt{15}$ (b) 30 (c) 24
   (d) 14 (e) $4\sqrt{3}$ (f) 9
3. (a) $11+5\sqrt{5}$ (b) $18+7\sqrt{6}$ (c) $11+6\sqrt{2}$
   (d) $7-4\sqrt{3}$ (e) $\sqrt{3}-5$ (f) $2+\sqrt{2}$
4. (a) $\frac{\sqrt{2}}{2}$ (b) $\frac{\sqrt{6}}{6}$ (c) $2\sqrt{3}$
   (d) $\frac{4\sqrt{6}}{3}$ (e) $\frac{\sqrt{21}}{7}$ (f) $2\sqrt{3}-\sqrt{6}$

1.6 Sets

Set notation

1. (a) $B=\{1, 2, 5, 10\}$
   (b) {1}, {2}, {5}, {10} {1, 2}, {1, 5}, {1, 10}, {2, 5}, {2, 10}, {5, 10}, {1, 2, 5}, {1, 2, 10}, {1, 5, 10}, {2, 5, 10}, {1, 2, 5, 10}, ∅
   (c) 4
2. (a) $C=\{a, b, l\}$
   (b) {a}, {b}, {l}, {a, b}, {a, l}, {b, l}, {a, b, l}, ∅
   (c) 3
3. (a) $D=\{-5, 5\}$
   (b) {–5}, {5}, {–5, 5}, ∅
   (c) 2
4. (a) {25} (b) {20, 25, 30}
   (c) ∅
5. (a) {3} (b) {11}
   (c) {2, 5, 7, 11, 13}
6. (a) (i) {Monday} (ii) ∅
   (iii) {Monday, Tuesday, Thursday, Saturday}
   (b) No, because it contains all the elements in the universal set.

Venn diagrams

1. (a)

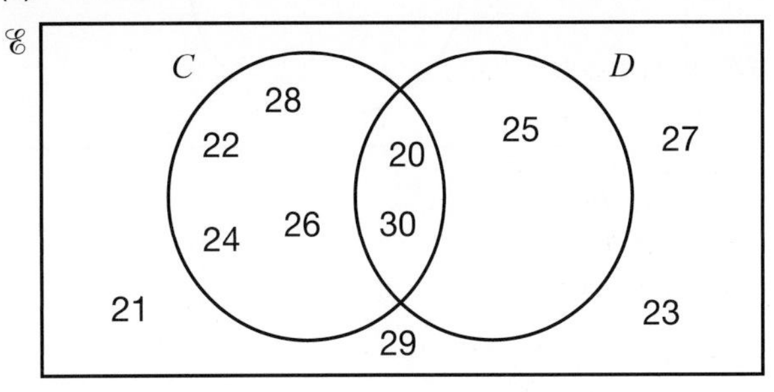

   (b) (i) {20, 30}
   (ii) {20, 22, 24, 25, 26, 28, 30}
   (iii) {25}

2. (a)

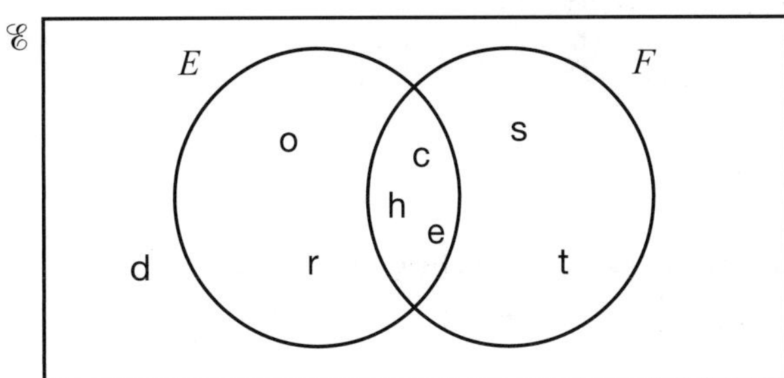

   (b) (i) {c, d, e, h, s, t}
   (ii) {o, r}
   (iii) {d}

3. (a)

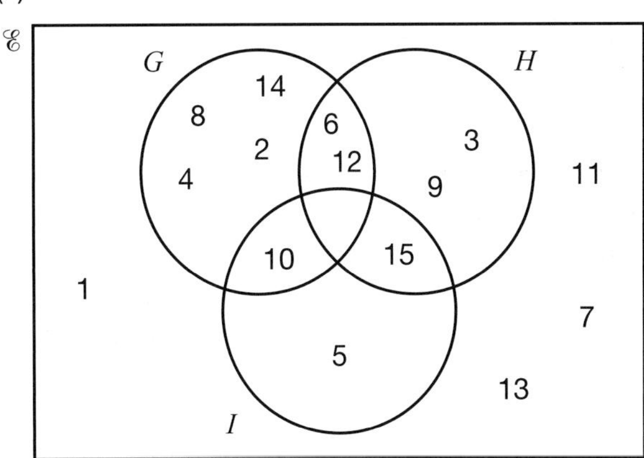

   (b) (i) {10, 15}
   (ii) {2, 4, 6, 8, 10, 12, 14, 15}
   (iii) {3, 9}

4. (a)

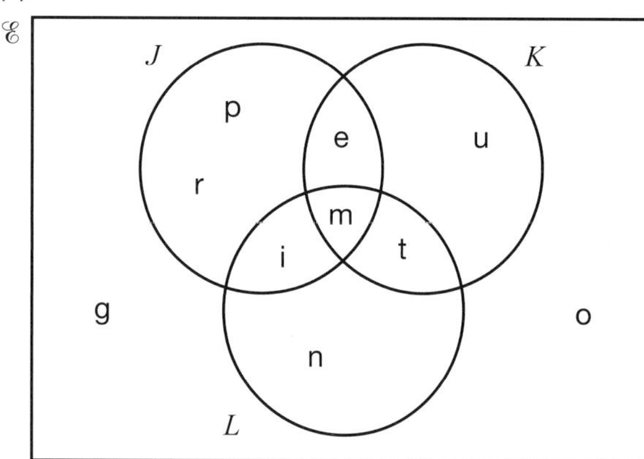

(b) (i) {m}
(ii) {i, m, n, t, u}
(iii) {g, o}

5. (a)

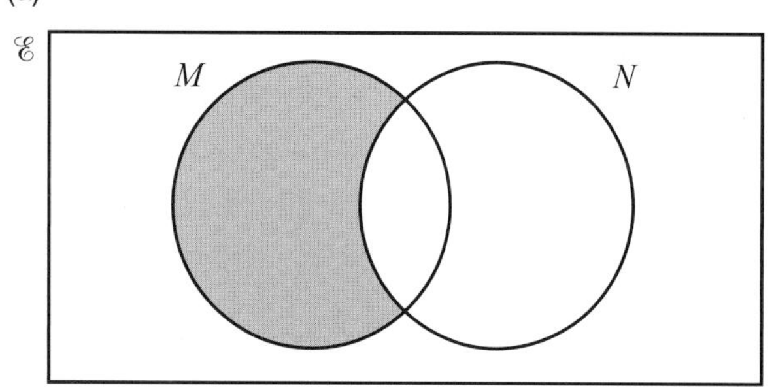

(b)

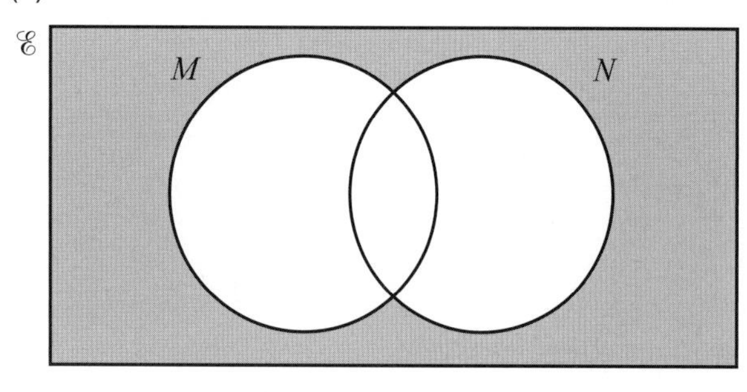

(c)

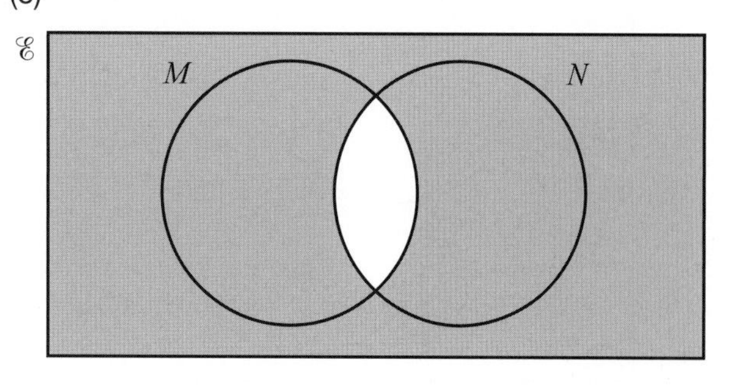

(d)

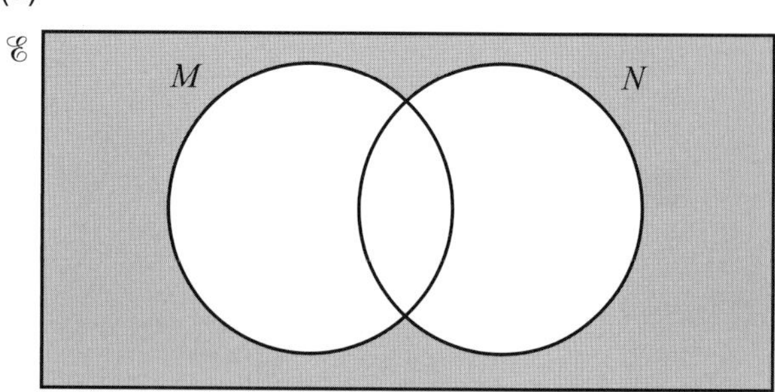

6. (a)

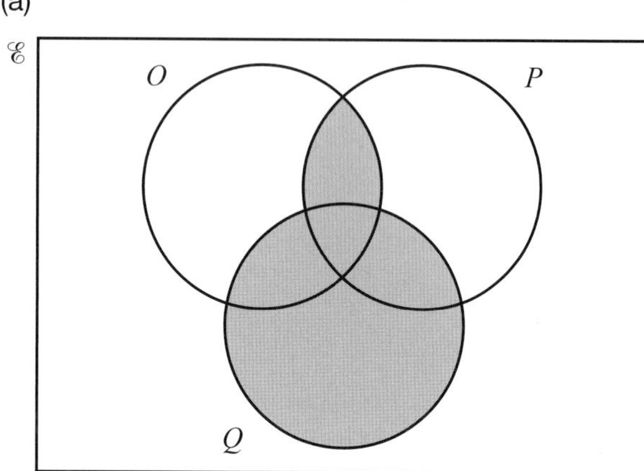

(b)

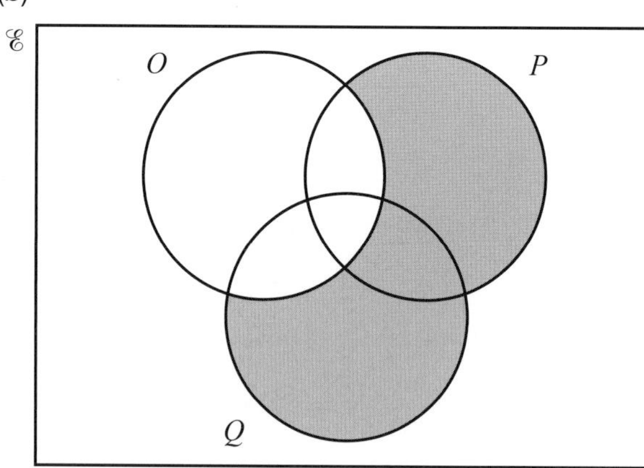

(c)

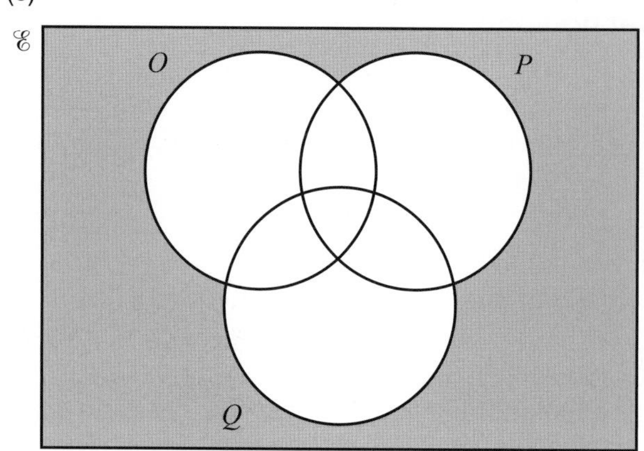

(d)

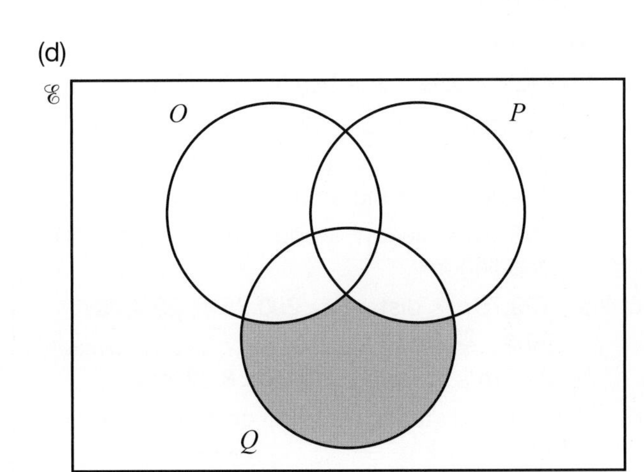

Solving problems with sets

1. (a) 27 (b) 5 (c) 16 (d) 40
2. (a) 8 (b) 23 (c) 36 (d) 17
3. (a)

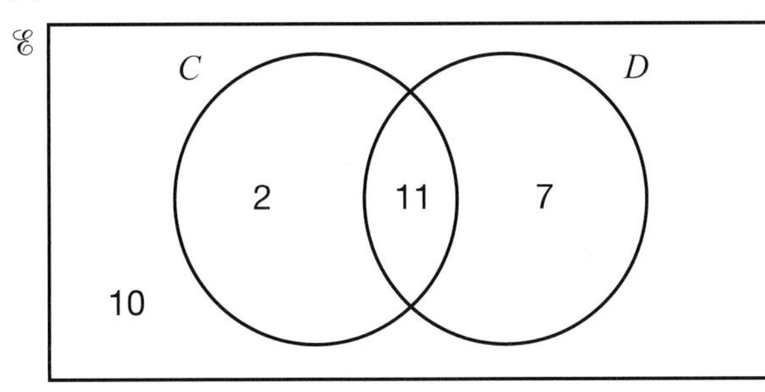

(b) 10

4. (a)

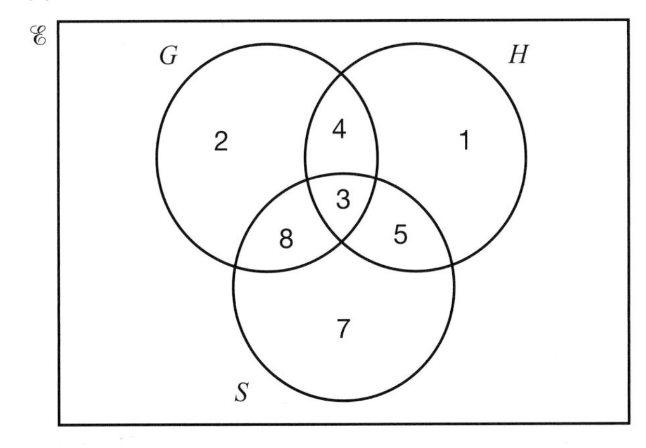

(b) 10

1.7 Ratio and proportion

Ratio

1. (a) (i) 3 : 5 (ii) 1 : 1.67
   (b) (i) 4 : 15 (ii) 1 : 3.75
   (c) (i) 4 : 7 (ii) 1 : 1.75
   (d) (i) 3 : 20 (ii) 1 : 6.67
   (e) (i) 9 : 1 (ii) 1 : 9
   (f) (i) 4 : 25 (ii) 1 : 6.25
2. £120 : £210
3. 125 adults, 225 children
4. 0.15 litres (150 ml) syrup, 1.35 litres (1350 ml) water
5. 125 g butter, 225 g flour, 150 g sugar
6. 90 teas, 135 coffees and 225 other drinks
7. 350 ml apple juice, 50 ml raspberry puree, 100 ml boysenberry juice
8. 133 adults
9. 200 concessionary tickets
10. £24 000
11. 300 ml lime juice, 450 ml mango puree
12. Rachel: 32 sweets; Megan: 36 sweets
13. 280 g flour, 175 g sugar

Increasing and decreasing quantities by a ratio

1. (a) 1000 (b) 375 (c) 300
   (d) 562.5 (e) 700 (f) 475
2. (a) 100 (b) 80 (c) 140
   (d) 75 (e) 32 (f) 137.5
3. 1250 g potatoes, 50 g butter, 5 teaspoons chopped fresh parsley, 75 g grated cheese, 125 g flour, 125 ml vegetable oil
4. 30 g butter, 165 g risotto rice, 337.5 ml boiling water, 75 g cooked peas, 37.5 g grated cheese, 22.5 ml lemon juice

Rates

1. (a) 48 cm (b) 183 days
2. (a) 6 litres/min (b) 15 minutes
3. (a) 12.5 litres (b) 3 litres
4. (a) 22.25 litres (b) 561.8 km
   (c) 11.2 km/litre
5. (a) 7.875 kg (b) 114.3 km
6. 1.55 p.p.m./year

Average speed

1. 100 km/h
2. 8 m/s
3. 14.1 km/h
4. 3 cm/min
5. 764 km/h
6. 4.8 km/h
7. 2.5 hours (or 2 hours and 30 minutes)
8. 2.4 hours (or 2 hours and 24 minutes)
9. 7 minutes 41.5 seconds
10. 5197.5 km
11. 3 km
12. 220 km
13. (a) 43.2 km/h (b) 72 km/h
    (c) 1.8 km/h (d) 115.2 km/h
    (e) 270 km/h (f) 630 km/h

14. (a) 5 m/s (b) 6.7 m/s (c) 13.9 m/s
(d) 25 m/s (e) 44.4 m/s (f) 208.3 m/s

Direct proportion

1. 5.25 kg
2. 224 km
3. $162.50
4. £6.29
5. 61.6 seconds
6. 310 g of butter, 520 g of flour and 210 g of sugar

Inverse proportion

1. £15
2. 20.6 km/h
3. 8.4 hours (or 8 hours and 24 minutes)
4. 6 days
5. 83 complete documents
6. 104 m of the $0.75/m wallpaper, 74.3 m of the $1.05/m wallpaper

1.8 Accuracy

Decimal places and significant figures

1. (a) (i) 300 (ii) 350 (iii) 346
(iv) 346.3 (v) 346.26 (vi) 346.258
(b) (i) 70 (ii) 67 (iii) 67.4
(iv) 67.4 (v) 67.39 (vi) 67.386
(c) (i) 4 (ii) 3.6 (iii) 3.62
(iv) 3.6 (v) 3.62 (vi) 3.622
(d) (i) 0.5 (ii) 0.53 (iii) 0.529
(iv) 0.5 (v) 0.53 (vi) 0.529
(e) (i) 0.09 (ii) 0.092 (iii) 0.0918
(iv) 0.1 (v) 0.09 (vi) 0.092
(f) (i) 0.005 (ii) 0.0054 (iii) 0.00538
(iv) 0 (v) 0.01 (vi) 0.005

Upper and lower bounds

1. (a) $95 \leqslant$ number of apples < 105
(b) 8.5 million $\leqslant$ population $<$ 9.5 million (or $8\,500\,000 \leqslant$ population $\leqslant 9\,499\,999$)
(c) $1.65\text{ m} \leqslant$ length $< 1.75\text{ m}$
(d) $245\text{ g} \leqslant$ mass $< 255\text{ g}$
(e) $20.5\text{ cm} \leqslant$ length $< 21.5\text{ cm}$
(f) $57.5\text{ km} \leqslant$ distance $< 58.5\text{ km}$

Calculations with upper and lower bounds

1. $293.05\text{ cm}^3 \leqslant$ volume $< 307.05\text{ cm}^3$
2. (a) 29.95 litres $\leqslant$ volume of liquid $<$ 30.05; 0.325 litre $\leqslant$ volume of bottle $<$ 0.335 litre
(b) 89 bottles $\leqslant$ number of bottles $\leqslant$ 92 bottles
3. (a) $64.5\text{ kg} \leqslant$ mass of average person $< 65.5\text{ kg}$; $1745\text{ kg} \leqslant$ mass carried by lift $< 1755\text{ kg}$
(b) $26 \leqslant$ number of people $\leqslant 27$
4. (a) 16.75 million $\leqslant$ population $<$ 16.85 million; $41\,450\text{ km}^2 \leqslant$ land area $< 41\,550\text{ km}^2$
(b) 403.1 people/km^2 $\leqslant$ population density $<$ 406.5 people/km^2
5. (a) $199.75\text{ m} \leqslant$ distance $< 200.25\text{ m}$; $22.45\text{ s} \leqslant$ time $< 22.55\text{ s}$
(b) $8.86\text{ m/s} \leqslant$ average speed $< 8.92\text{ m/s}$
6. $13.25\text{ km} \leqslant$ distance travelled on 1 litre of petrol $< 13.42\text{ km}$

1.9 Applying number

Estimating quantities

1. (a) 15 cm, 5–10 g
(b) length, 30 cm; width, 20 cm; thickness, 1 cm; mass, between 0.5 and 1 kg
(c)–(e) Student's own answer
(f) length, between 10 and 15 cm; mass between 100 and 200 g

Time

1. (a) (i) 10.35 am (ii) 1035
(b) (i) 11.20 pm (ii) 2320
(c) (i) 3.10 pm (ii) 1510
(d) (i) 8.05 am (ii) 0805
(e) (i) 12.50 am (ii) 0050
(f) (i) 3.45 am (ii) 0345
2. 50 minutes
3. 2 hours and 35 minutes
4. 1 hour and 45 minutes
5. 10 hours and 52 minutes
6. 8 hours and 25 minutes
7. (a) 34 minutes (b) 1 minute
(c) 16 minutes

Money and currency conversions

1. (a) MXN$576.90 (b) US$23.40
2. (a) R$188.10 (b) £146.20
3. (a) S$85.50 (b) A$307.02
4. (a) Lkr9722.79 (b) MYR12.74
5. (a) ₹4631.92 (b) HK$31.74
6. (a) R254.28 (b) RMB469.57

1.10 Electronic calculators

1. (a) 68.78 (b) 10.81 (c) –31.71
(d) 2.52 (e) 0.771 (f) 1.44

Practice questions

1. (a) $\frac{1.93649}{17.1}$ **(1)** $= 0.113$ **(1)**
   (b) $\sqrt{\frac{23.8}{10.81}}$ **(1)** $= \sqrt{2.201665} = 1.484$ **(1)**
2. $5(5.92 \times 10^9)$ **(1)** $= 2.96 \times 10^{10}$ **(1)**
3. $\frac{\frac{4}{35}}{\frac{10+14}{35}} = \frac{\frac{4}{35}}{\frac{24}{35}}$ **(1)** $= \frac{4}{35} \times \frac{35}{24}$ **(1)** $= \frac{4}{24}$ **(1)** $= \frac{1}{6}$
4. $14 \times 6 + 1$ **(1)** $= 85$ trains **(1)**
5. (a) 5.1 **(1)** (b) 0.0319 **(1)**
   (c) 0.0508 **(1)**
6. 1 tablet: £47.50 ⩽ cost < £48.50 **(1)** 780 tablets: lower bound = £47.50 × 780 = £37 050; upper bound = £48.50 × 780 = £37 830 **(1)**
7. $1 + \frac{16+4+9}{24}$ **(1)** $= 1 + \frac{29}{24}$ **(1)** $= 2\frac{5}{24}$ **(1)**
8. 560 m.p.h. = 560 × 1.609 km/h **(1)**
   $= 560 \times 1.609 \times \frac{1000}{60 \times 60}$ m/s **(1)** = 250 m/s **(1)**
9. (a) $4^{-2} = 0.0625$ **(1)**, $p = -2$ **(1)** (b) $2^{3q} = 512$ **(1)**, $3q = 9$, $q = 3$ **(1)** (c) $8^{-\frac{1}{3}} = 0.5$ **(1)**, $r = -\frac{1}{3}$ **(1)**
10. 1 part = \$600 ÷ 8 = \$75**(1)**; amount spent on travel = \$75 × 3 = \$225 per month **(1)**
11. (a) 127 **(1)** (b) 125 **(1)**
12. $\left(\frac{6}{5}\right)^{-4}$ **(1)** $= \frac{625}{1296}$ **(1)**
13. (a) 1.358×10^6 **(1)**
    (b) 1.3575×10^6 **(1)** ⩽ population < 1.3585×10^6 **(1)**
14. £1200 × 1.14 × 1.14 **(1)** = £1559.52 **(1)**
15. $\frac{1}{9} + \frac{1}{8}$ **(1)** $= \frac{8+9}{72}$ **(1)** $= \frac{17}{72}$ **(1)**
16. 1 − −4 = 5 °C **(1)**
17. 9 × 1.2 = 10.8 hours **(1)**; 0.8 hours = 60 × 0.8 minutes = 48 minutes **(1)**; 10 hours and 48 minutes **(1)**
18. £400 = 400 × 1.167 = €466.80 **(1)**; amount left = €466.80 − €300 = €166.80 **(1)**; amount in pounds = €166.80 ÷ 1.243 = £134.19 **(1)**
19. 79.9 kg ÷ 0.94 **(1)** = 85 kg **(1)**
20. Fill in the numbers on the Venn diagram.

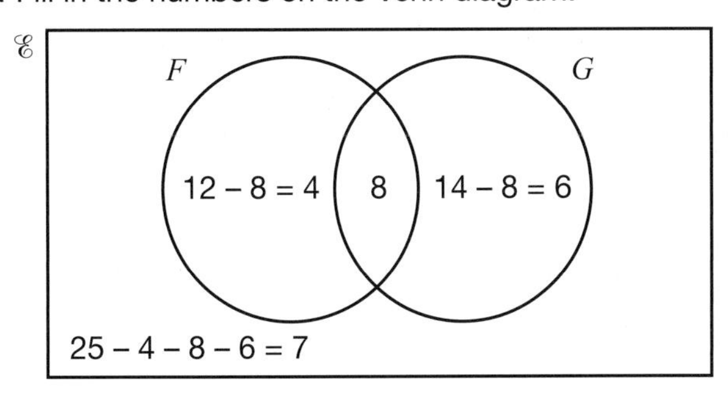

   (a) 4 + 8 + 6 = 18 **(1)** (b) 6 **(1)** (c) 17 **(1)**

21. (a) (i) £11 000 × 0.65 **(1)** = £7150 **(1)**
    (ii) 65 : 35 = 13 : 7 **(1)**
    (b) 2450 ÷ (7 + 5 + 2) = 2450 ÷ 14 = 175; Farid's share = £175 × 7 = £1225 **(1)**; Ryan's share = £175 × 5 = £875 **(1)**; Sunni's share = £175 × 2 = £350 **(1)**
    (c) (i) £11 000 × 0.79^3 **(1)** = £5423.43 **(1)**
    (ii) (£11 000 − £5423.43) ÷ £11 000 × 100% **(1)** = 50.7% **(1)**
    (iii) £5423.43 × 0.65 = £3525.23 **(1)**
22. (a) 208 = 2 × 2 × 2 × 2 × 13 **(2)**
    (b) 2 × 2 × 2 × 2 = 16 **(1)**
    (c) 2 × 2 × 2 × 2 × 3 × 13 = 624 **(1)**
23. (a) £7.50 × 44 × 0.85 **(1)** = £280.50 **(1)**
    (b) £59.28 ÷ 0.78 **(1)** = £76.00 **(1)**
    (c) 44 ÷ 11 × 2 **(1)** = 8 **(1)**
    (d) time taken = 1008 − 0838 = 1 hour and 30 minutes = 1.5 hours **(1)**; average speed = 150 ÷ 1.5 **(1)** = 100 km/h **(1)**
24. (a) 250 ÷ 200 × 20 **(1)** = 25 **(1)**
    (b) 250 ÷ 200 × 140 g **(1)** = 175 g **(1)**
25. (a) $\frac{36.9}{25.9} + 1.8^2 = 1.424710424 + 3.24$ **(1)** $= 4.664710424$ **(1)**
    (b) 4.66 **(1)**
26. $\frac{16-15}{18}$ **(1)** $= \frac{1}{18}$ **(1)**
27. 110 cm ÷ (6 + 3 + 2) = 110 cm ÷ 11 = 10 cm **(1)**; 10 cm × 6 = 60 cm **(1)**
28. (a) {15} **(1)** (b) {5, 6, 9, 10, 12, 15} **(1)**
29. £7000 × 1.03^4 **(2)** = £7878.56 **(1)**
30. (a) 28 322 773 ÷ 86 613 986 × 100% **(1)** = 32.7% **(1)**
    (b) 86 613 986 ÷ 1.055 **(1)** = 82 098 565 **(1)** = 82 099 000 to the nearest thousand **(1)**
31. $B = \{7, 8, 9, 10\}$ **(2)**
32. $x = 0.5\dot{7}$; $10x = 5.\dot{7}$ **(1)** $9x = 5.2$, $90x = 52$ **(1)**, $x = \frac{52}{90} = \frac{26}{45}$
33. (a) 64.8 ÷ 7 = 9.2571 **(1)** length = 9.2571 × 8 = 74.1 m **(1)**
    (b) 37 cm : 74.1 m = 37 cm : 7410 cm **(1)** = 1 : 7410 ÷ 37 **(1)** = 1 : 200 **(1)**
34. 1.335 × 1.317 **(1)** = 1.758 195 **(1)**; increase is 75.8% **(1)**
35. £19.99 × 0.65 **(1)** = £12.99 **(1)**
36. 1 hour and 15 minutes = 1.25 hours **(1)**; 90 ÷ 1.25 **(1)** = 72 km/h **(1)**
37. (a) £120 × 0.01 × 15 + £120 + £5 **(1)** = £143 **(1)**
    (b) £23 ÷ £120 × 100% **(1)** = 19.2% **(1)**
38. $\sqrt{28 \times 5} + \sqrt{7 \times 5}$ **(1)** $= \sqrt{4} \times \sqrt{7} \times \sqrt{5} + \sqrt{7} \times \sqrt{5}$ $= 2\sqrt{7} \times \sqrt{5} + \sqrt{7} \times \sqrt{5}$ **(1)** $= 3\sqrt{7} \times \sqrt{5}$, so $k = 3\sqrt{7}$ **(1)**

2 Algebra

2.1 Use of symbols and indices

Using letters

1. (a) $4n$ (b) $4n+5$ (c) $n-3$
2. $\$(M-N)$
3. Josie: $x+3$, Maria: $2x$, Alice: $x-5$
4. $£\frac{P}{5}$
5. (a) $\frac{t}{2}$ (b) $\frac{t}{2}+4$
6. $12a$

Using indices

1. (a) $\frac{4}{x^2}$ (b) $\frac{7}{p^5}$ (c) $\frac{8}{y^3}$
2. (a) $5m^{-6}$ (b) $2y^{-4}$ (c) $9x^{-1}$
3. (a) $20a^7$ (b) $9a^6$ (c) $6a^{-3}$
   (d) $2a^4$ (e) $6a^7$ (f) $3a$
   (g) $10a^5b^9$ (h) $12ab$ (i) $30b^{-2}$
   (j) $3ab^2$ (k) $4a^7b^2$ (l) $3a^{-9}b$
   (m) $3ab^3c^2$ (n) $9b^4c$ (o) $\frac{12}{5}ab^5c^4$

Fractional indices

1. (a) $x=-\frac{1}{3}$ (b) $x=-\frac{3}{2}$ (c) $x=-\frac{1}{2}$
   (d) $x=-\frac{5}{2}$ (e) $x=-\frac{3}{4}$ (f) $x=-\frac{1}{2}$
2. (a) $2x^{-\frac{7}{2}}$ (b) $\frac{25}{4}d^5$ (c) $6x^{\frac{1}{2}}$
   (d) $16y^2$ (e) $10x^{-\frac{3}{2}}$ (f) $24y^{\frac{7}{2}}$

2.2 Algebraic manipulation

Simplifying expressions

1. (a) $18xy^2$ (b) $8p^3q^2$
   (c) $-6q^3r^2$ (d) $9x^3y^3$
   (e) $12m^3t^2$ (f) $12x^3y^2$
   (g) $26xy+12xy^2$ (h) $10p^3q^2-14p^2q^2$
   (i) $4q^2r^2+18q^3r^2$ (j) $-9x^2y+12xy^2$
   (k) $22pq^2+12p^2q$

Brackets

1. (a) $21+18h$ (b) $3x+5y$
   (c) $7k-22$ (d) $29k-17$
   (e) $14np+12mp+15mn$ (f) $7x^2+7x$
2. (a) $x^2+9x+14$ (b) $x^2+2x-15$
   (c) $y^2-10y+21$ (d) y^2-y-12
   (e) m^2-4 (f) x^2-25
   (g) $6x^2+5x+1$ (h) $10x^2+31x+15$
   (i) $12m^2+m-6$ (j) $15n^2-13n-20$
   (k) $42-11x-20x^2$ (l) $12+18x-12x^2$
   (m) $x^2-12x+36$ (n) $4x^2+16x+16$
   (o) $25-30x+9x^2$

Factorisation

1. (a) $x(y+2)$ (b) $8p(1-q)$
   (c) $5n(m+2n)$ (d) $6x(y-2xz)$
   (e) $3ab(b+2a-3)$ (f) $4pq(r-2p+4qr)$

Factorising quadratic expressions

1. (a) $(x+3)(x+8)$ (b) $(x+4)(x+5)$
   (c) $(x-3)(x+5)$ (d) $(x+6)(x-7)$
   (e) $(x-2)(x-8)$ (f) $(x-3)(x-9)$
   (g) $(2x+2)(3x+3)$ (h) $(2x+5)(5x+2)$
   (i) $(3x-3)(4x+5)$ (j) $(2x-6)(5x+3)$
   (k) $(2x-4)(2x-6)$ (l) $(3x-7)(5x-2)$

Algebraic fractions

1. (a) $\frac{11x-21}{21}$ (b) $\frac{-5x+45}{6}$
   (c) $\frac{-32x-118}{15}$ (d) $\frac{5(3x^2+x+3)}{3(3x+1)}$
   (e) $\frac{9x+1}{(x+1)(x-1)}$ (f) $\frac{-x-5}{(x+1)(x-1)}$
   (g) $\frac{2}{x+1}$ (h) $\frac{2y}{3y+9}$
   (i) $\frac{3(5y+2)}{5y-3}$ (j) $\frac{9}{2}$
   (k) $\frac{x+3}{3x}$ (l) $\frac{15x^2}{(x-2)^2}$
2. (a) $\frac{3x-1}{(x-2)(x+3)}$ (b) $\frac{(2x-3)(x+1)}{(x-1)(x-2)}$
   (c) $\frac{2(x+1)(x-2)}{(3x+4)(2x+1)}$

2.3 Expressions and formulae

Substituting numbers into expressions and formulae

1. (a) $A=l^2$
   (b) (i) $144\,\text{cm}^2$ (ii) $26.01\,\text{cm}^2$
   (iii) $13.69\,\text{m}^2$
2. (a) $A=3.14r^2$
   (b) (i) $78.5\,\text{cm}^2$ (ii) $200.96\,\text{mm}^2$
   (iii) $3.14\,\text{m}^2$
3. (a) -8 (b) 57 (c) -104
4. (a) -16 (b) -78 (c) 72
5. (a) 31 (b) 21 (c) 73
6. (a) 204 (b) 480 (c) -225

Rearranging formulae

1. (a) $p=3(T-4)$ (b) $p=Av$
   (c) $p=\frac{C-5q}{4}$ (d) $p=\sqrt{m-4}$
   (e) $p=\frac{C-q^2}{5}$ (f) $p=\frac{\sqrt{k}}{2}$

Rearranging more complex formulae

1. (a) $m=\frac{T}{R^2+t}$ (b) $m=\frac{B+2}{pq+4s}$

 (c) $m=\sqrt{\frac{2p}{2-p}}$ (d) $m=\sqrt{\frac{c}{1-cR^2}}$

 (e) $m=\frac{3c^2}{1-c^2}$ (f) $m=\frac{1}{A^2-C+t}$

2.4 Linear equations

Linear equations

1. (a) $x=6$ (b) $x=9$ (c) $x=-3$
 (d) $x=60$ (e) $x=11$ (f) $x=3$
 (g) $x=12$ (h) $x=-2$ (i) $x=-15$
 (j) $x=1$ (k) $x=5$ (l) $x=12$

Solving problems with equations

1. chair = £20, table = £65
2. 35°, 85° and 60°
3. girl is 12 years old, mother is 35 years old and grandmother is 62 years old
4. side = 21 cm, perimeter = 84 cm
5. £0.39 or 39p
6. 14 m^2

2.5 Proportion and variation

Direct variation and direct proportion

1. (a) $d=600t$, 10 hours (b) 3300 km
2. (a) $C=0.09d$, £33.75 (b) 600 km
3. (a) $E=25d$, $E=225$ J
 (b) $d=-6.4$ m (6.4 m downwards)
4. (a) $M=0.375d^2$, 294 g (b) 23 cm
5. (a) $P=3Q^2$, $Q=\pm9$ (b) $P=75$
6. (a) $E=5v^2$, $E=10\,125$ J (b) $v=\pm12$ m/s
7. (a) $V=4.5r^3$, 6 cm (b) 562.5 cm^3
8. (a) $y=10x^3$, $x=12$ (b) $y=2160$
9. (a) $m=5r^3$, $m=78.125$ g (b) $r=4$ cm
10. (a) $T=0.2\sqrt{l}$, $T=0.8$ s (b) $l=100$ cm (1 m)
11. (a) $v=1.5\sqrt{w}$, $v=\pm10.5$ (b) $w=36$
12. (a) $g=0.3\sqrt{h}$, $g=\pm3.3$ (b) $h=36$

Inverse variation and inverse proportion

1. (a) $y=\frac{4}{x}$, $y=0.4$ (b) $x=12$
2. (a) $p=\frac{25}{q}$, $p=6.25$ (b) $q=10$
3. (a) $n=\frac{0.1}{m}$, $n=0.5$ (b) $m=0.4$
4. (a) $p=\frac{15}{q^2}$, $p=0.234$ (b) $q=\pm4$
5. (a) $y=\frac{100}{x^2}$, $x=\pm10$ (b) $y=0.694$
6. (a) $n=\frac{0.25}{m^2}$, $m=\pm10$ (b) $n=0.003\,91$

2.6 Quadratic equations

Solving quadratic equations by factorisation

1. (a) $x=0$ or $\frac{3}{4}$ (b) $x=-2$ or -4

 (c) $x=5$ or -6 (d) $x=1$ or $1\frac{2}{3}$

 (e) $x=-2$ or $2\frac{1}{2}$ (f) $x=1\frac{1}{2}$ or $-\frac{3}{4}$

Solving quadratic equations using the formula

1. (a) $x=-0.42$ or -1.58 (b) $x=1.59$ or 0.16
 (c) $x=-2$ or 0.75 (d) $x=2.91$ or -0.91
 (e) $x=1.23$ or 0.27 (f) $x=2.35$ or -0.85

Solving quadratic equations by completing the square

1. (a) $x=7.74$ or 0.26 (b) $x=-0.88$ or -9.12
 (c) $x=6.28$ or 0.72
2. (a) $x=-3\pm\sqrt{6}$ (b) $x=6\pm\sqrt{29}$

 (c) $x=-\frac{9}{4}\pm\frac{\sqrt{113}}{4}$
3. 5 cm and 9 cm

2.7 Simultaneous linear equations

Solving simultaneous equations

1. (a) $x=3, y=-1$ (b) $x=2, y=6$
2. (a) $x=-2, y=7$ (b) $x=3, y=-8$ (c) $x=7, y=4$
 (d) $x=-3, y=-5$

Simultaneous equations and graphs

1. (a) (–2, –3) (b) (1.5, 2.5)

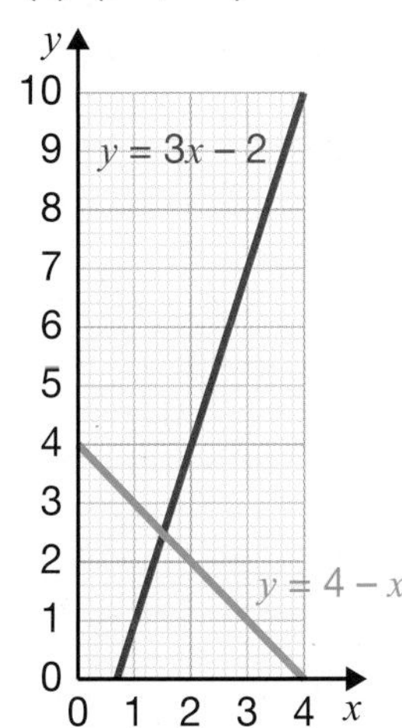

(c) (–0.4, 3.2)

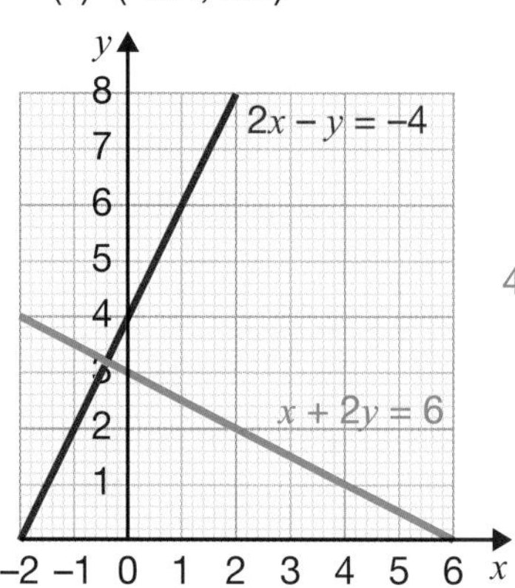

(d) (–1, 1)

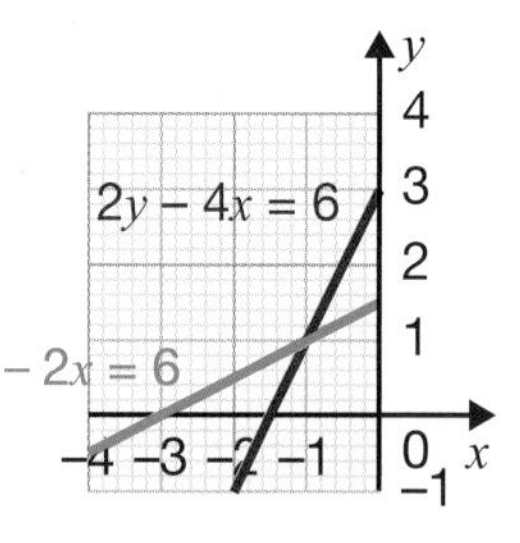

(e) (–2, 0) and (2.5, 2.2)

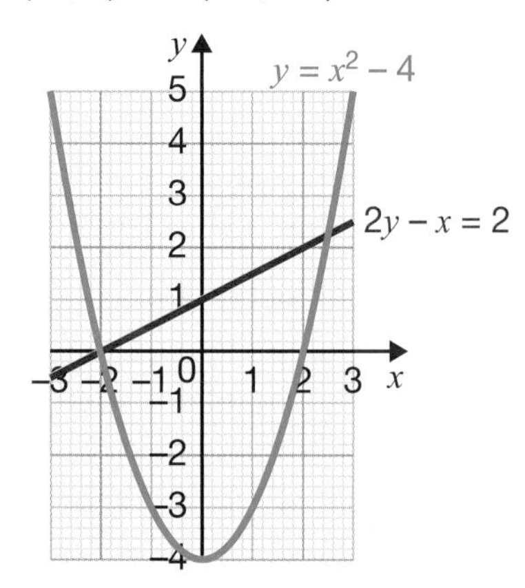

(f) Graphs do not intercept, so there is no solution.

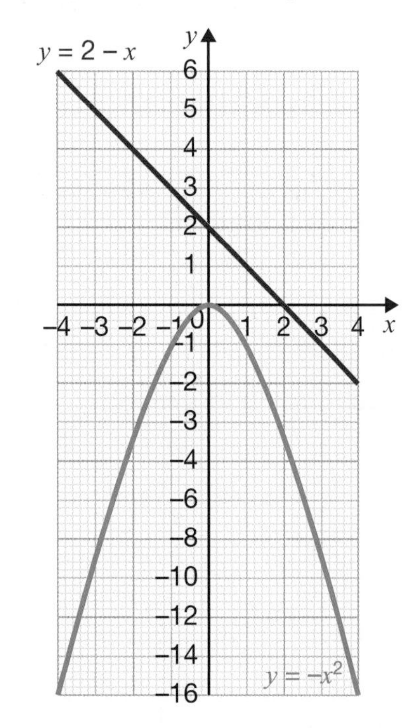

Simultaneous non-linear and linear equations

1. (a) (–1, 0), (2, 3)
   (b) (–1, 7), (5, 13)
   (c) (–3, 4), (5, 0)
   (d) (–1, 5), (3, –3)
   (e) (–1, –4), (2, 2)
   (f) (0, 4), (4, –4)
2. 10 cm and 20 cm

2.8 Graphs

Coordinates and gradients

1.

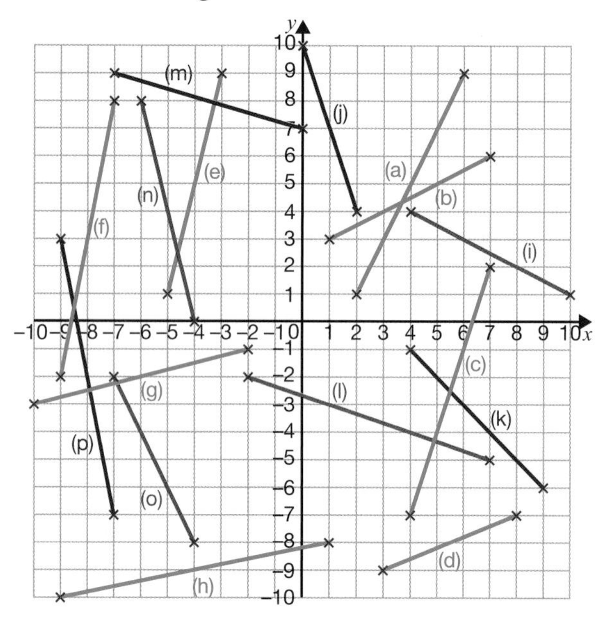

2. (a) 2 (b) $\frac{1}{2}$ (c) 3
   (d) $\frac{2}{5}$ or 0.4 (e) 4 (f) 5
   (g) $\frac{1}{4}$ (h) $\frac{1}{5}$ (i) $-\frac{1}{2}$
   (j) –3 (k) –1 (l) $-\frac{1}{3}$
   (m) $-\frac{1}{4}$ (n) –4 (o) –2
   (p) –5

Length and midpoint of a line segment

1. (a) (4, 5), 8.94 units
   (b) (4, 4.5), 6.71 units
   (c) (5.5, –2.5), 9.49 units
   (d) (5.5, –8), 5.39 units
   (e) (–4, 5), 8.25 units
   (f) (–8, 3), 10.20 units
   (g) (–6, –2), 8.25 units
   (h) (–4, –9), 10.20 units
   (i) (7, 2.5), 6.71 units
   (j) (1, 7), 6.32 units
   (k) (6.5, –3.5), 7.07 units
   (l) (2.5, –3.5), 9.49 units
   (m) (–4, 8), 8.25 units
   (n) (–5, 4), 8.25 units
   (o) (–5.5, –5), 6.71 units
   (p) (–8, –2), 10.20 units

$y = mx + c$

1. (a)

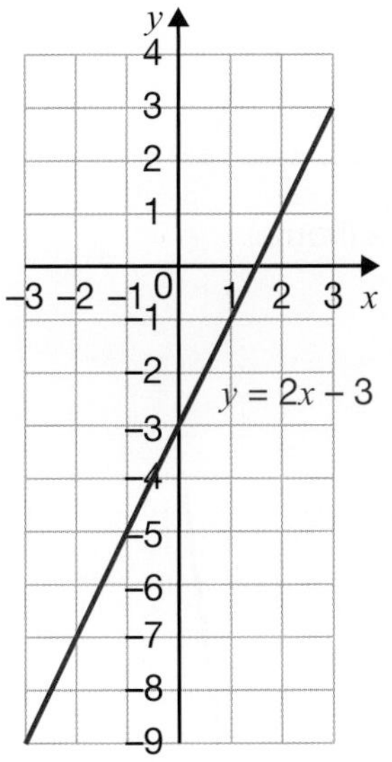

(b)

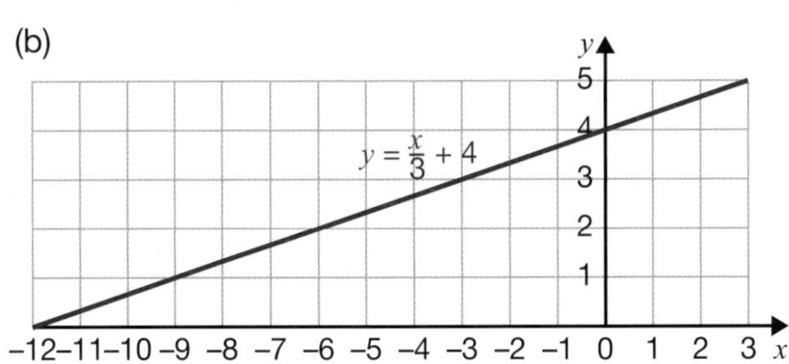

(c)

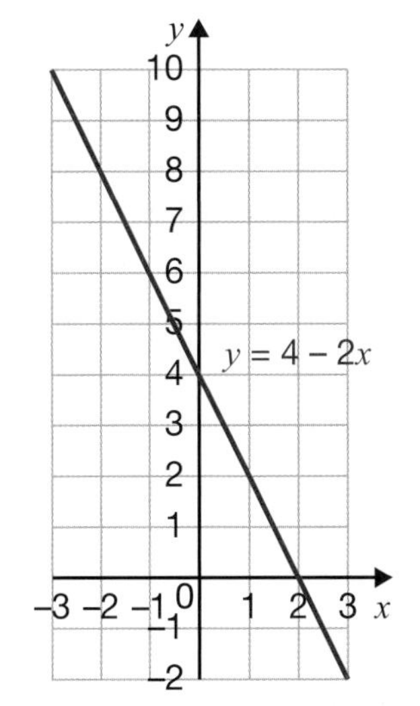

(d)

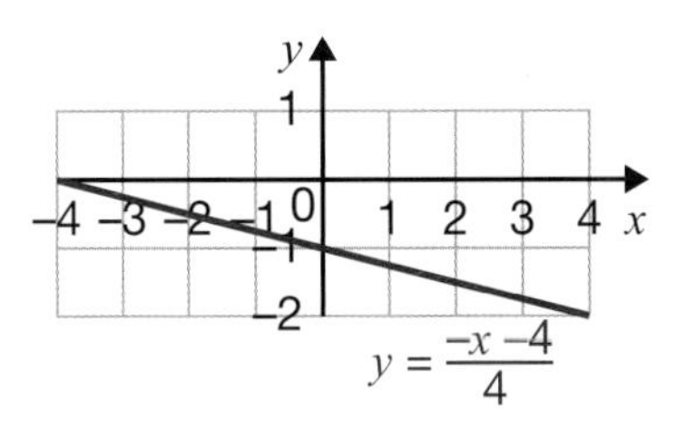

(e)

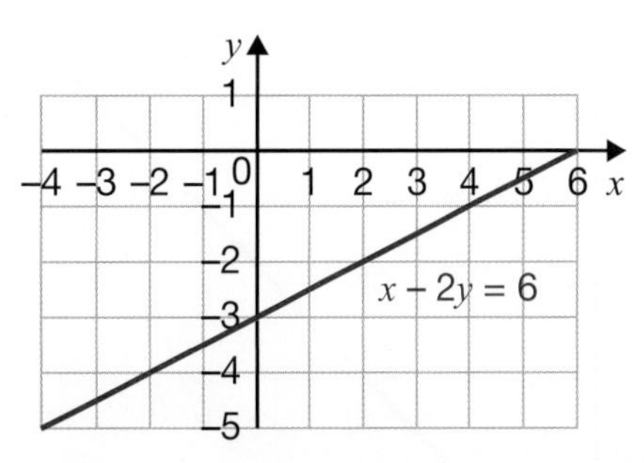

(f)

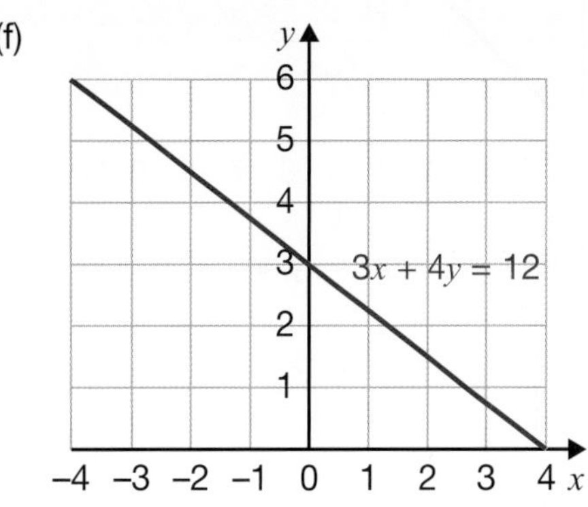

2. (a) $y = x - 4$ (b) $y = 2x + 5$ (c) $y = 3 - x$
   (d) $y = 7 - 3x$ (e) $y = 0.25x + 5$ (f) $y = 2 - 0.5x$

Parallel and perpendicular lines

1. (a) $y = 2x - 4$ (b) $y = 3x - 6$ (c) $y = 0.5x$
   (d) $y = -4x - 1$ (e) $y = 2 - \frac{x}{4}$ (f) $x + 2y = 14$
2. (a) $y = \frac{19 - x}{2}$ (b) $y = \frac{x}{3} - 4$ (c) $y = 2 - 2x$
   (d) $y = 6x + 5$

Conversion graphs

1. (a) 3.5 pints (b) 9.6 pints (c) 26.2 litres
   (d) 2.9 litres (e) 4.9 litres (f) 17.1 litres
2. (a) 70 rand (b) 119 rand (c) 1050 rand
   (d) €1.10 (e) €5.70 (f) €17.90
3. (a) (i) £32.50 (ii) £60 (iii) £270
   (b) (i) 50 units (ii) 600 units (iii) 1800 units
4. (a)

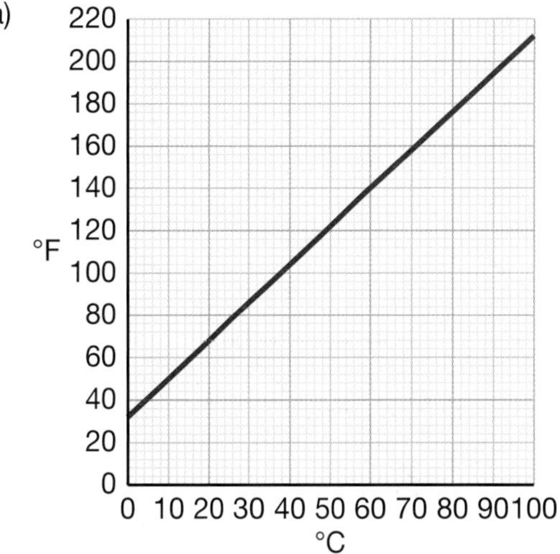

(b) (i) 20 °C (ii) 95 °F

5. (a)

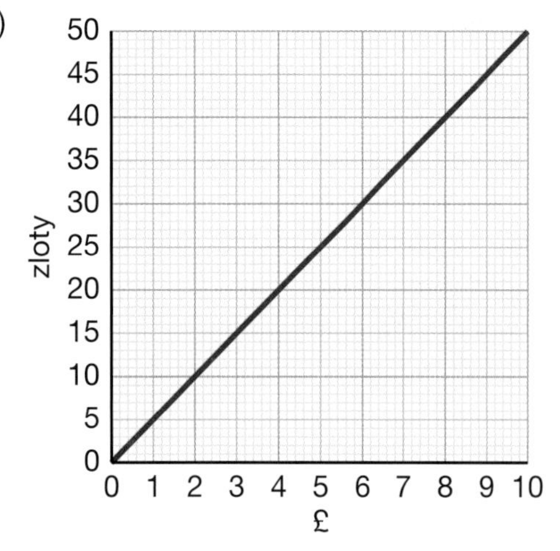

(b) (i) 40 zloty (ii) £13.60

6. (a)

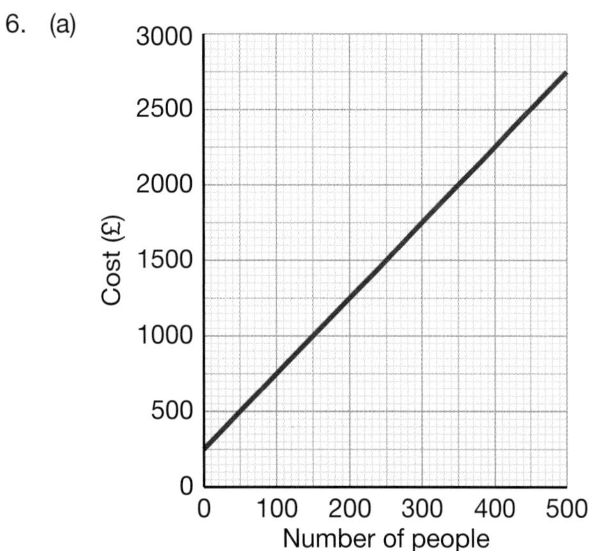

(b) £1750

(c) 130 people

Travel graphs

1. (a) 120 km/h (b) between 10:30 and 11:00
   (c) 64 km/h (d) The car was stationary.
2. (a) Ade (b) between 90 and 125 s
   (c) 8.57 m/s
   (d) Ade 6.4 m/s, Ben 6.15 m/s, Charlie 5.71 m/s
3. (a) 15 m/s (b) –0.75 m/s^2 (c) 7500 m (7.5 km)
   (d) 14.4 m/s
4. (a) 1.4 m/s (b) –0.2 m/s^2 (c) 99 000 m (99 km)
5. (a)

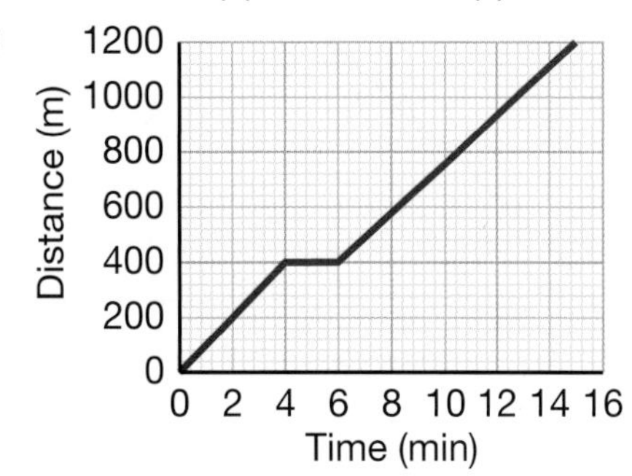

(b) 4.8 km/h

6. (a)

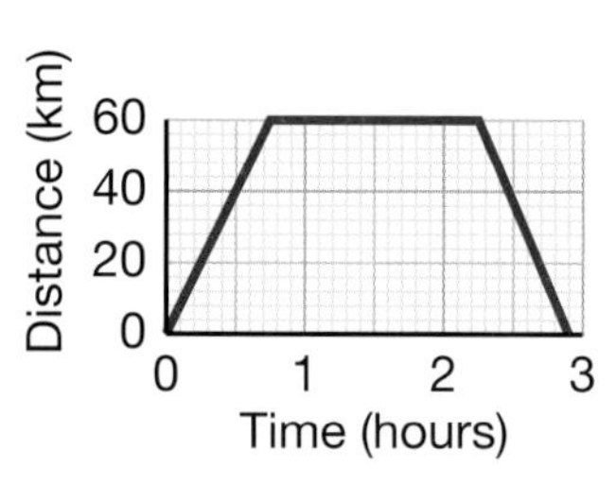

(b) 90 km/h

Quadratic graphs

1. (a)

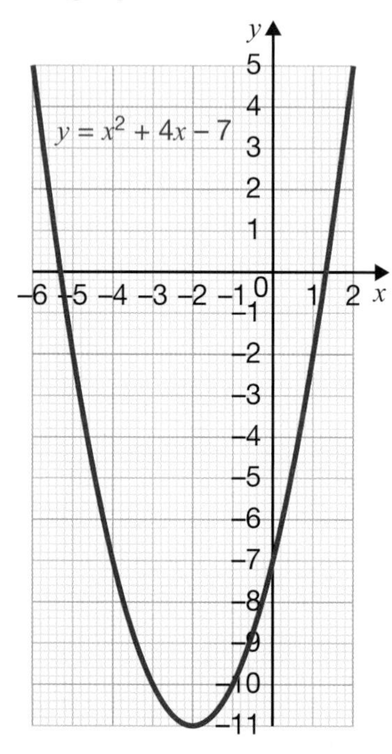

(b) $y = -7.8$ (c) $x = -4.4$ and 0.4

2. (a)

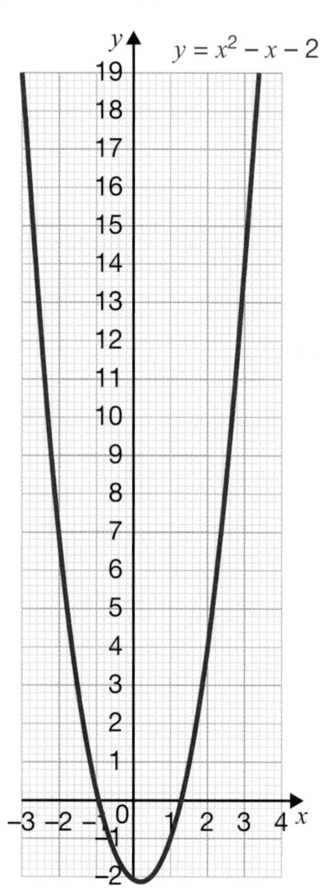

(b) $y=7.1$ (c) $x=-1.8$ and 2.2

3. (a)

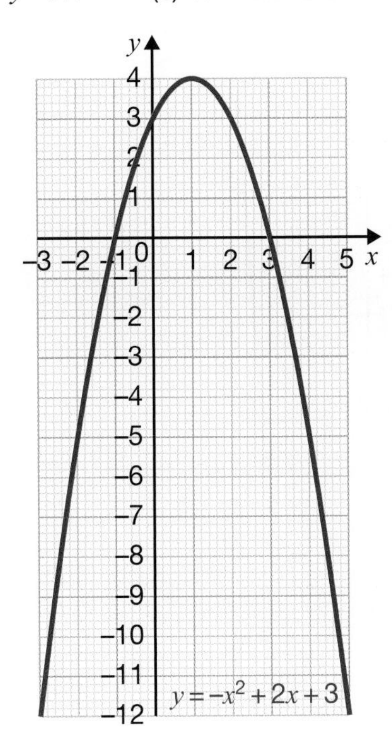

(b) $y=1.7$ (c) $x=-1.7$ and 3.7

4. (a)

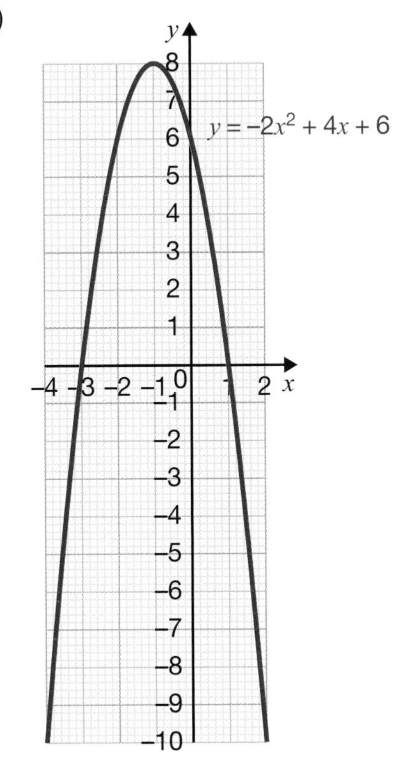

(b) $y=7.7$ (c) $x=-2.4$ and 0.4

Cubic graphs

1. (a)

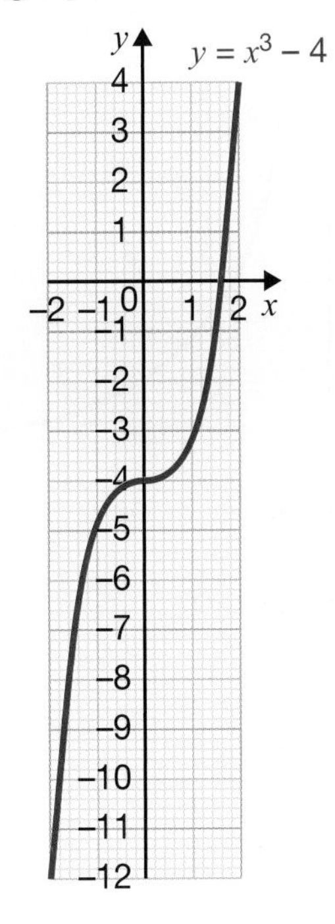

(b) $x=1.4$

2. (a)

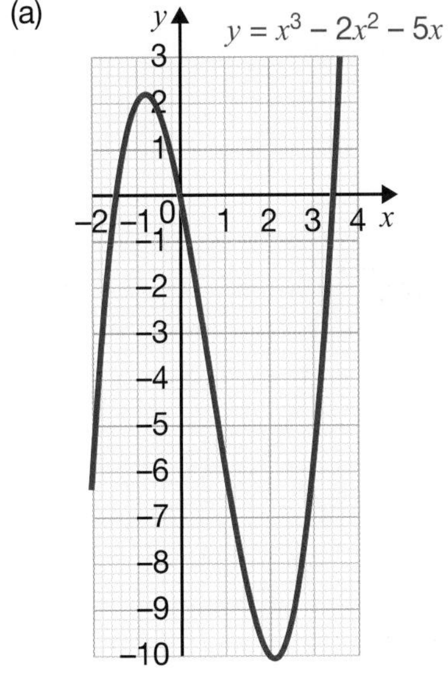

(b) $x=-1.4$, 0 and 3.4

3. (a)

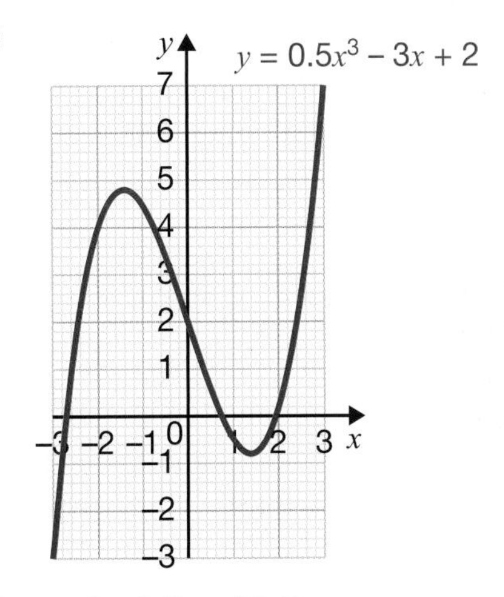

(b) $x=-2$, -0.7 and 2.7

Reciprocal graphs

1. (a)

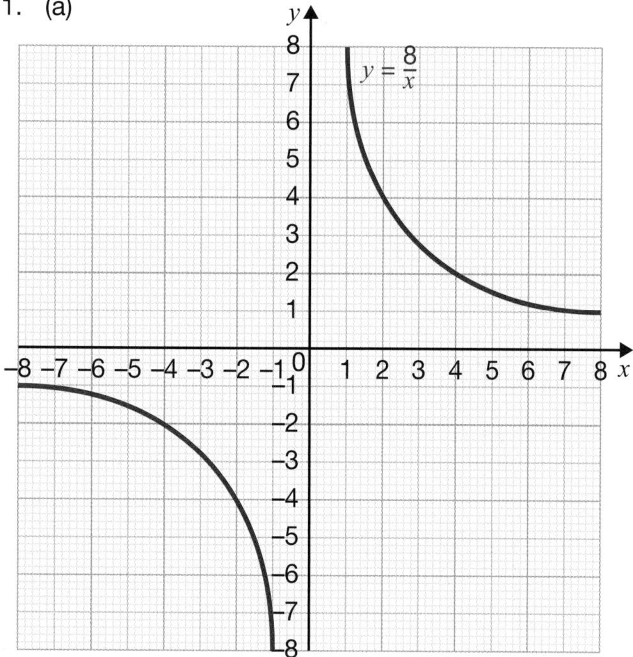

(b) (i) $x = 5.5$ (ii) $x = -1.7$

2. (a)

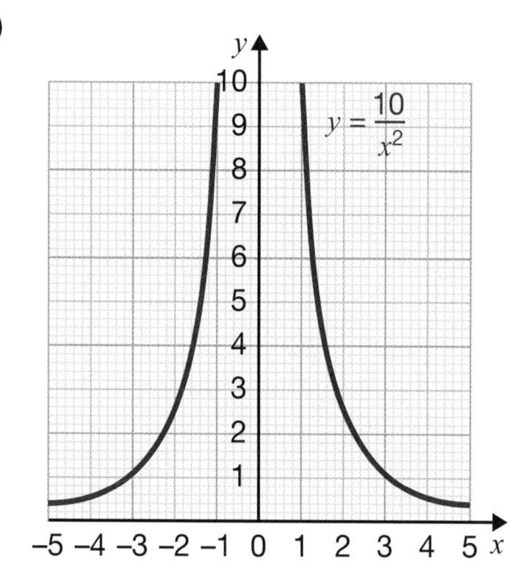

(b) $x = -1.6$ and 1.6

Tangents to curves

1. (a)

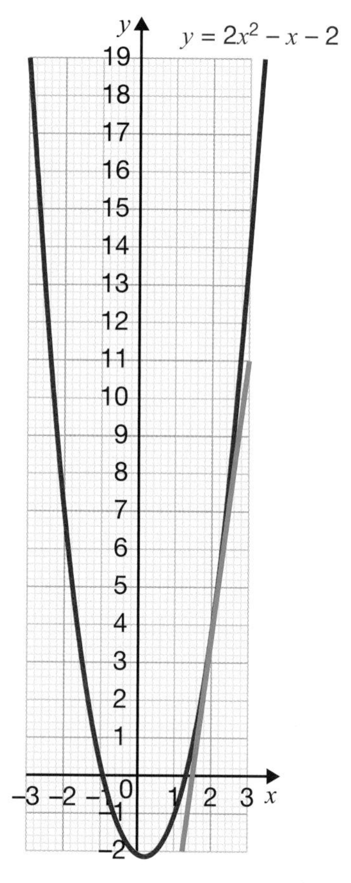

(b) 7

2. (a)

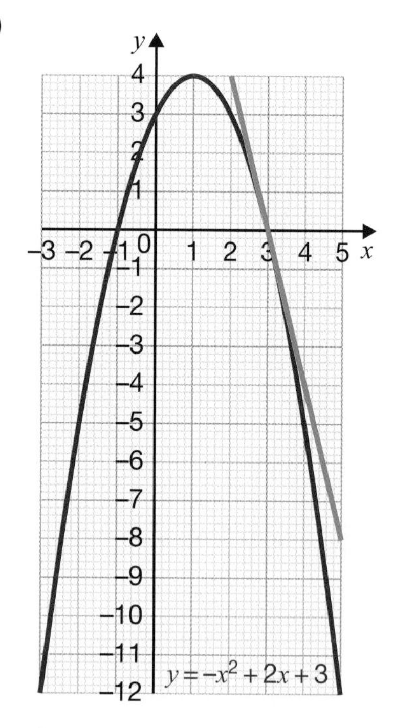

(b) –4

3. (a)

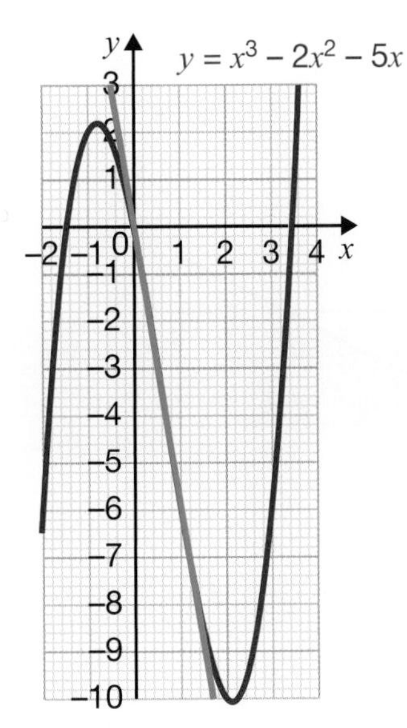

(b) −6

4. (a)

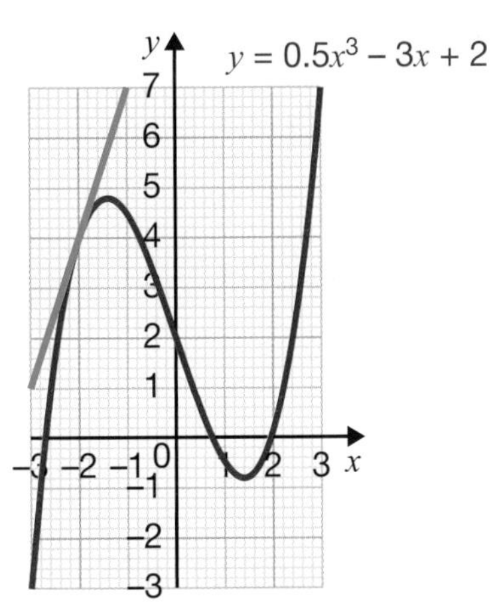

(b) 3

5. (a)

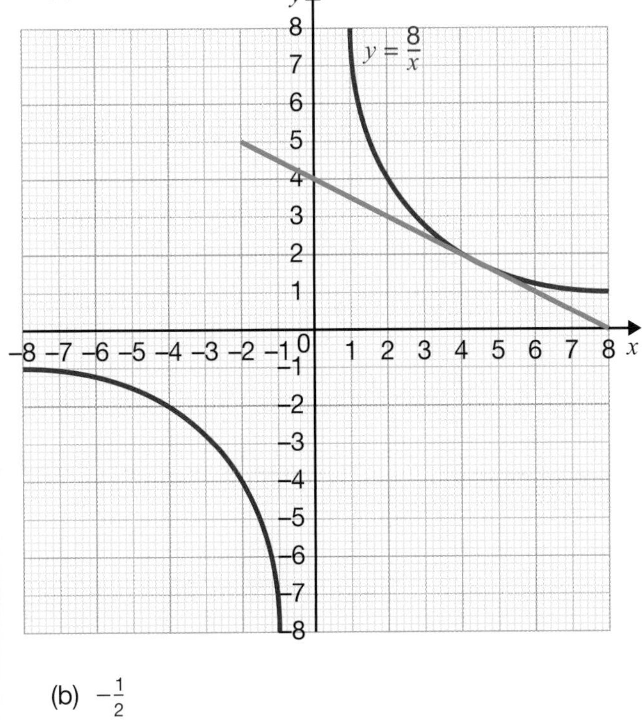

(b) $-\frac{1}{2}$

Exponential graphs

1.

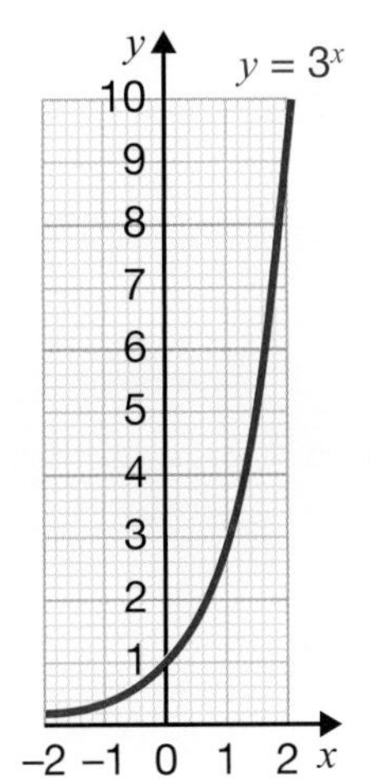

2.

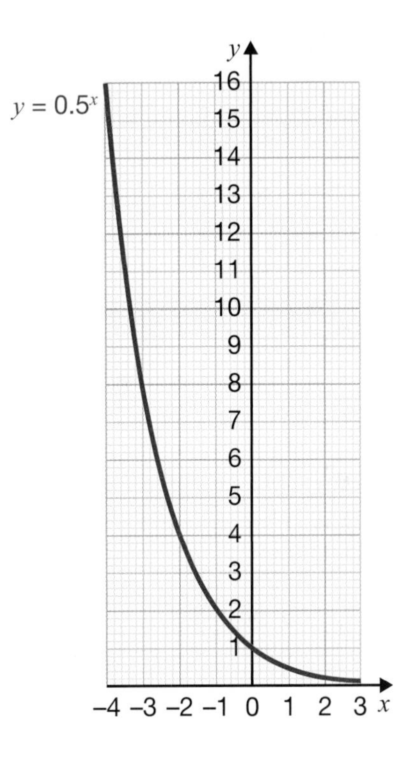

2.9 Inequalities

Inequalities

1. (a) $x \leqslant 5$

0 1 2 3 4 5

(b) $x \geqslant -2$

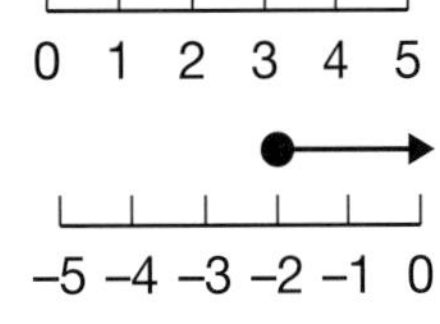

(c) $x \leqslant 4\frac{1}{2}x$

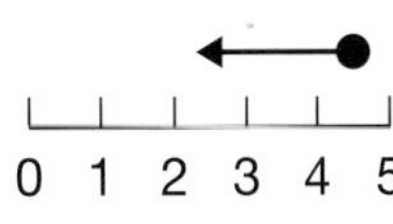

(d) $x > 1$

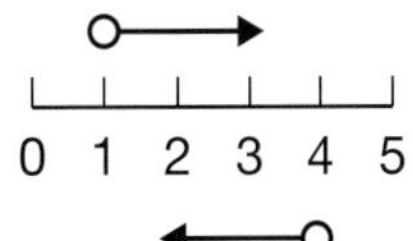

(e) $y < 6$

2 3 4 5 6 7

(f) $t > 1\frac{2}{3}$

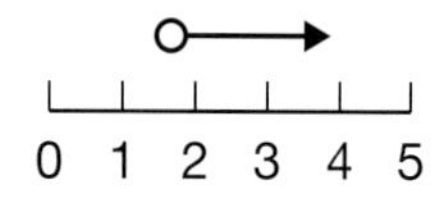

(g) $p < 6$

2 3 4 5 6 7

(h) $y \geqslant \frac{3}{4}$

0 1 2 3 4 5

(i) $y \geqslant \frac{2}{3}$

0 1 2 3 4 5

(j) $q < 2$

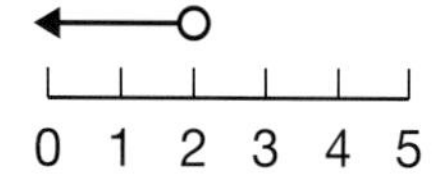

(k) $y \leqslant 17$

15 16 17 18 19 20

(l) $y > 1\frac{1}{5}$

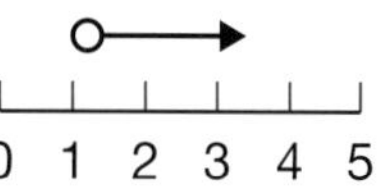

Inequalities on graphs

1. (a)

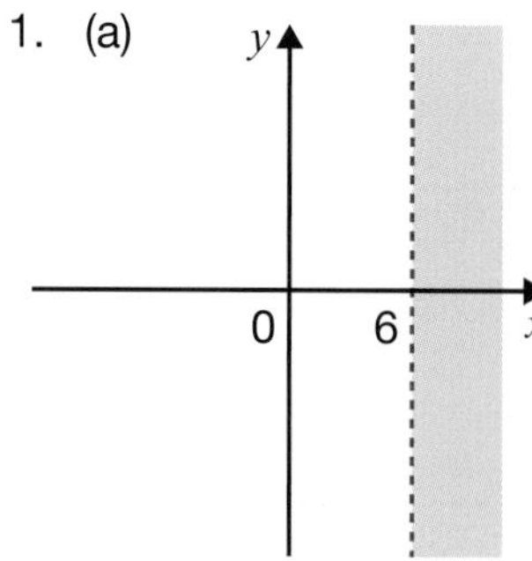

(b)

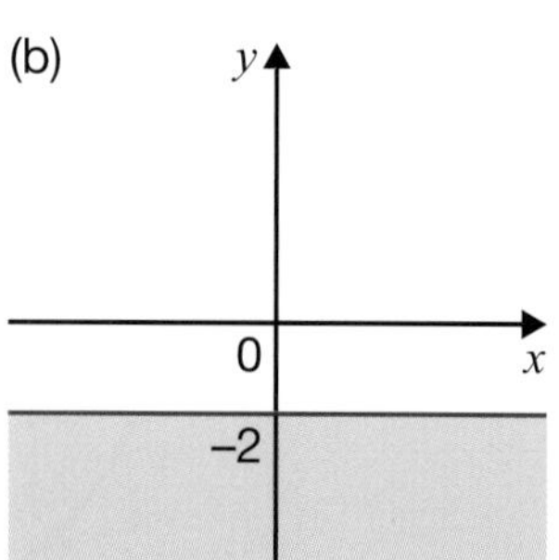

(c)

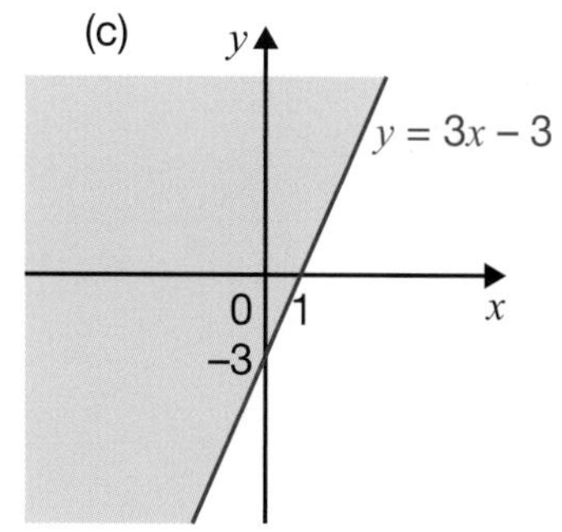

(d)

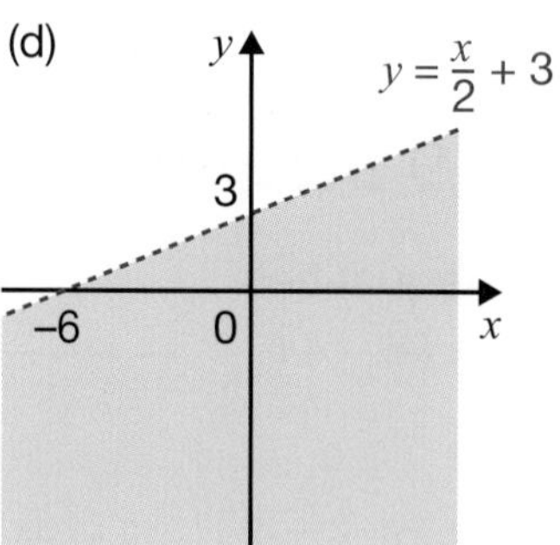

(e)

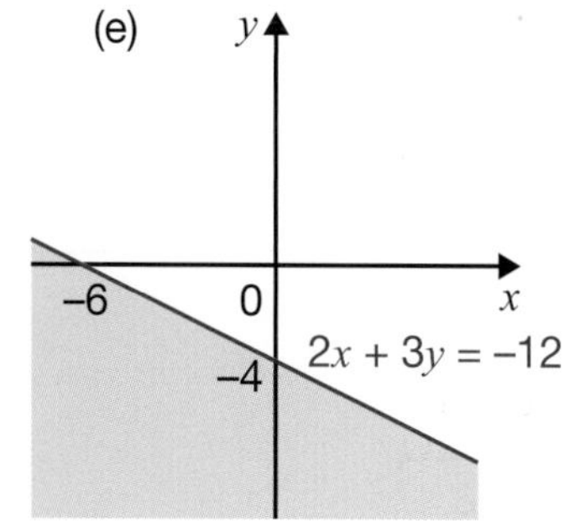

(f)

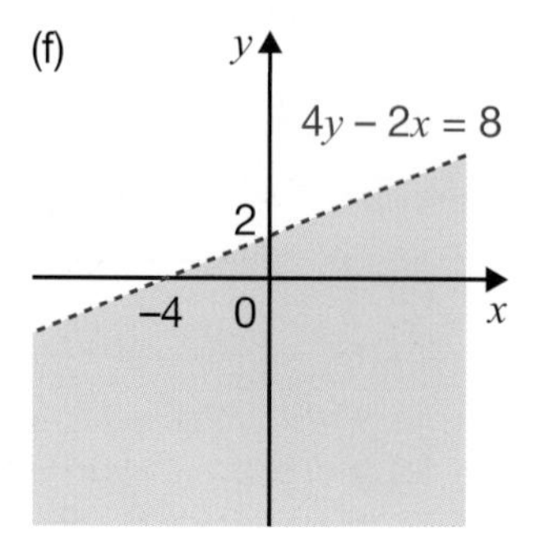

More inequalities

1. (a)

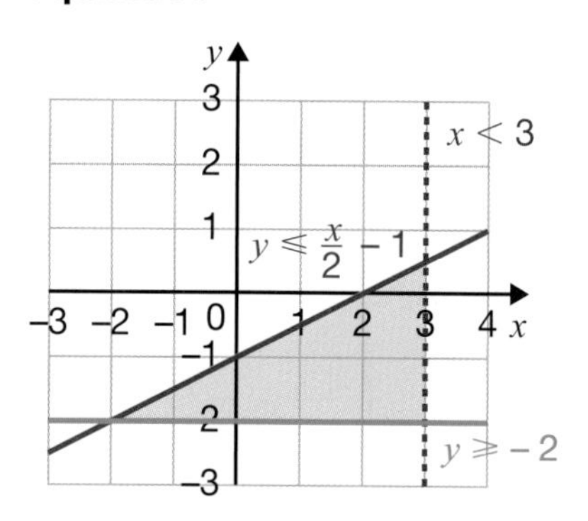

(b)

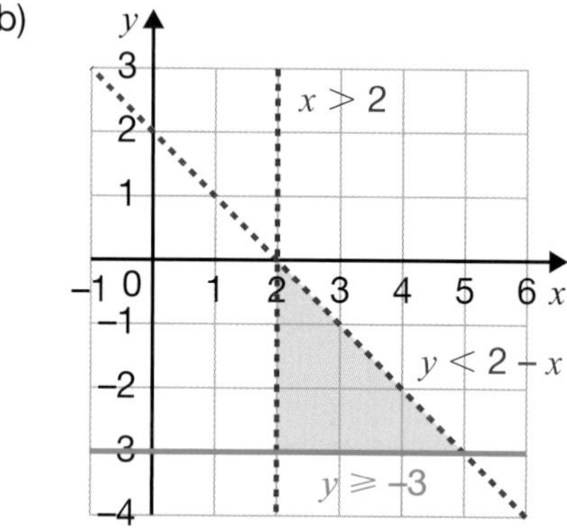

(c)

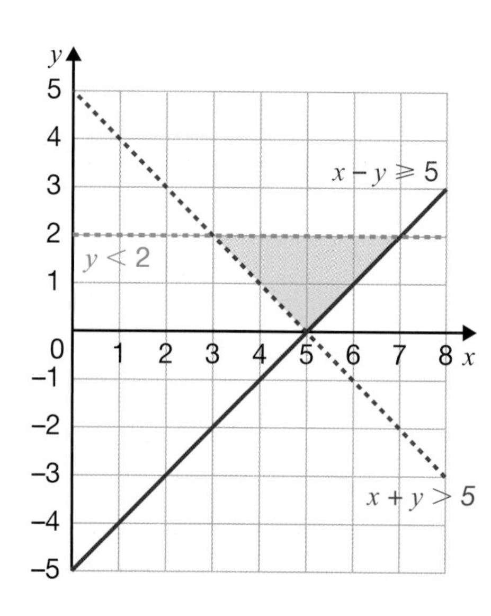

(d)

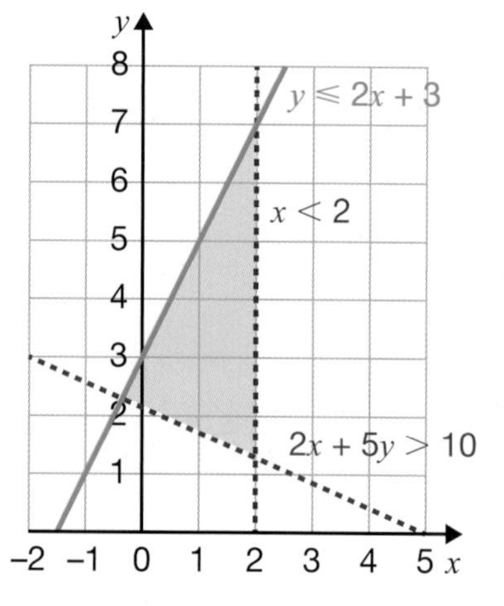

(e)

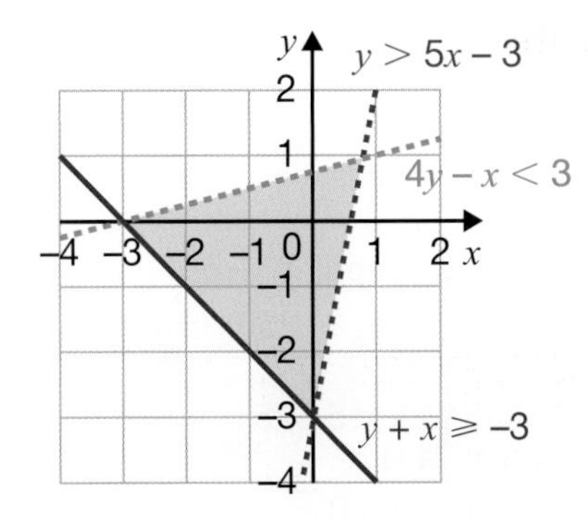

(f)

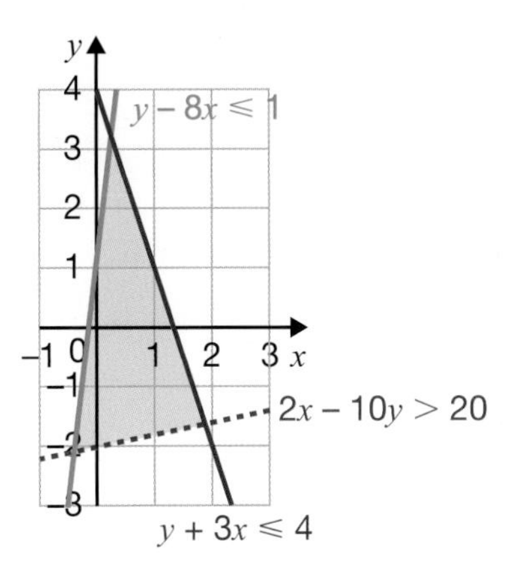

Quadratic inequalities

1. (a) $-7 < x < 7$

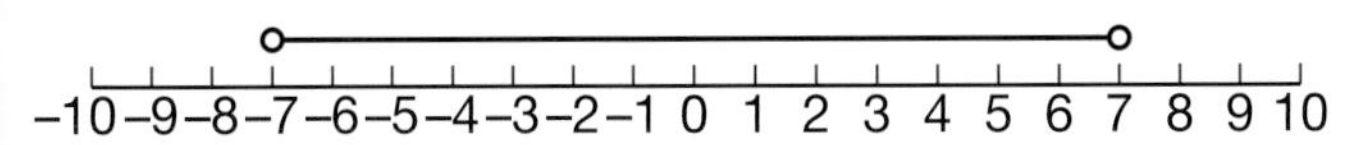

(b) $-1.2 > x > 1.2$

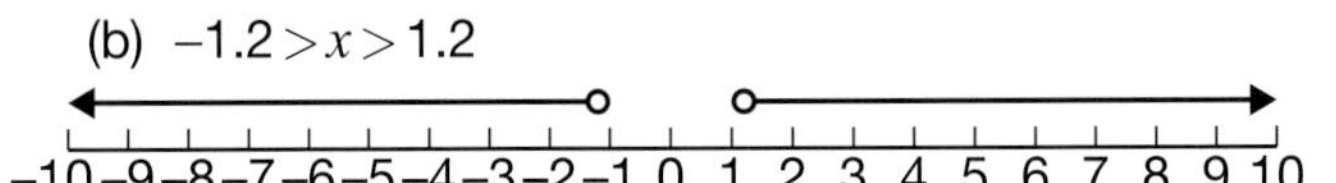

(c) $-3 \geqslant x \geqslant 3$

(d) $-5 \leqslant x \leqslant 5$

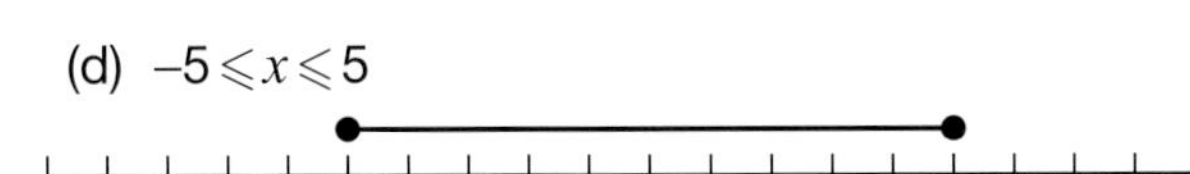

(e) $-6 > x > 6$

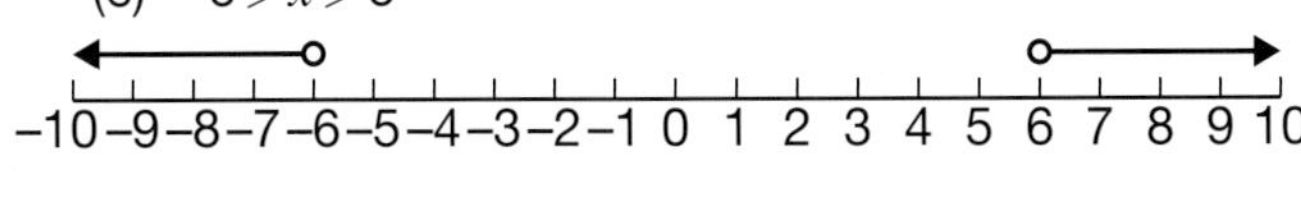

(f) $-8 \leqslant x \leqslant 8$

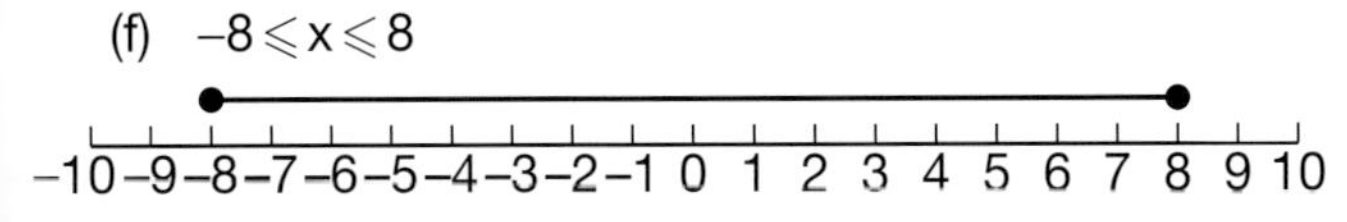

(g) $-3 > x > 3$

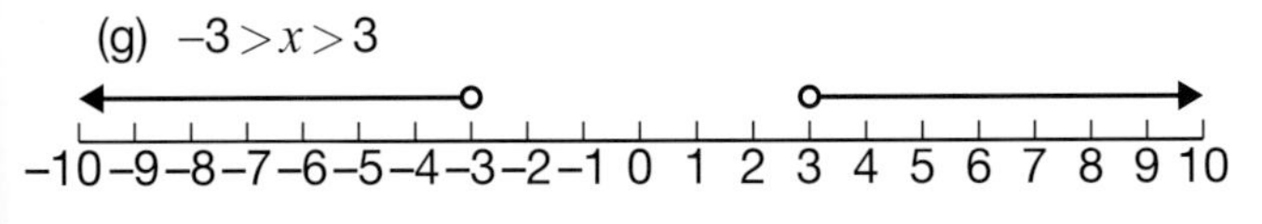

(h) $-4 \leqslant x \leqslant 4$

Linear programming

1. (a) x=number of coaches, y=number of minibuses
   $12x+5y \leqslant 100$; $x \geqslant 5$, $y \geqslant 3$
   (b) There are 10 possible combinations of coaches and minibuses.

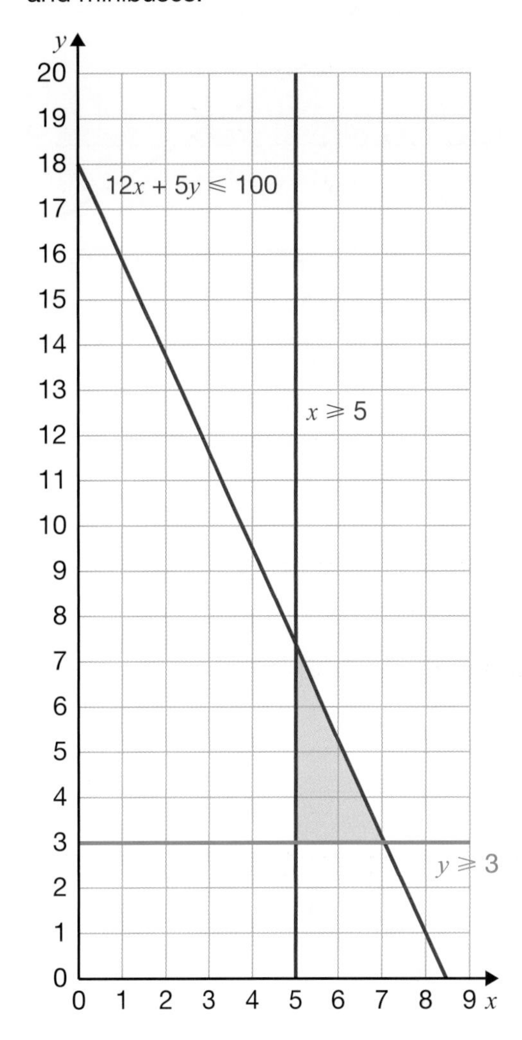

2. (a) x=number of adult tickets,
   y=number of child tickets
   $x+y \leqslant 5000$, $3x+2y \geqslant 12\,500$, $y \geqslant x$

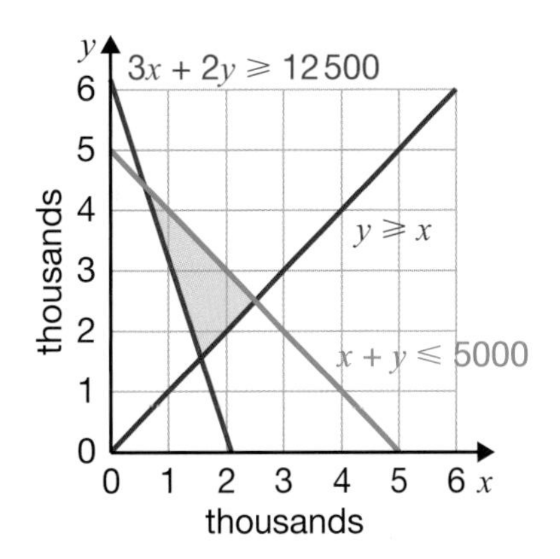

   (b) about 700

3. (a) x=number of cartons of milk,
   y=number of bottles of water
   $x \geqslant 2$, $y \geqslant 3$, $0.6x+y \leqslant 10$

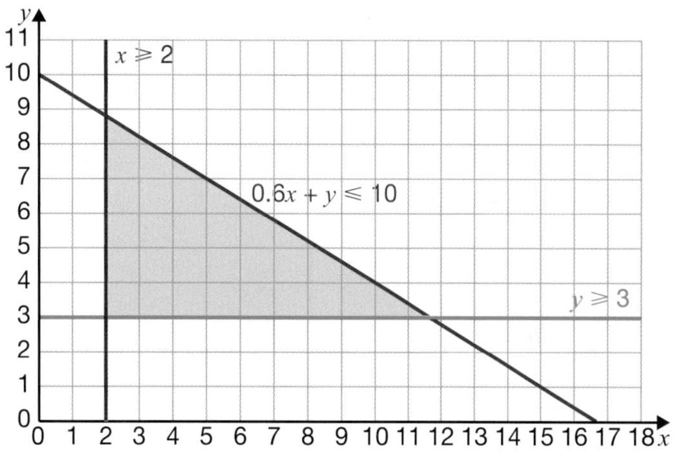

(b) 11 cartons of milk

4. (a) x=number of wins, y=number of draws
$3x+y \geqslant 34$, $x+y \leqslant 15$

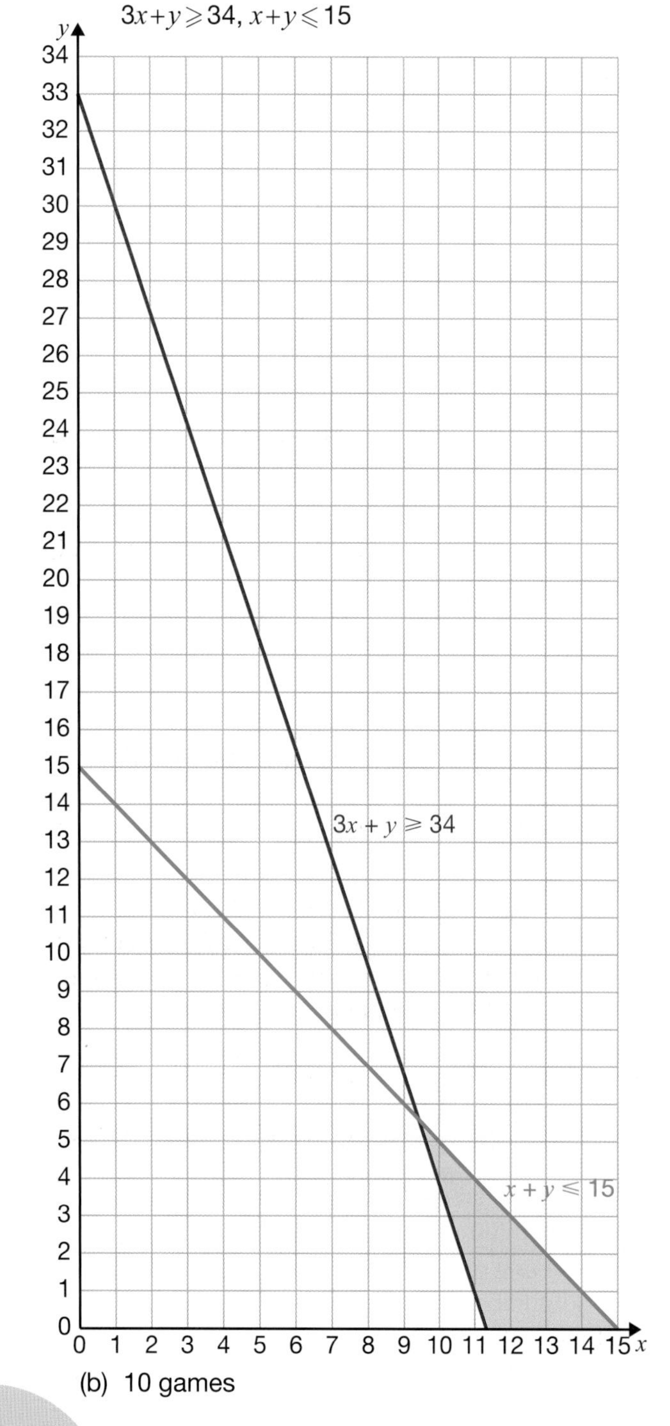

(b) 10 games

2.10 Sequences

Sequences

1. (a) add 4; 19, 23, 27
(b) add 9; 42, 51, 60
(c) multiply by 4; 512, 2048, 8192
(d) multiply by 5; 6250, 31 250, 156 250
(e) double; 48, 96, 192
(f) halve; 62.5, 31.25, 15,625
(g) divide by 3; 9, 3, 1
(h) subtract 6; 40, 34, 28

Finding the nth term

1. (a) $3n+2$, 152 (b) $8n-5$, 395
(c) $5n+17$, 267 (d) $4n+3$, 203
(e) $102-3n$, –48 (f) $131-6n$, –169
2. (a) 2, 8, 18, 32, 50 (b) 6, 9, 14, 21, 30
(c) 2, 6, 12, 20, 30 (d) 0, $\frac{1}{4}, \frac{2}{5}, \frac{1}{2}\left(\frac{3}{6}\right), \frac{4}{7}$

Number patterns

1. (a) $4n+2$ (b) 50 people
2. (a) $5n+1$ (b) 251 matchsticks
3. (a) $3n+2$ (b) 227 squares
4. (a) $4n-1$ (b) 119 matchsticks

2.11 Functions

Function notation

1. (a) 13 (b) 48 (c) 27 (d) 4
2. (a) –3 (b) 72 (c) 60 (d) –3
3. (a) 61 (b) –24 (c) 2028 (d) –2
4. (a) 2 (b) 1 (c) 10 (d) 4
5. (a) 3 (b) 1.5 (c) 0 (d) –7
6. (a) ±2 (b) ±3 (c) ±1 (d) ±2.5

Inverse functions

1. (a) $f^{-1}(x)=\dfrac{x-2}{3}$ (b) $f^{-1}(x)=2x-10$
(c) $f^{-1}(x)=\dfrac{x-9}{6}$ (d) $f^{-1}(x)=\dfrac{4x+7}{2}$
2. (a) $f^{-1}(x)=\dfrac{2-3x}{x}$, $-4\frac{1}{3}$ (b) –4.8
(c) –5.4 (d) –9

Composite functions

1. (a) 3 (b) $\frac{7}{3}$ (c) $\frac{2}{3}x+1$ (d) $\dfrac{2x+1}{3}$
2. (a) $\frac{3}{4}$ (b) $\frac{3}{7}$ (c) $\dfrac{3}{x+2}$ (d) $\dfrac{3}{x}+2$
3. (a) 1.5 (b) –3 (c) $\dfrac{2x-9}{2}$ (d) $x-9$
4. (a) 21 (b) 351
(c) $8x^2-22x+15$ (d) $4x^2+2x-3$

5. (a) $-x^2+5x+5$ (b) x^2-5x
   (c) 9 (d) -4

6. (a) $\frac{1}{2x}$ (b) $f^{-1}(x)=\frac{1-5x}{x}$, $gf^{-1}(x)=\frac{2-15x}{x}$
   (c) $\frac{1}{6}$ (d) -14

Domain and range of a function

1. (a) $\{x: x \geqslant 0\}$ (b) $\{x: x \geqslant -6\}$ (c) $\{x: x \geqslant 3\}$
   (d) $\{x: x \neq -2\}$ (e) $\{x: x \neq -3\}$ (f) $\{x: x > 9\}$
2. (a) {3, 19, 73, 201}
   (b) {–7, 81, 2268, 19 100}
   (c) {–1, 687, 46 479, 999 503}
   (d) {–10, –6, –3, –1, 1, 3, 6, 10}
   (e) $\left\{\frac{1}{3}, \frac{1}{11}, \frac{1}{38}, \frac{1}{102}\right\}$
   (f) $\left\{\frac{1}{6}, \frac{1}{2}, \frac{8}{13}, \frac{200}{309}\right\}$

2.12 Calculus

Differentiation

1. (a) $2x+2$, 10 (b) $6x^2+12x$, 18
   (c) $16x^3-16x$, 96 (d) $2-\frac{5}{x^2}$, 1.8
   (e) $4x-\frac{4}{x^3}$, –7.5 (f) $6x^2-10$, 140
2. $\frac{dy}{dx}=3-\frac{4}{x^2}$, (–1, –5) and (1, 9)

Turning points

1. (a) $4x+6$, (–1.5, –9.5), minimum
   (b) $3-8x$, $\left(\frac{3}{8}, 10\frac{9}{16}\right)$, maximum
   (c) $3x^2+10x$, $\left(-3\frac{1}{3}, 21\frac{14}{27}\right)$, maximum; (0, 3), minimum
   (d) $-12x-3x^2$, (–4, –26), minimum; (0, 6), maximum
   (e) $2-\frac{8}{x^2}$, (–2, –5), maximum; (2, 11), minimum
   (f) $2-\frac{16}{x^3}$, (2, 1), minimum

Practical problems

1. (a) $v=6t-6$, $t=1$ s (b) $s=2$ m, $a=6$ m/s^2
2. (a) $v=9.8t$, 49 m/s (b) 9.8 m/s^2
3. (a) $v=12-2t=-8$ m/s, $a=-2$ m/s^2
   (b) $t=6$ s
   (c) 36 m
4. (a) $v=24t-6t^2$, $t=0$ s and 4 s (b) $a=24-12t$, $t=2$ s
5. (a) $v=\frac{1}{2}-\frac{10}{t^2}$, $t=\sqrt{20}$ s (b) $2\sqrt{5}$ m or 4.47 m
   (c) $v=0.4$ m/s, $a=\frac{20}{t^3}$, 0.02 m/s^2
6. (a) $v=4t^3-12t$, $t=0$ s and $\sqrt{3}$ s
   (b) $a=12t^2-12$, when $t=0$, $a=-12$ m/s^2; when $t=\sqrt{3}$ s, $a=24$ m/s^2

Practice questions

1. $F=\frac{k}{d^2}$ **(1)**, $k=1.28$ **(1)**, $F=0.163$ **(1)**
2. (a) $v=\sqrt{\frac{6-2}{3.5}}$ **(1)** $v=1.07$ **(1)**
   (b) $v^2=\frac{k+u}{d}$ **(1)** $v^2d=k+u$ **(1)** $u=v^2d-k$ **(1)**
3. (a) distance = area under graph **(1)**
   $=\frac{10.5}{60}\times 60$ **(1)** $+\frac{14.75}{60}\times 40$ **(1)**
   [Area of two trapezia – this is the easiest way of calculating the area.]
   $= 10.5+9.8333=20.3$ km **(1)**
   (b) $20.3 \div 0.25$ **(1)** $=81.3$ km/h **(1)**
4. (a) (5.5, –1.5) **(1)**
   (b) $(7-2)^2+(0-7)^2$ **(1)** distance $=\sqrt{5^2+7^2}$ **(1)**
   $=\sqrt{74}=8.60$ units **(1)**
   (c) $m=\frac{-3-7}{4-2}=-5$ **(1)** $7=-5\times 2+c$,
   $c=17$ **(1)** $y=17-5x$ **(1)**
5. (a) $h(1)=\frac{1}{1-2}=-1$ **(1)**, $g(-1)=2\times(-1)^3-3=-5$ **(1)**
   (b) $x^3=\frac{y-3}{2}$ **(1)** $\sqrt[3]{\frac{y-3}{2}}$ **(1)**
   (c) $x^2-x-12=0$ **(1)** $(x+3)(x-4)=0$ **(1)** $x=-3$ or 4 **(1)**
6. $p(q+s)+r(q+s)$ **(1)** $(p+r)(q+s)$ **(1)**
7. (a) $3n+2$ **(1)** $\sqrt{3n+2}$ **(1)** (b) $\sqrt{104}$ or 10.2 **(1)**
8. $\frac{8(x+2)-2(x+8)\,\mathbf{(1)}}{(x+8)(x+2)\,\mathbf{(1)}}=\frac{6x}{(x+8)(x+2)}$ **(1)**
9. $y<5-x$ **(2)** $y \leqslant 2x+2$ **(2)** $y \geqslant 1$ **(1)**
10. (a) $\frac{6\times 10^3}{\sqrt{1.44\times 10^{-2}}}$ **(1)** $=\frac{6\times 10^3}{1.2\times 10^{-1}}$ **(1)** $=5\times 10^4$ **(1)**
    (b) $p^2=\frac{q^2}{rs}$ **(1)** $p^2r=\frac{q^2}{s}$ **(1)** $r=\frac{q^2}{p^2s}$ **(1)**
11. $(4x+6y=26)-(4x+2y=14)$ **(1)** $4y=12$, $y=3$ **(1)** $2x+9=13$, $2x=4$, $x=2$ **(1)** [Note that this is just one way of solving the simultaneous equations. There are many other ways of doing it.]
12. $bx-ax=by$ **(1)** $x(b-a)=by$ **(1)** $x=\frac{by}{b-a}$ **(1)**
13. (a) $t=k\sqrt{l}$ **(1)** $1=k\sqrt{25}$, $5k=1$, $k=0.2$, $t=0.2\sqrt{l}$ **(1)**
    (b) $t=0.2\sqrt{144}=0.2\times 12=2.4$ **(1)**
14. $\frac{(2+x)(2x-1)-x(2x+3)\,\mathbf{(1)}}{x(2x-1)\,\mathbf{(1)}}=\frac{4x+2x^2-2-x-2x^2-3x}{x(2x-1)}$
    (1) $=-\frac{2}{x(2x-1)}$ **(1)**

15. (a) Acceleration $= 30\,\text{m/s} \div 12\,\text{s}$ **(1)** $= 2.5\,\text{m/s}^2$ **(1)**
(b) Distance car A travels = area under graph
$= \frac{1}{2}(20+8) \times 30$ **(1)** $= 420\,\text{m}$ **(1)**
Distance car B travels $= \frac{1}{2} \times 20 \times 30 = 300\,\text{m}$ **(1)**
difference in distance $= 420\,\text{m} - 300\,\text{m} = 120\,\text{m}$ **(1)**

16. (a) $-6 < 3x \leqslant 6$ **(1)** $-2 < x \leqslant 2$ **(1)** $x = -1, 0, 1, 2$ **(1)**
(b) $x^2 - 36 = (x+6)(x-6)$ **(1)**
$x^2 - 9x + 18 = (x-6)(x-3)$ **(1)** $\dfrac{x+6}{x-3}$ **(1)**
(c) $3(x-1) - 2(x-5) = 4(x-1)(x-5)$ **(1)**
$3x - 3 - 2x + 10 = 4x^2 - 24x + 20$ **(1)**
$x + 7 = 4x^2 - 24x + 20$, $4x^2 - 25x + 13 = 0$ **(1)**
(d) $x = \dfrac{--25 \pm \sqrt{(-25)^2 - 4 \times 4 \times -13}}{2 \times 4}$ **(2)**
$= \dfrac{25 \pm \sqrt{625+208}}{8} = \dfrac{25 \pm 28.8617...}{8} = -0.48$ **(1)**
or 6.73 **(1)**

17. (a) From left to right: 5 **(1)**, 9 **(1)**, 1 **(1)**, –7 **(1)**, –3 **(1)**
(b) **(3)** for points plotted correctly,
(1) for smooth curve drawn through points
(c) $x = -4.2$ **(1)**, -0.8 **(1)** and 4.8 **(1)**
(d) $k > 9.6$ **(1)** $k < -7.6$ **(1)**
(e) **(1)** for straight line with gradient 2
(1) for intercept (0, –3)
(1) for line starting at $x = 0$ and finishing at $x = 5$
(f) $b = -28$ **(1)**, $c = 16$ **(1)**
(g) $x = 0.6$ **(1)** and 5 **(1)**

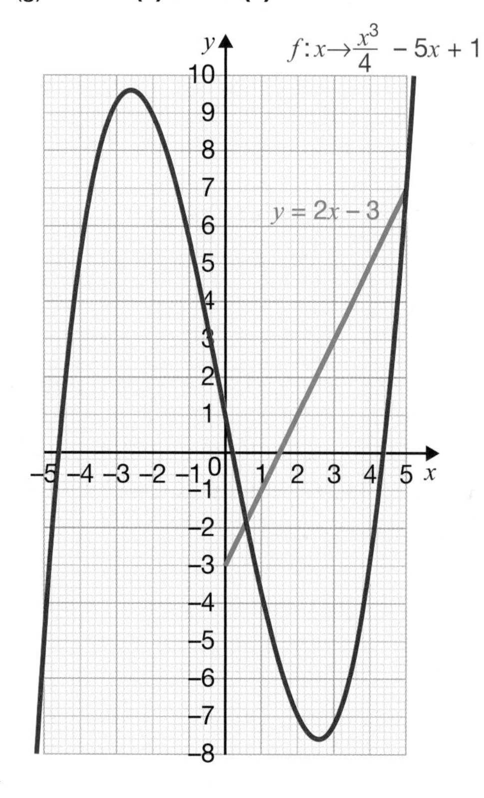

18. (a) (i) $x \leqslant 6$ **(1)**
(ii) $y \leqslant 6$ **(1)**
(iii) $30x + 45y \geqslant 360$ **(1)** $2x + 3y \geqslant 24$ **(1)**
(b) $x = 6$ drawn correctly **(1)** $y = 6$ drawn correctly **(1)**
$2x + 3y = 24$ drawn correctly **(2)**
unwanted regions shaded correctly **(1)**

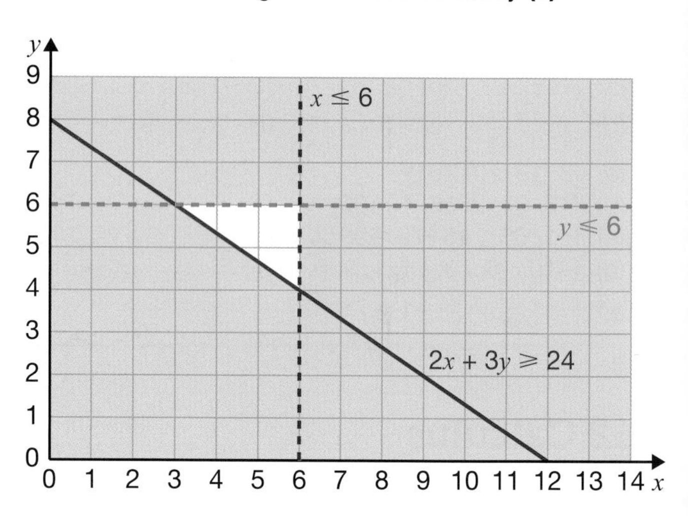

(c) (i) $x = 3$ **(1)**, $y = 6$ **(1)**
(ii) $3 \times £350 + 6 \times £500 = £1050 + £3000 = £4050$ **(1)**

19. $2(3x+2) + 5(x-4) = 5 \times 10$ **(1)**
$6x + 4 + 5x - 20 = 50$, $11x = 66$ **(1)** $x = 6$ **(1)**

20. $2x = -10$ **(1)** $x = -5$ **(1)**

21. (a) $\dfrac{dV}{dx} = 6x$ **(1)** -12 **(1)**
(b) $6x - 12 = 0$ **(1)** $6x = 12$, $x = 2$ **(1)**
(c) The coefficient of x^2 is positive. **(1)**
(d) 18 **(1)**

22. (a) $M = kN^3$ **(1)** $12.4 = 64k$, $k = 0.2$, $M = 0.2N^3$ **(1)**
(b) 5.4 **(1)**

23. (a) $y = \dfrac{8}{x-4}$, $xy - 4y = 8$ **(1)**
$xy = 8 + 4y$, $f^{-1}(x) = \dfrac{8+4x}{x}$ **(1)**
(b) $3\left(\dfrac{8}{x-4}\right) + 5$ **(1)** $= \dfrac{24}{x-4} + 5 = \dfrac{24 + 5x - 20}{x-4} = \dfrac{5x+4}{x-4}$ **(1)**

24. (a) From left to right: –4.8 **(1)**, –3 **(1)**, –1, 3 **(1)**, 8.3 **(1)**
(b) Points plotted correctly **(2)**,
smooth curve drawn through all points **(1)**
(c) tangent drawn **(1)**
fall approx 7.2 squares over 2 squares along **(1)**
gradient = –3.5
(answers between 3.4 and 3.8 are acceptable) **(1)**
(d) $k \geqslant 3$ **(1)**
(e) line drawn correctly with gradient 1 **(1)**
passing through (0, –6) **(1)**
(f) $x = 0.3$ **(1)**
(g) $x^2 - x - 2 - \dfrac{2}{x} = 0$ **(1)** $-\dfrac{2}{x} + x^2 = x + 2$ **(1)**

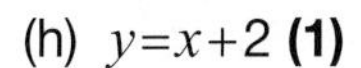

(h) $y=x+2$ **(1)**

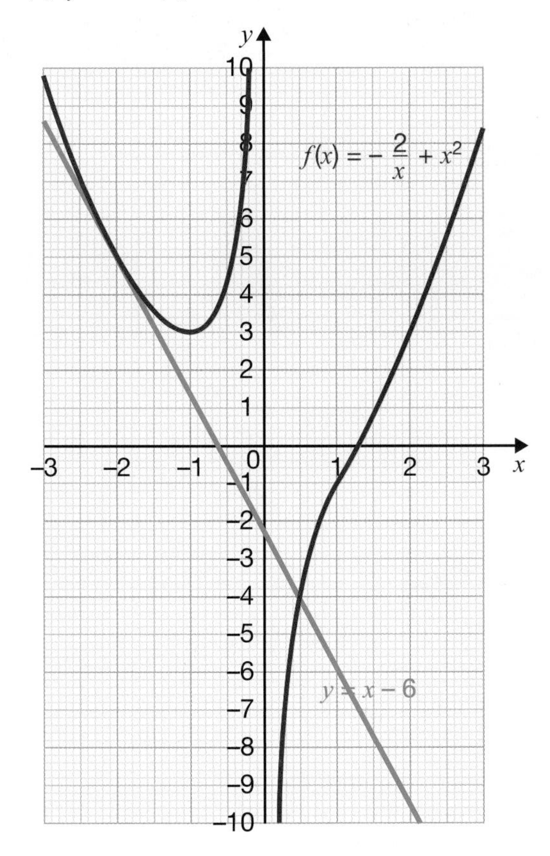

3 Geometry and measure

3.1 Lines and angles

Angles and triangles

1. No, because you can have an isosceles right-angled triangle.
2. $a=b=71°$, $c=80°$, $d=60°$, $e=52°$, $f=76°$, $g=49°$, $h=90°$, $i=45°$, $j=72°$, $k=54°$

Lines and angles

1. $a=b=90°$, $c=e=f=h=58°$, $d=g=i=122°$
2. $a=d=f=h=i=63°$, $b=e=g=117°$, $c=54°$

3.2 Polygons

Quadrilaterals

1. (a) $a=39°$, $b=123°$, $c=57°$, $d=123°$, $e=75°$, $f=39$
   (b) $a=49°$, $b=139°$, $c=41°$, $d=139°$, $e=41°$, $f=103°$, $g=113°$, $h=77°$, $i=139°$, $j=41°$ $k=103°$
2. (a) $x=20°$, $y=20°$; angles in the kite: 20°, 112°, 112° and 116°; other angle: 160°
   (b) $x=25°$, $y=24°$, so angles are 53°, 127°, 142° and 38°
3. $x=50°$
4. Yes, both a square and a rectangle have four right angles and opposite sides are the same length.
5. Yes, both a rhombus and a parallelogram have opposite angles equal in size and opposite sides are the same length.
6. Yes, both a square and a rhombus have opposite angles equal in size and all four sides are the same length.
7. No, a kite will only be a rhombus when all four sides are the same length.

Polygons

1. (a) 10 sides (b) 6 sides (c) 5 sides
2. (a) 8 sides (b) 12 sides (c) 15 sides
3. (a) 9 sides (b) 11 sides (c) 14 sides
4. (a) $x=31°$ (b) $x=35°$ (c) $x=36°$

3.3 Construction

Construction

1. (a) 48°, 6 cm, 5 cm (b) 118°, 8 cm, 6.5 cm
   (c) 193°, 6.2 cm, 7.3 cm (d) 270°, 8.5 cm, 7.5 cm
   (e) 307°, 5.9 cm, 6.8 cm
2. Student's own drawings (a) 117°, 5.1 cm, 4.2 cm
   (b) 37°, 10.3 cm, 4.9 cm (c) 7.9 cm, 46°, 29°
3. Student's own drawings
4. Student's own drawings

Scale drawings

1. (a) 60 cm wide by 45 cm deep
   (b) 2.5 m
   (c) yes (space is 90 cm wide)
   (d) 1:20
2. (a) (i) 110 km (ii) 225 km (iii) 130 km
   (b) 1:2 500 000
3. Student's own accurate scale drawings

Bisectors

1. Student's own diagram
2. (a) Construct an angle of 60° and bisect it.
   (b) Construct the perpendicular to a line and bisect the right angle formed.
   (c) 160° = 180° − 15°. To construct an angle of 15°, construct an angle of 60°, bisect it to create an angle of 30° and then bisect again.

Loci

1. The locus is a circle.
2.

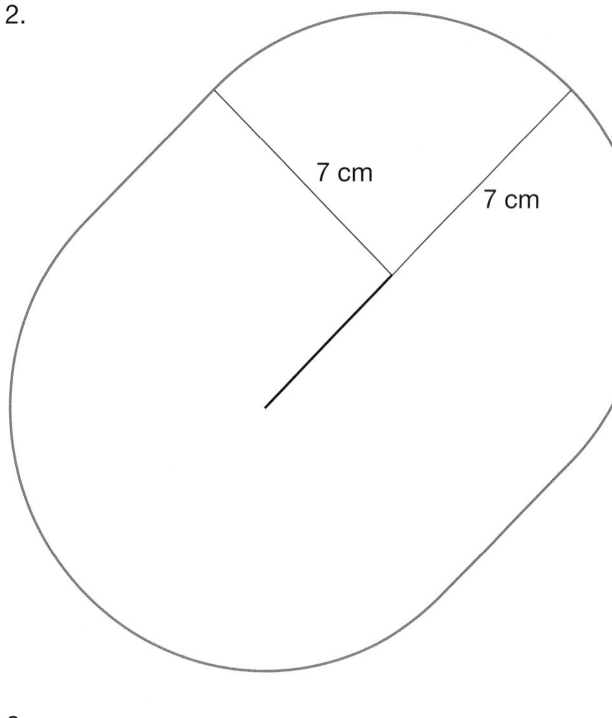

3.

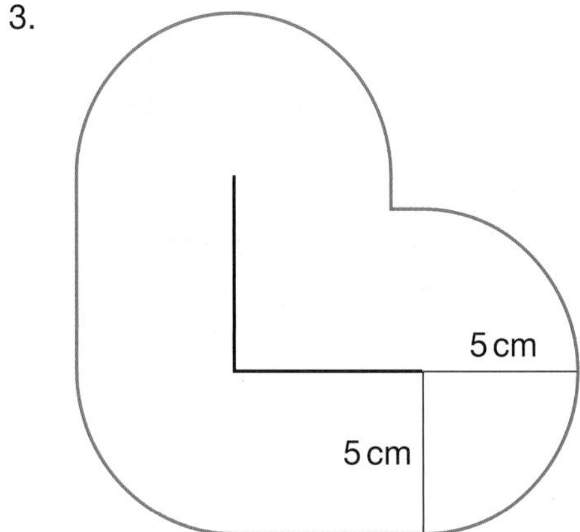

4.

5.

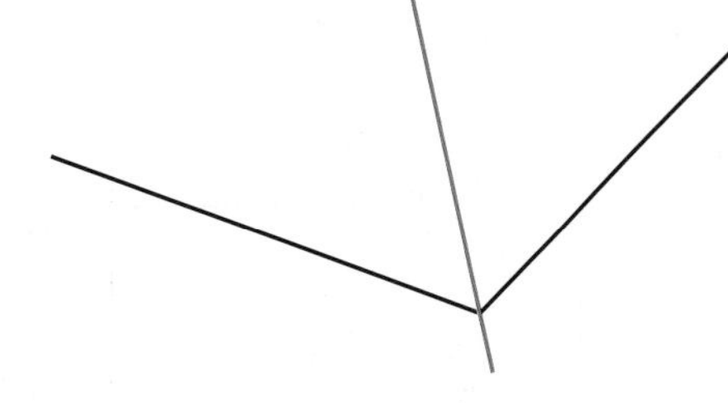

6. No, the goat cannot. The shaded area shows the area where the goat can eat the grass.

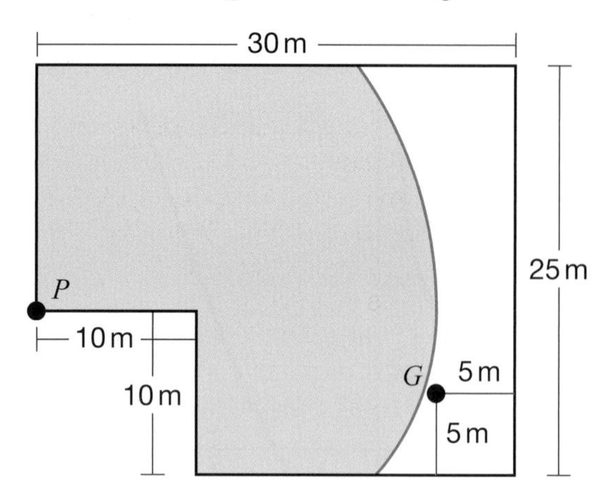

3.4 Circles

Circles, tangents and chords

1. (a) $a=142°$, $b=71°$ (b) $c=53°$, $d=26.5°$
   (c) 36° and 144°
2. (a) $a=38°$, $b=52°$, $c=52°$ (b) 5 cm
3. (a) 74° (b) 8 cm
   (c) (i) 3.5 cm (ii) 1 cm
4. (a) 3 cm (b) 6 cm
   (c) 12.5 m (d) 6 cm

Circle theorems

1. (a) $a=48°$ (angles subtended on circumference are equal)
   $b=100°$ (angles in a triangle add up to 180°)
   $c=100°$ (vertically opposite angles)
   $d=32°$ (angles in a triangle add up to 180°)
   $e=96°$ (angle at centre is twice angle at circumference)
   $f=g=42°$ (angles in an isosceles triangle)
   $h=16°$ (angle subtended from each end of diameter is a right angle)
   $i=132°$ (opposite angles in a cyclic quadrilateral are supplementary)
   (b) $j=42°$ (angle between radius and tangent is a right angle)
   $k=96°$ (angles in an isosceles triangle)
   $l=48°$ (angle at circumference is half angle at centre)
   $m=48°$ (angles subtended on circumference are equal)
   $n=42°$ (angle subtended from diameter is a right angle)
   $o=60°$ (angles subtended on circumference are equal)
   $p=30°$ (angles in a triangle)

2. (a) $a = 71°$ (angles in an isosceles triangle)
$b = 71°$ (alternate segment theorem)
$c = 71°$ (angles in an isosceles triangle)
$d = 38°$ (angles on a straight line add up to 180°)
$e = 109°$ (angles in a cyclic quadrilateral are supplementary)
$f = 38°$ (alternate segment theorem)
(b) $g = 78°$ (alternate segment theorem)
$h = 78°$ (angles in an isosceles triangle)
$i = 24°$ (angles in a triangle)
$j = 156°$ (angle at centre is twice angle at circumference)
$k = 12°$ (angles in an isosceles triangle)

3.5 Trigonometry and Pythagoras' theorem

Three-figure bearings

1. (a) 120° (b) 300° (c) 166°
(d) 346° (e) 234° (f) 194°
(g) 056° (h) 034°

Pythagoras' theorem and right-angled triangles

1. (a) 10 cm (b) 15 cm (c) 11.66 m
(d) 13.04 mm (e) 13.75 m (f) 17.32 mm
2. (a) 6.93 cm (b) 5.20 m (c) 3.00 cm
(d) 5.40 cm (e) 6.68 cm (f) 30.91 cm

Angles of depression and elevation

1. (a) 162 m (b) 919 m
2. (a) 114 m (b) 46.2 m
3. (a) 37.3 m (b) 236 m
4. (a) 240 m (b) 560 m

Obtuse angles

1. (a) 90° (b) 0° or 180°
(c) 104.5° (d) 14.5° or 165.5°
(e) 120° (f) 44.4° or 135.6°
(g) 138.6° (h) 48.6° or 131.4°
2. (a) 26.6° (b) 135°
(c) 143.1° (d) 108.4°

Sine and cosine rules

1. (a) 17.4 m (b) 7.13 cm (c) 20.3 cm
2. (a) 45.6°
(b) 20.7° (There are two possible answers, but as the angle you are given is obtuse, this angle must be acute.)
(c) 128°
3. (a) 10.3 mm (b) 10.9 m (c) 14.3 cm
4. (a) 26.4° (b) 138° (c) 46.7°

5. (a) 26.0 cm^2 (b) 61.4 cm^2 (c) 52.6 cm^2
6. 127°

3-D problems

1. (a) 9.05 m (b) 46.7 m
2. (a) 1.36 m (b) 39.8°
3. (a) 20.8 cm (b) 22.6°

3.6 2-D shapes

Perimeter and area

1. (a) 54 cm^2 (b) 40 cm^2 (c) 96 cm^2
(d) 98 cm^2
2. 30 cm
3. (a) 131 cm^2 (b) 78 cm^2 (c) 65.5 cm^2
(d) 42 cm^2 (e) 136.5 cm^2 (f) 182 cm^2
4. (a) 234 cm^2 (b) 560 cm^2

Circles

Note: in working out answers involving π, the value from a calculator has been used.

1. (a) 28.3 cm^2, 18.8 cm (b) 78.5 cm^2, 31.4 cm
(c) 113 cm^2, 37.7 cm (d) 254 cm^2, 56.5 cm
2. (a) 4π cm, 12π cm^2 (b) 4π cm, 16π cm^2
(c) 12.5π cm, 62.5π cm^2 (d) 4π cm, 24π cm^2

Compound shapes

1. (a) 54.1 cm^2 (b) 303 cm^2 (c) 254 cm^2
2. 21.5% (area of card = 486 cm^2, area of circles = 381.7 cm^2, wasted card = 104.3 cm^2)

3.7 3-D shapes and volume

Nets

1. Accurate drawings showing the following:

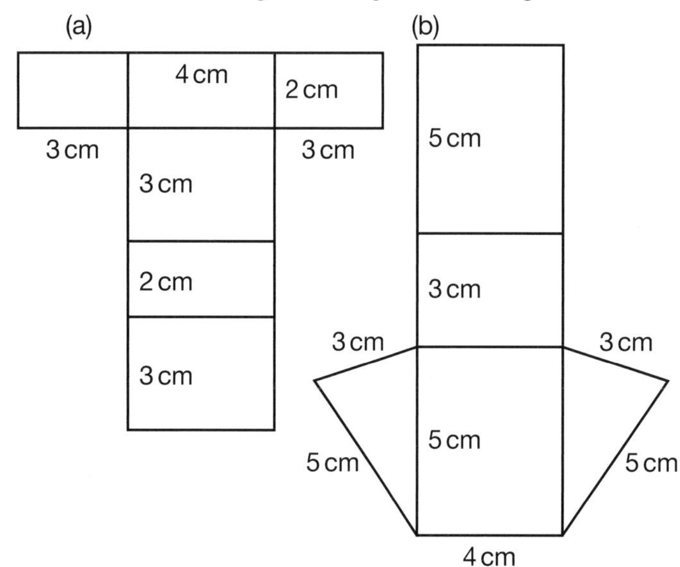

(c)

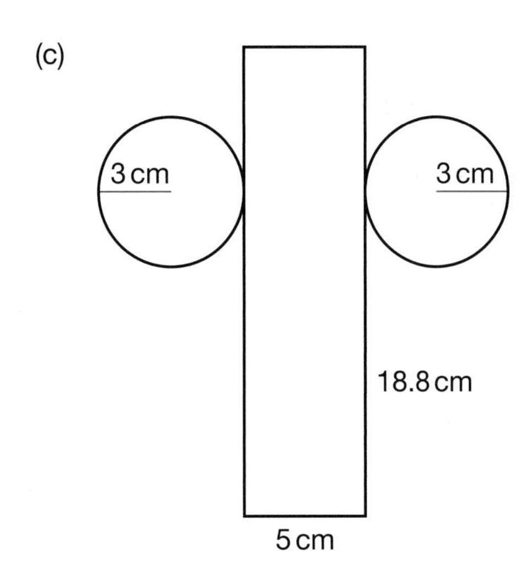

Volume and surface area of prisms

1. (a) 108 cm^3, 150 cm^2 (b) 188 cm^3, 214 cm^2
   (c) 2121 m^3, 1696 m^2 (d) 1.44 m^2, 7.92 m^2
2. (a) 48 cm^3 (b) 483 cm^3
   (c) 318 cm^3 (d) 1244 cm^3

Converting between units

1. (a) 1.857 m (b) 560 cm
   (c) 23 650 kg (d) 250 g
   (e) 37.4 cm^2 (f) 0.65 m^2
   (g) 230 000 cm^2 (h) 4500 mm^2
   (i) 330 000 mm^3 (j) 0.33 litres
   (k) 6.5 cm^3 (l) 370 000 cm^3
2. (a) 1.08×10^5 mm^3, 1.08×10^{-4} m^3; 1.88×10^5 mm^3, 1.88×10^{-4} m^3
   (b) 1.5×10^4 mm^2, 1.5×10^{-2} m^2; 2.14×10^4 mm^2, 2.14×10^{-2} m^2

Other 3-D shapes

1. (a) 905 cm^3, 452 cm^2 (b) 3054 cm^3, 1018 cm^2
   (c) 524 cm^3, 314 cm^2 (d) 4189 cm^3, 1257 cm^2
   (e) 302 cm^3, 302 cm^2 (f) 670 cm^3, 523 cm^2
   (g) 251 cm^3, 245 cm^2 (h) 616 cm^3, 459 cm^2
2. (a) 90 cm^3 (b) 315 cm^3
   (c) 213 cm^3 (d) 864 cm^3

Compound shapes

1. 300π m^3
2. 153 cm^3
3. 8.84 litres
4. 1925 m^3

3.8 Symmetry

2-D symmetry

1. (a) 1 (b) 0 (c) 1
   (d) 2 (e) 1 (f) 1
   (g) 3 (h) 2 (i) 8
   (j) 4 (k) 1 (l) 1
2. (a) 2 (b) 2 (c) 2
   (d) 0 (e) 2 (f) 0
   (g) 3 (h) 2 (i) 8
   (j) 4 (k) 2 (l) 2
3. (a)

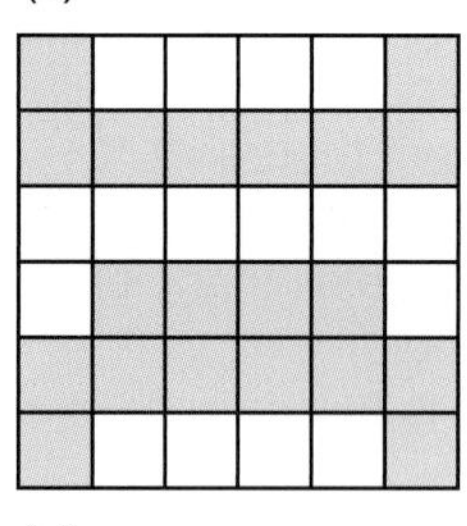

(b)

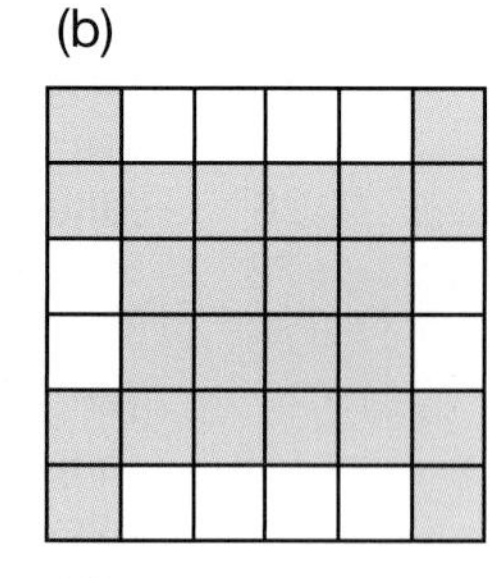

(c)

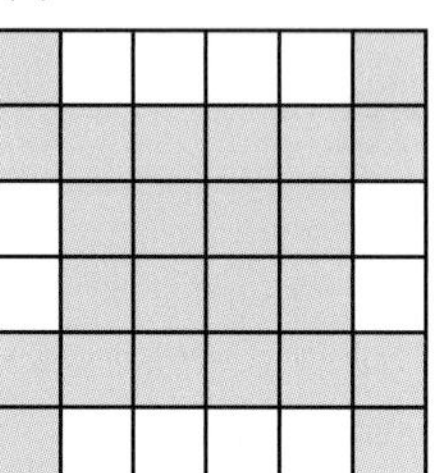

(d)

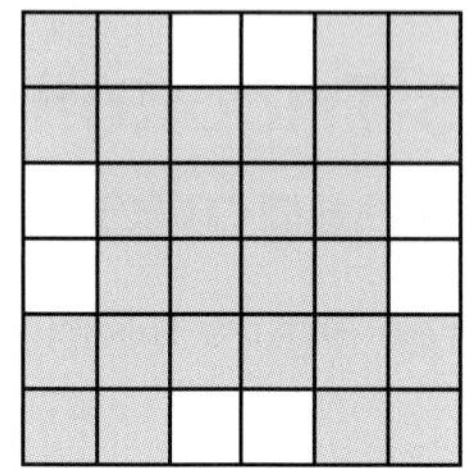

4. kite

3-D symmetry

1. (a) (i) 3 planes of symmetry, 3 axes of symmetry
   (ii) 2
   (b) (i) infinite number of planes of symmetry and axes of symmetry
   (ii) infinite for axis going through centre of circular faces, 2 for axes going midway between circular faces
   (c) (i) infinite planes of symmetry, 1 axis of symmetry
   (ii) infinite
   (d) (i) 2 planes of symmetry, no axes of symmetry
   (ii) 0
   (e) (i) 4 planes of symmetry, 1 axis of symmetry
   (ii) 4
   (f) (i) 6 planes of symmetry, 1 axis of symmetry
   (ii) 6

3.9 Similarity

Lengths and areas of similar shapes

1. (a) $x = 9.6$ cm, $y = 10$ cm (b) $x = 8$ cm, $y = 21$ cm
   (c) $x = 60$ cm, $y = 33$ cm (d) $x = 20$ cm, $y = 19.2$ cm
2. 59.4 cm^2
3. 27 cm^2
4. 827 cm^2

Areas and volumes of similar shapes

1. 2.13 g, 204.8 mm^2
2. 1114 cm^3, 630 cm^2
3. 7.5 cm
4. 614 cm^3, 550 cm^2

3.10 Vectors

Vectors

1. $\begin{pmatrix} 5 \\ 2 \end{pmatrix}, \begin{pmatrix} 2 \\ -3 \end{pmatrix}, \begin{pmatrix} -3 \\ -4 \end{pmatrix}, \begin{pmatrix} -2 \\ 4 \end{pmatrix}$

2. (a) $\begin{pmatrix} -3 \\ -5 \end{pmatrix}$ (b) $\begin{pmatrix} 3 \\ 5 \end{pmatrix}$ (c) $\begin{pmatrix} -7 \\ 2 \end{pmatrix}$ (d) $\begin{pmatrix} 1 \\ 8 \end{pmatrix}$

3. (a) $\begin{pmatrix} -1 \\ 7 \end{pmatrix}$ (b) $\begin{pmatrix} -5 \\ 1 \end{pmatrix}$ (c) $\begin{pmatrix} 7 \\ 0 \end{pmatrix}$ (d) $\begin{pmatrix} -19 \\ 16 \end{pmatrix}$

Magnitude of a vector

1. (a) 5.39 (b) 10 (c) 6.08
   (d) 14.9 (e) 14.9 (f) 20

Vector geometry

1. (a) $-\mathbf{b}$ (b) $2\mathbf{a}$ (c) $2\mathbf{b}-\mathbf{a}$
   (d) $2\mathbf{a}-3\mathbf{b}$ (e) $-2\mathbf{a}-2\mathbf{b}$ (f) $3\mathbf{a}+2\mathbf{b}$

2. (a) (i) $\frac{1}{2}\mathbf{b}$ (ii) $\frac{1}{2}(\mathbf{a}+\mathbf{b})$
   (b) $\overrightarrow{CD}=\frac{1}{2}\mathbf{a}$ and is a multiple of $\overrightarrow{OA}$, so it is parallel to $\overrightarrow{OA}$.

3. (a) (i) $\mathbf{a}+\mathbf{b}$ (ii) $3\mathbf{a}+\frac{1}{2}\mathbf{b}$
   (b) halfway between M and C

4. (a) (i) $2\mathbf{a}$ (ii) $\mathbf{a}+2\mathbf{b}$ (iii) $\mathbf{a}+\mathbf{b}$
   (b) $\overrightarrow{FD}=2\mathbf{a}+2\mathbf{b}$, which is a multiple of $\overrightarrow{EF}$, so it is a straight line.

3.11 Transformations

Translations

1. (a) $\begin{pmatrix} -2 \\ 1 \end{pmatrix}$ (b) $\begin{pmatrix} 5 \\ 1 \end{pmatrix}$ (c) $\begin{pmatrix} 4 \\ -6 \end{pmatrix}$ (d) $\begin{pmatrix} -3 \\ -4 \end{pmatrix}$

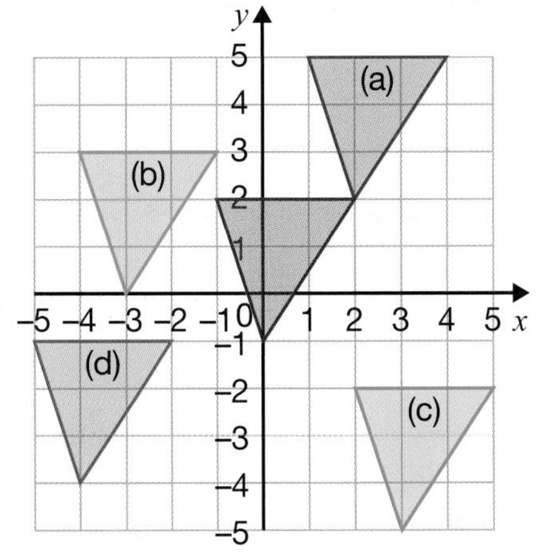

Reflections

1. (a) reflection in line $y=-1$
   (b) reflection in line $x=1$
   (c) reflection in line $y=x$
   (d) reflection in line $y=-x$

2.

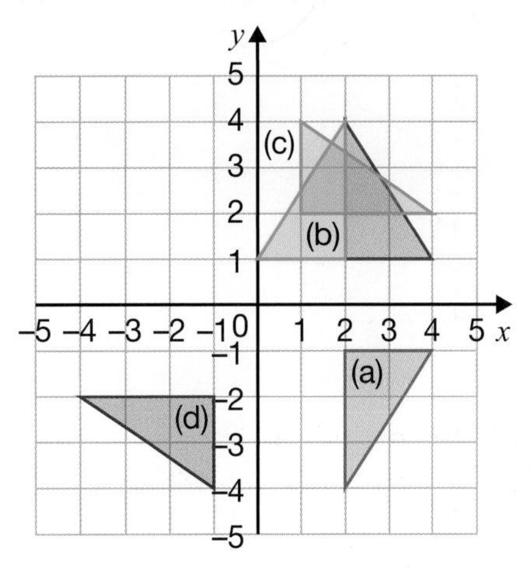

Rotations

1. (a) 90° clockwise about (0, 0)
   (b) 180° about (2, 0)
   (c) 90° anticlockwise about (2, 2)
   (d) 90° anticlockwise about (1, –1)

2.

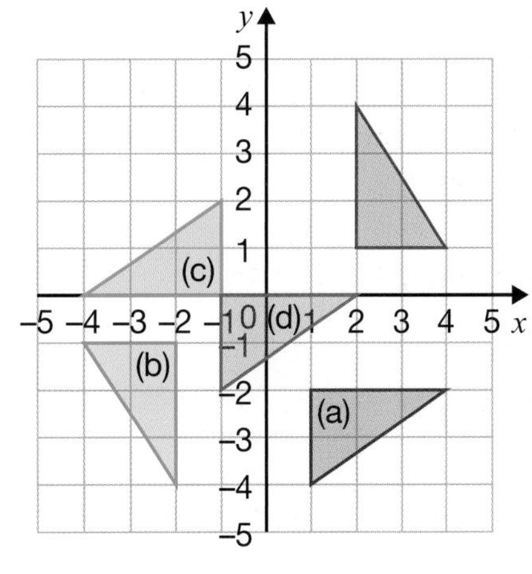

Enlargements

1.

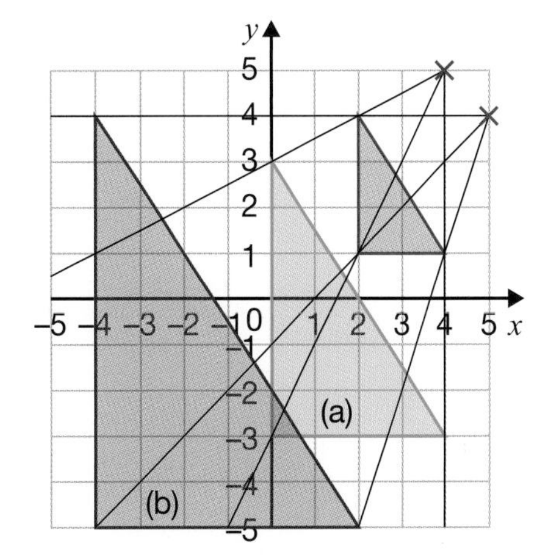

2.

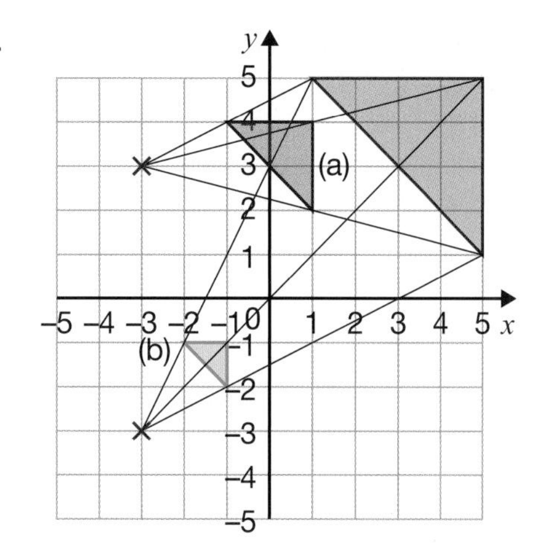

3.

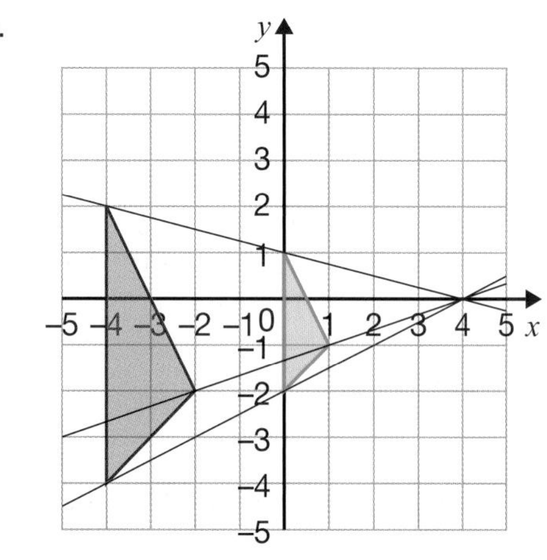

centre of enlargement is (4, 0)

4.

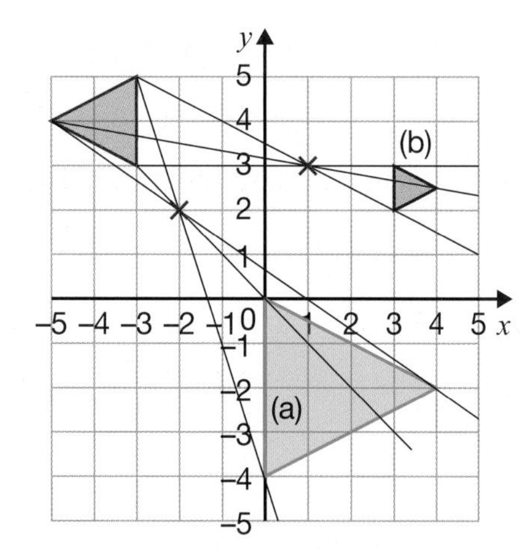

Combined transformations

1. (a), (b)

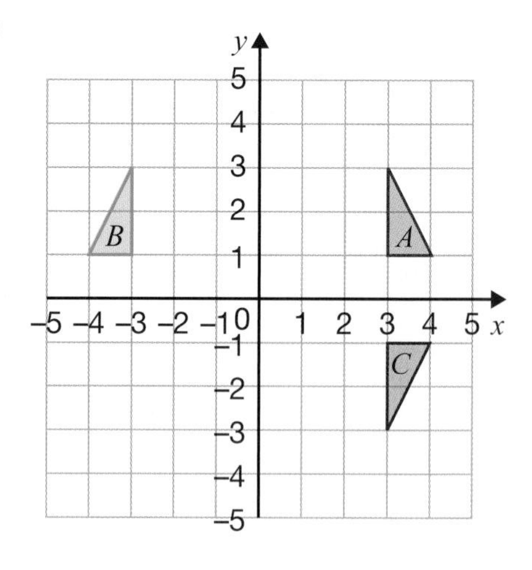

(c) reflection in the line $y=0$ / x-axis

2. (a), (b)

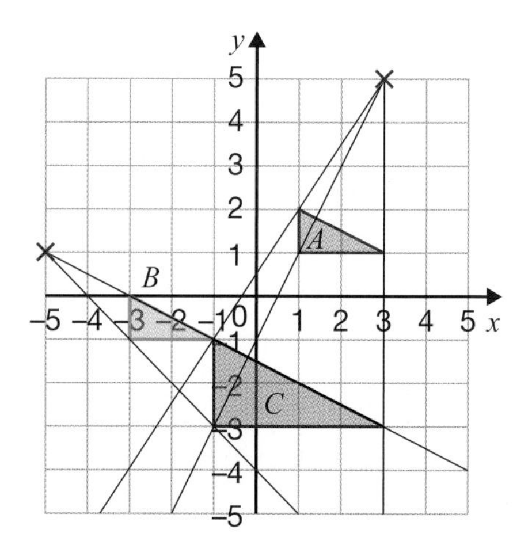

(c) enlargement by scale factor 2 about the centre of enlargement (3, 5)

3. (a), (b)

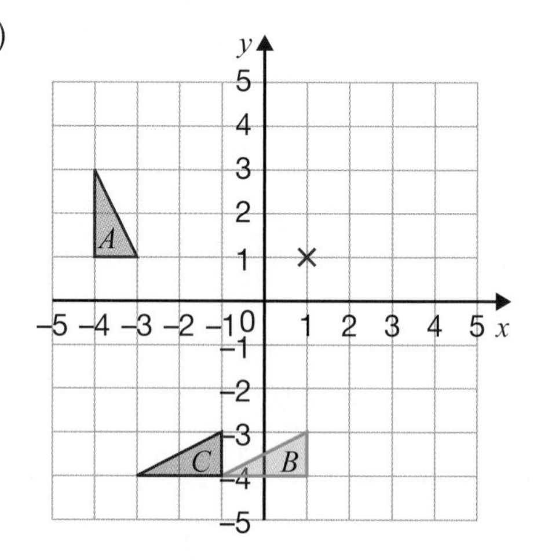

(c) rotation 90° anticlockwise about the centre of rotation (0, 0)

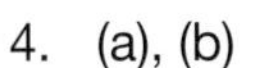

4. (a), (b)

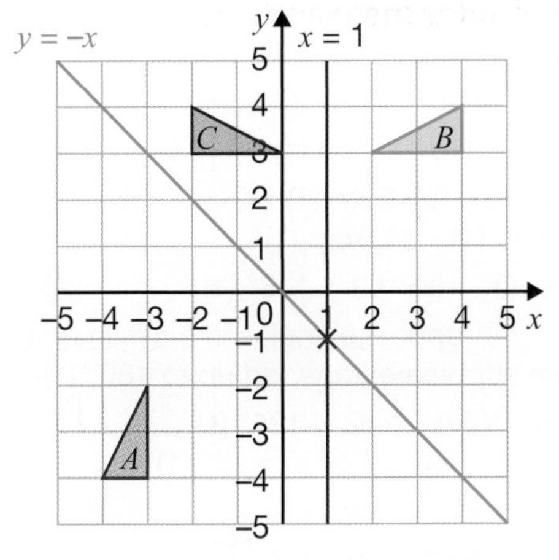

(c) rotation 90° clockwise about the centre of rotation (1, –1)

3.12 Matrices

Matrices

1. (a) $\begin{pmatrix} 2 & 0 \\ 4 & -4 \end{pmatrix}$ (b) $\begin{pmatrix} 4 & 10 \\ -14 & 6 \end{pmatrix}$ (c) $\begin{pmatrix} 3 & -9 \\ 10 & -9 \end{pmatrix}$

(d) $\begin{pmatrix} 7 & 6 \\ -15 & 4 \end{pmatrix}$ (e) $\begin{pmatrix} -3 & 14 \\ -14 & 12 \\ 8 & 6 \end{pmatrix}$ (f) $\begin{pmatrix} -8 \\ 6 \end{pmatrix}$

(g) $\begin{pmatrix} -12 & 8 \\ -3 & 2 \end{pmatrix}$ (h) $\begin{pmatrix} 13 & 4 \\ -3 & 24 \end{pmatrix}$

2. $x=-3$, $y=2$

2×2 matrices

1. (a) $\begin{pmatrix} \frac{2}{3} & -1 \\ -\frac{1}{2} & 1 \end{pmatrix}$ (b) $\begin{pmatrix} -1 & 3 \\ 1 & -2 \end{pmatrix}$

(c) matrix is singular (d) $\begin{pmatrix} 1 & -\frac{1}{2} \\ -\frac{1}{2} & \frac{1}{2} \end{pmatrix}$

2. **QP**=**I**

Transformations

1. (a)

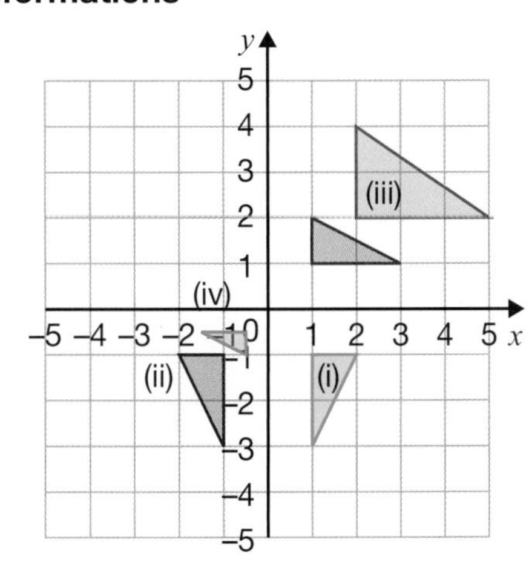

(b) (i) rotation 90° clockwise about (0, 0)
(ii) reflection in the line $y=-x$
(iii) enlargement about (0, 0) with scale factor 2
(iv) enlargement about (0, 0) with scale factor –0.5

2. (a) $\begin{pmatrix} -1 & 0 \\ 0 & -1 \end{pmatrix}$ (b) $\begin{pmatrix} -1 & 0 \\ 0 & 1 \end{pmatrix}$

(c) $\begin{pmatrix} 1 & 0 \\ 0 & -1 \end{pmatrix}$ (d) $\begin{pmatrix} 3 & 0 \\ 0 & 3 \end{pmatrix}$

Practice questions

1. cos 135°, sin 35°, sin 135°, cos 35° **(2)**
2. (a) area$=\pi\times40^2$ **(1)** $=5027\text{ cm}^2$ **(1)**
   (b) 0.503 m^2 **(1)**
3. $(8-2)\times180=1080$ **(1)** $180+6x=1080$ **(1)**
   $6x=900$, $x=150°$ **(1)**
4. $a=62°$ **(1)** ($b+c$ is a right angle, and angles in a triangle add up to 180°) **(1)** $b=59°$ **(1)** (angles in an isosceles triangle) **(1)** $c=31°$ **(1)** ($b+c$=right angle) **(1)**
5. (a) $-1\begin{pmatrix} 3 & -2 \\ -5 & 3 \end{pmatrix}$ **(1)** $\begin{pmatrix} -3 & 2 \\ 5 & -3 \end{pmatrix}$ **(1)**
   (b) $\begin{pmatrix} 19 & 12 \\ 30 & 19 \end{pmatrix}$ **(2)** (**(1)** if 2 or 3 elements correct)
6. (a) (i) $\overrightarrow{OC}+\overrightarrow{CD}$ or $3\mathbf{b}+\frac{2}{3}\mathbf{a}-2\mathbf{b}$ **(1)** $=\frac{2}{3}\mathbf{a}+\mathbf{b}$ **(1)**
   (ii) $\overrightarrow{OD}-\overrightarrow{OB}$ or $\frac{2}{3}\mathbf{a}+\mathbf{b}-2\mathbf{b}$ **(1)** $=\frac{2}{3}\mathbf{a}-\mathbf{b}$ **(1)**
   (b) $\overrightarrow{DE}=\overrightarrow{DA}+\overrightarrow{AE}$ or $\frac{1}{3}\mathbf{a}-\mathbf{b}+\frac{1}{3}\mathbf{a}$ **(1)** $=\frac{2}{3}\mathbf{a}-\mathbf{b}$ **(1)** $\overrightarrow{BD}$ and $\overrightarrow{DE}$ are the same so they are in a straight line **(1)**
7. $4x=-8$ **(1)** $x=-2$ **(1)** $y=3$ **(1)**
8. (a) $COB=58°$, $AOB=122°$ **(1)** $OBA=58°\div2=29°$ **(1)**
   (b) $OAB=29°$; bearing of B from $A=180°+OAB$ **(1)** $=180°+29°=209°$ **(1)**
9. (a) $\begin{pmatrix} 4 \\ -2 \end{pmatrix}$ **(1)**
   (b) correct arcs **(1)** to construct a perpendicular bisector through (4, 4) **(1)**
10. (a) $\begin{pmatrix} 6 \\ -2 \end{pmatrix}$ **(1)**
    (b) correct arcs **(1)** to construct a perpendicular bisector through (3, 4) **(1)**
    (c) (i) AB or $BC=\sqrt{2^2+4^2}$ **(1)** $\sqrt{20}=4.47$ units **(1)**
    (ii) area$=0.5\times\sqrt{20}\times\sqrt{20}$ **(1)** $=10\text{ cm}^2$ **(1)**
11. $\frac{1}{3}\pi r^2\times2r$ **(1)** $\div8r^3$ **(1)** $=\frac{2}{3}\pi\div8\times100\%=26.2\%$ **(1)**

12. area of sector $=\frac{70}{360}\times\pi\times 8^2$ **(1)** area of triangle $=0.5\times 8\times 8\times \sin 70°$ **(1)** shaded area $=$ area of sector $-$ area of triangle $=39.09\,\text{cm}^2-30.07\,\text{cm}^2$ **(1)** $=9.03\,\text{cm}^2$ **(1)**

13. (a) $\cos ABC=\frac{8.5^2+5.1^2-7.5^2}{2\times 8.5\times 5.1}$ **(2)** $=0.48454$ **(1)**
$ABC=\cos^{-1} 0.48544=61°$ **(1)**
(b) $222°+61°=283°$ **(1)**

14. (a) angles in same segment on circumference **(1)**
(b) $\frac{CE}{5.78}=\frac{7.53}{9.26}$ **(1)** $CE=4.70\,\text{cm}$ **(1)**
(c) $\frac{BEC}{22.4}=\left(\frac{5.78}{9.26}\right)^2$ **(1)** area of $BEC=8.73\,\text{cm}^2$ **(1)**

15. (a) $\begin{pmatrix}-4\\1\end{pmatrix}$ **(1)** (b) (i) $\begin{pmatrix}7\\1\end{pmatrix}$ **(1)** (ii) $\begin{pmatrix}6\\-2\end{pmatrix}$ **(1)**

16. (a) $\overrightarrow{RS}=\overrightarrow{RQ}+\overrightarrow{QS}$ **(1)** $\overrightarrow{QS}=\frac{3}{4}\mathbf{q}$ **(1)**
$\overrightarrow{QS}=\frac{2}{3}(\mathbf{p}-\mathbf{q})$ **(1)** $\overrightarrow{RS}=\frac{2}{3}\mathbf{p}+\frac{1}{12}\mathbf{q}$ **(1)**
(b) $\overrightarrow{OM}=\overrightarrow{OR}+\frac{1}{2}\overrightarrow{RS}$ **(1)** $=\frac{1}{4}\mathbf{q}+\frac{1}{2}\left(\frac{2}{3}\mathbf{p}+\frac{1}{12}\mathbf{q}\right)=\frac{1}{3}\mathbf{p}+\frac{7}{24}\mathbf{q}$ **(1)**

17. (a) $5^2+12^2=169$ **(1)** $169+15^2=394$ **(1)**
$CE=\sqrt{394}=19.85\,\text{cm}$ **(1)**
(b) $\sin ECA=5\div 19.85$ **(1)** $=0.25189$,
$ECA=14.59°$ **(1)**
(c) $\tan BCF=5\div 12$ **(1)** $=0.41667$, $BCF=22.62°$ **(1)**
(d) $\frac{BG}{\sin 22.62°}=\frac{12}{\sin 120°}$ **(1)**
$BG=12\times \sin 22.62°\div \sin 120°$ **(1)** $=5.33\,\text{cm}$ **(1)**
(e) volume $=0.5\times 5\,\text{cm}\times 12\,\text{cm}\times 15\,\text{cm}$ **(1)**
$=450\,\text{cm}^3$ **(1)**

18. (a) $\sqrt{6^2+9^2}$ **(1)** $=10.82\,\text{cm}$ **(1)**
(b) $\frac{1}{3}\times\pi\times 6^2\times 9$ **(1)** $=339\,\text{cm}^3$ **(1)**
(c) (i) $9\,\text{cm}\div 3$ **(1)** $=3\,\text{cm}$ **(1)**
(ii) $\frac{1}{3}\times\pi\times 2^2\times 3$ **(1)** $=12.6\,\text{cm}^3$ **(1)**
(d) volume of cylinder $=\pi\times 6^2\times 8=904.78\,\text{cm}^3$ **(1)**
volume of truncated cone
$=339.3\,\text{cm}^3-12.6\,\text{cm}^3=326.7\,\text{cm}^3$ **(1)**
total volume $=904.78\,\text{cm}^3+326.7\,\text{cm}^3$ **(1)**
$=1231\,\text{cm}^3$ **(1)**

19. (a) (i) enlargement **(1)** of scale factor 0.5 **(1)** about centre of enlargement (4, 8) **(1)**
(ii) translation **(1)** of $\begin{pmatrix}-10\\4\end{pmatrix}$ **(1)**
(iii) rotation **(1)** of 90° anticlockwise **(1)** about the centre of rotation (6, 4) **(1)**
(b) (–6, –6) **(1)** (–8, 2) **(1)** (–8, 6) **(1)**
(c) (i) (–4, –2) **(1)** (–8, –4) **(1)** (–8, –2) **(1)**
(ii) rotation **(1)** 90° clockwise **(1)** about the centre of rotation (0, 0) **(1)**

20. area $=$ area of rectangle $+$ area of semicircle **(1)**
$8.9\times 7.2=64.08\,\text{cm}^2$ **(1)** $0.5\times\pi\times 3.6^2=20.36\,\text{cm}^2$ **(1)**
total area $=64.08+20.36=84.4\,\text{cm}^2$ **(1)**

21. (a) $0.5(10+15)\times 9$ **(1)** $=112.5\,\text{cm}^2$ **(1)**
(b) $15-10=5\,\text{cm}$ **(1)** $BC^2=9^2+5^2=106$ **(1)** $BC=\sqrt{106}$ **(1)** $=10.3\,\text{cm}$ **(1)**

22. (a) (i) $180-62°=118°$ **(1)**
(ii) opposite angles in a cyclic quadrilateral **(1)** are supplementary/add up to 180° **(1)**
(b) $DOB=2\times 62°=124°$ **(1)**
$OBD=(180°-124°)/2=28°$ **(1)**

23. volume of tennis balls $=3\times\frac{4}{3}\pi r^3=4\pi r^3$ **(1)** volume of cylinder $=\pi r^2\times 6r=6\pi r^3$ **(1)**
empty space $=6\pi r^3-4\pi r^3=2\pi r^3$ **(1)** $54\pi=2\pi r^3$, **(1)**
$r^3=27$, $r=3\,\text{cm}$ **(1)**

24. (a) $AB^2=13^2+8^2-2\times 13\times 8\times\cos 25°$ **(1)** $=44.49$ **(1)**
$AB=\sqrt{44.49}=6.67\,\text{cm}$ **(1)**
(b) $6.67\times AC=6\times 13$ **(1)** $AC=11.69\,\text{cm}$ **(1)**
$BC=11.69-6.67=5.02\,\text{cm}$ **(1)**

25. (a) rotation **(1)** 90° anticlockwise **(1)** about the centre of rotation (0, 0) **(1)**
(b) (–1, 3) **(1)** (1, 3) **(1)** (–1, 4) **(1)**
(c) rotation **(1)** 90° anticlockwise **(1)** about the centre of rotation (–3, –1) **(1)**

26. (a) $AC^2=7^2+9^2$ **(1)** $EC^2=AC^2+AE^2$ **(1)**
$=7^2+9^2+5^2=155$, $EC=\sqrt{155}$ **(1)** $=12.4\,\text{cm}$ **(1)**
(b) angle required $=ACE$, $\tan ACE=5\div\sqrt{7^2+9^2}=0.43852$ **(1)** $ACE=23.7°$ **(2)**

4 Statistics and probability

4.1 Representing data

Collecting data

1. (a)

Number of children	Frequency
1	6
2	12
3	5
4	4
5	2
6	1

(b)

Number of days absent	Frequency
0	9
1	12
2	5
3	3
4	2
5	4
6	1

2. (a)

Marks, m	Frequency
$20 \leqslant m < 30$	2
$30 \leqslant m < 40$	4
$40 \leqslant m < 50$	11
$50 \leqslant m < 60$	11
$60 \leqslant m < 70$	6
$70 \leqslant m < 80$	2

(b)

Height, h (cm)	Frequency
$140 \leqslant h < 150$	1
$150 \leqslant h < 160$	4
$160 \leqslant h < 170$	11
$170 \leqslant h < 180$	13
$180 \leqslant h < 190$	6
$190 \leqslant h < 200$	1

Pictograms, pie charts and bar charts

1. (a)

Number of children | Frequency

1
2
3
4
5
6

Key: represents 2 children

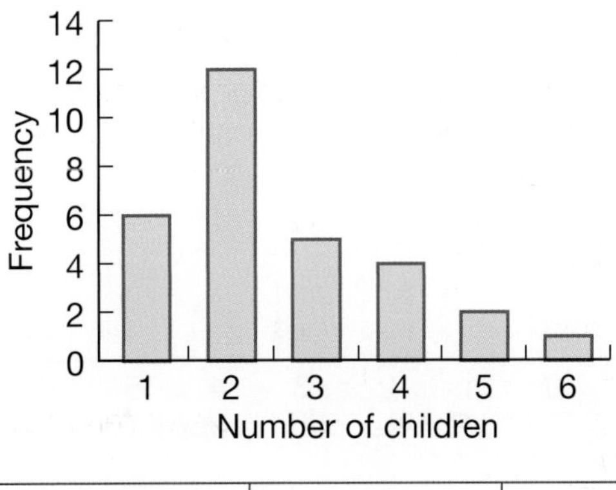

Number of children	Frequency	Angle
1	6	72°
2	12	144°
3	5	60°
4	4	48°
5	2	24°
6	1	12°
Total	30	360°

Number of children

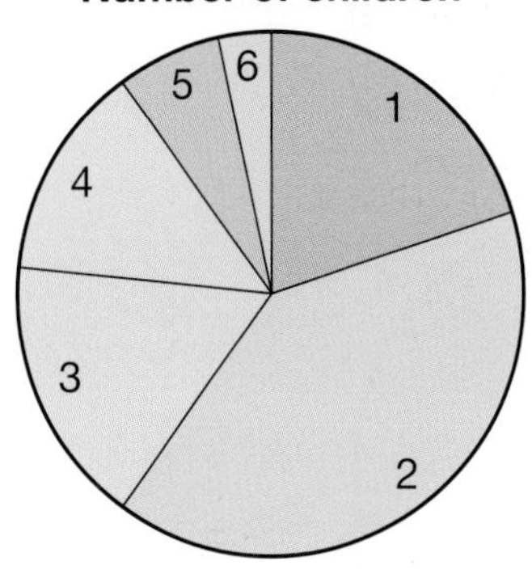

(b) Number of days absent | Frequency

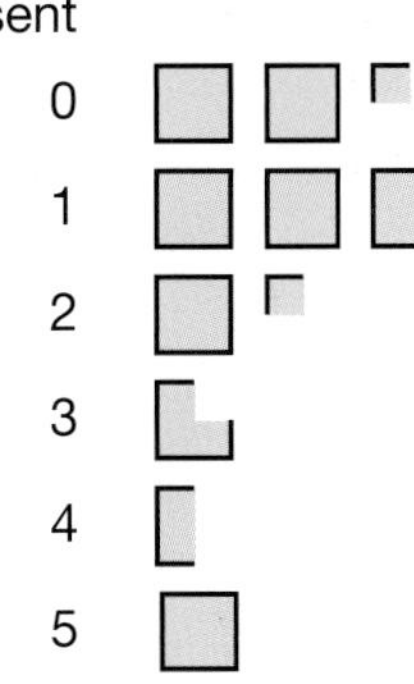

Key: represents 4 children

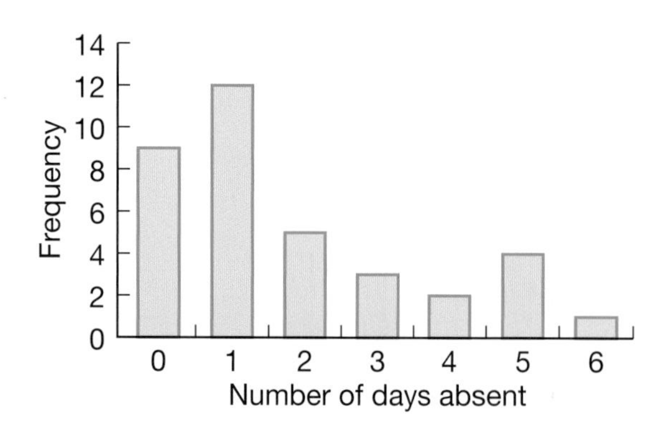

Number of days absent	Frequency	Angle
0	9	90°
1	12	120°
2	5	50°
3	3	30°
4	2	20°
5	4	40°
6	1	10°
Total	36	360°

Number of days students are absent in a term

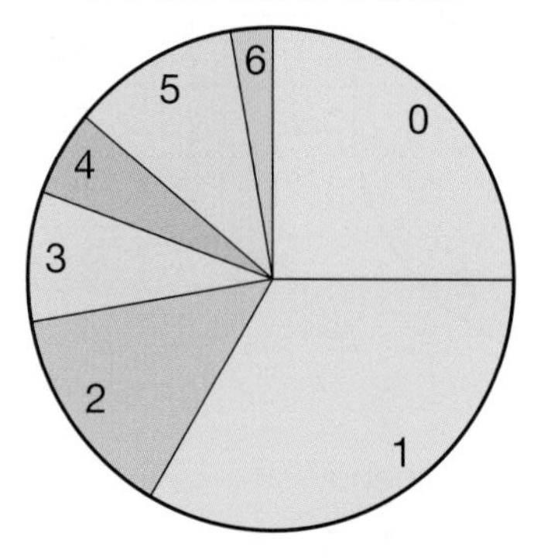

2.

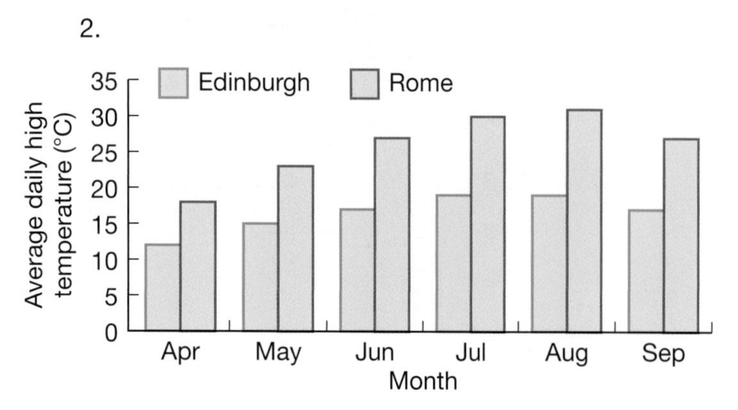

Histograms and cumulative frequency diagrams

1. (a)

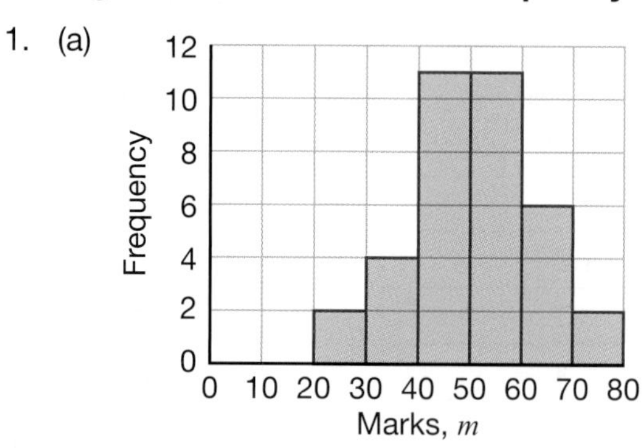

Marks, m	Frequency	Cumulative frequency
$20 < m \leqslant 30$	2	2
$30 < m \leqslant 40$	4	6
$40 < m \leqslant 50$	11	17
$50 < m \leqslant 60$	11	28
$60 < m \leqslant 70$	6	34
$70 < m \leqslant 80$	2	36

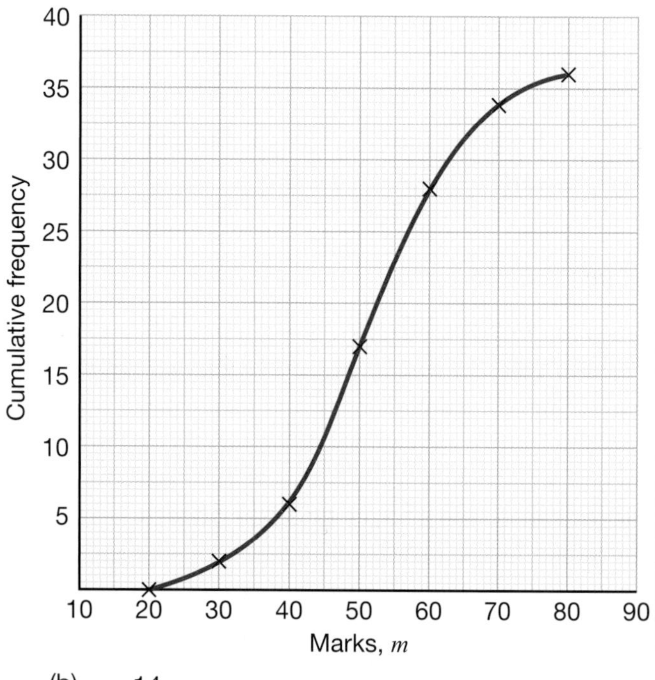

(b)

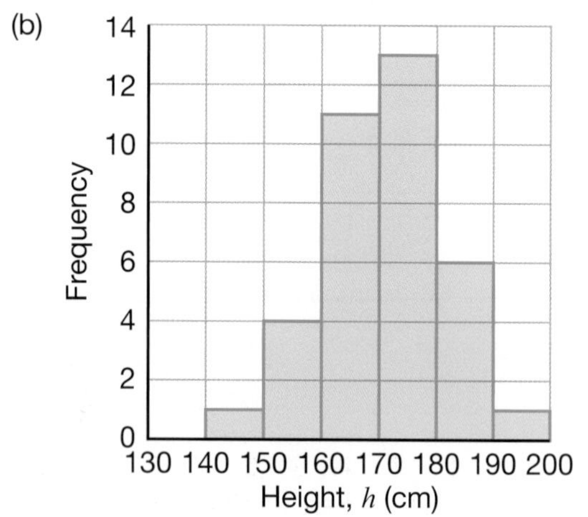

Height, h (cm)	Frequency	Cumulative frequency
$140 < h \leqslant 150$	1	1
$150 < h \leqslant 160$	4	5
$160 < h \leqslant 170$	11	16
$170 < h \leqslant 180$	13	29
$180 < h \leqslant 190$	6	35
$190 < h \leqslant 200$	1	36

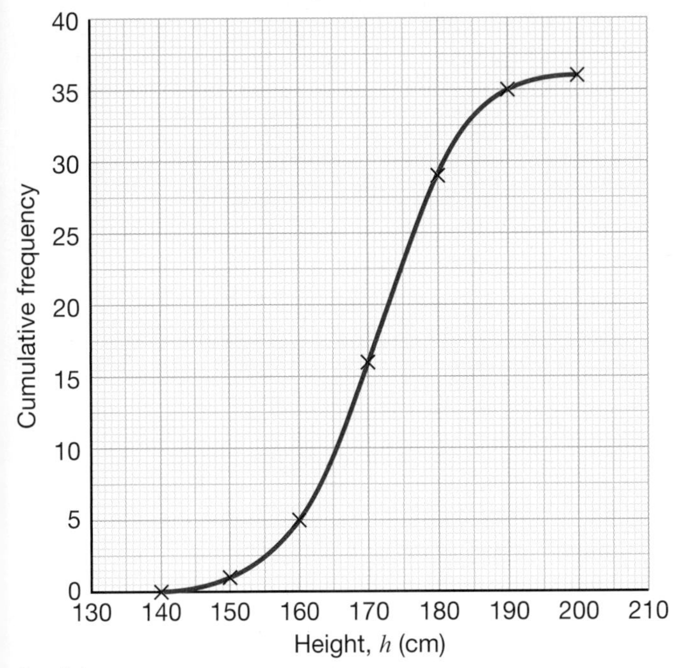

2. (a)

Time taken, t (minutes)	Frequency	Frequency density	Cumulative frequency
$0 < t \leqslant 2$	10	5	10
$2 < t \leqslant 3$	15	15	25
$3 < t \leqslant 4$	10	10	35
$4 < t \leqslant 5$	8	8	43
$5 < t \leqslant 7$	8	4	51
$7 < t \leqslant 10$	9	3	60

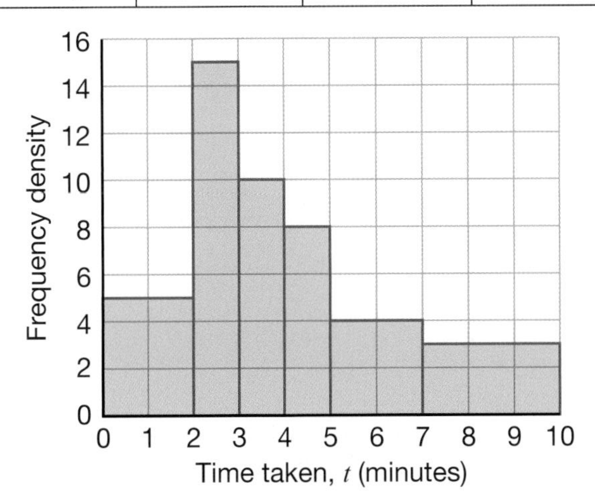

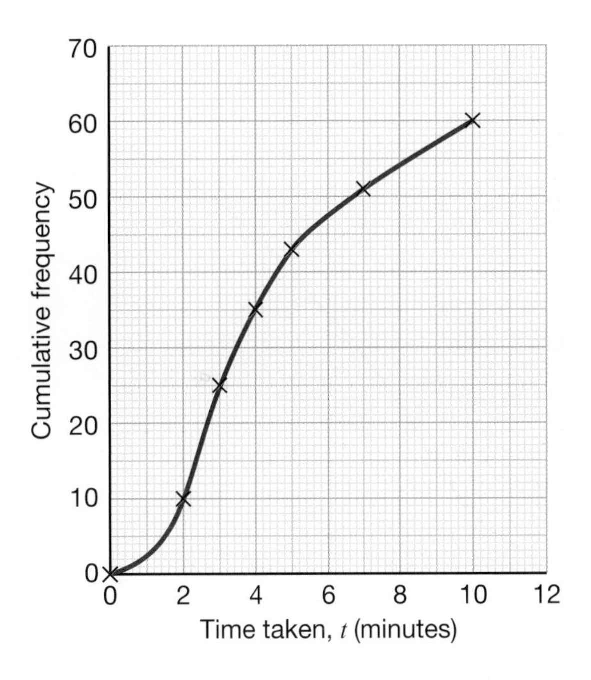

(b)

Time taken, t (minutes)	Frequency	Frequency density	Cumulative frequency
$0 < t \leqslant 10$	6	0.6	6
$10 < t \leqslant 15$	7	1.4	13
$15 < t \leqslant 20$	8	1.6	21
$20 < t \leqslant 30$	12	1.2	33
$30 < t \leqslant 40$	11	1.1	44
$40 < t \leqslant 50$	8	0.8	52
$50 < t \leqslant 70$	8	0.4	60

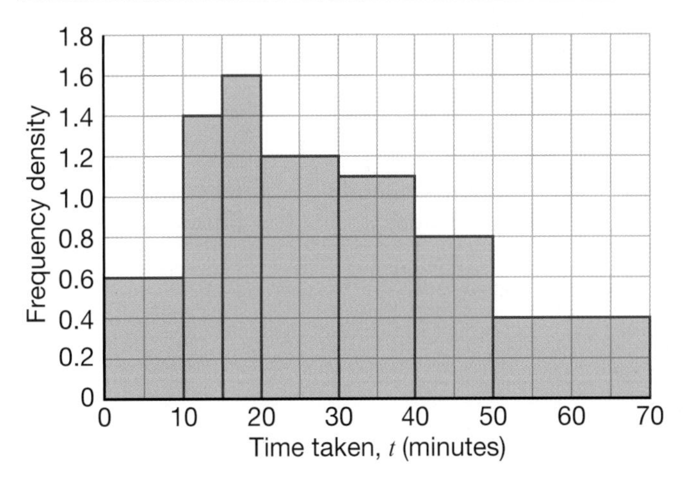

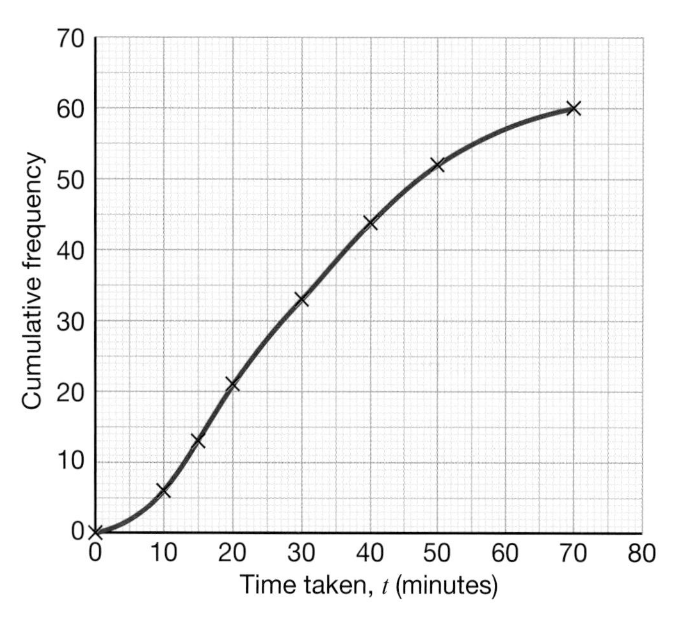

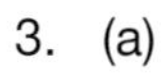

3. (a)

Time, t (seconds)	Frequency
$0 < t \leqslant 150$	375
$150 < t \leqslant 250$	350
$250 < t \leqslant 300$	225
$300 < t \leqslant 350$	210
$350 < t \leqslant 400$	175
$400 < t \leqslant 500$	200
$500 < t \leqslant 700$	200

(b) At 300 seconds 54.8% of people had been served and at 400 seconds, 76.9% of people had been served. So the first target is being met but not the second.

Scatter diagrams

1. (a), (b) mean point is (1.8, 6.2)

	Engine capacity (litres)	Fuel consumption (litres/100 km)
	2	6.3
	1.2	5
	1.4	5.7
	3	7.1
	1.1	5
	1.6	6.5
	1	4.6
	2.9	9.1
Mean	1.8	6.2

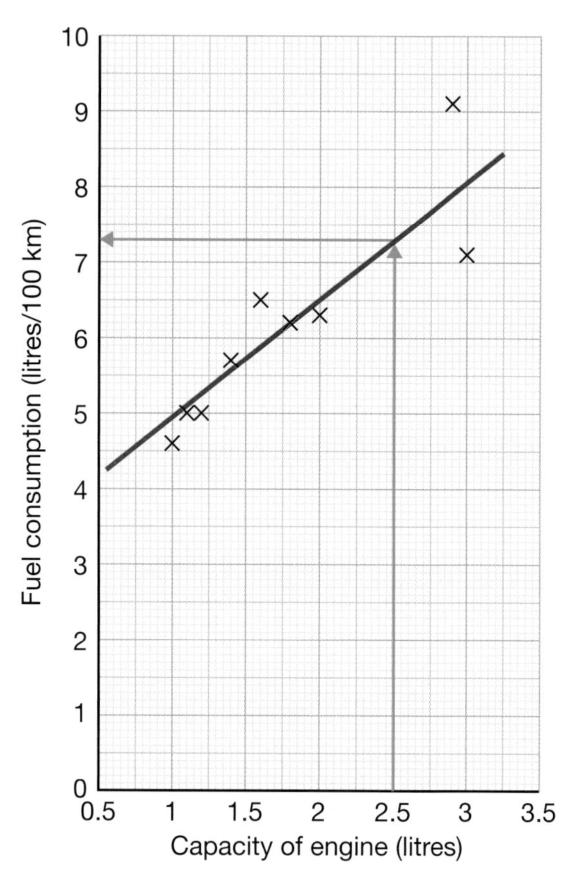

(c) 7.3 litres/100 km

2. (a), (b) mean point is (4.3, 5100)

	Age of car (years)	Value (£)
	2	9000
	1	10500
	4	6000
	6	2900
	7	2000
	8	1300
	4	4200
	6	1400
	2	6800
	3	7000
Mean	4.3	5100

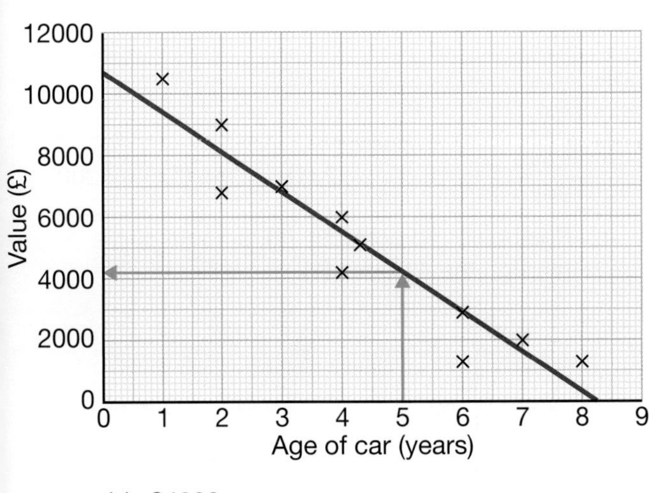

(c) £4200

4.2 Averages

Averages

1. (a) mean = 31.6, median = 30.5, mode = 28, range = 16
   (b) mean = 0.3, median = 0.5, mode = 2, range = 12
2. (a) mean = 2.5, median = 2, mode = 2, range = 5
   (b) mean = 1.8, median = 1, mode = 1, range = 6

Mean of grouped data

1. (a) 50.8 marks (b) 171 cm
   (c) 4.1 minutes (d) 29.7 minutes
2. (a) no modal class (b) $170 \leqslant h < 180$
   (c) $2 \leqslant t < 3$ (d) $20 \leqslant t < 30$

Using cumulative frequency diagrams

1. (a) (i) median = 51 marks, upper quartile = 59 marks, lower quartile = 44 marks, interquartile range = 15 marks
   (ii) 35 marks and 61 marks
   (b) (i) median = 171 cm, upper quartile = 178 cm, lower quartile = 165 cm, interquartile range = 13 cm
   (ii) 157 cm, 180 cm
   (c) (i) median = 27 minutes, upper quartile = 41 minutes, lower quartile = 16 minutes, interquartile range = 25 minutes
   (ii) 10 minutes, 45 minutes

4.3 Probability

Probability

1. (a) $\frac{1}{16}$, 0.0625, 6.25%
   (b) $\frac{3}{16}$, 0.1875, 18.75%
   (c) $\frac{13}{16}$, 0.8125, 81.25%
   (d) 0, 0%
2. (a) $\frac{1}{10}$ (b) $\frac{9}{10}$ (c) $\frac{2}{3}$
   (d) $\frac{1}{3}$ (e) 1

Relative frequency

1. (a) 1: 0.24, 2: 0.27, 3: 0.26, 4: 0.23
   (b) 25 times
2. (a) 0.1, 0.05, 0.06, 0.09, 0.095, 0.107
   (b) 0.167
   (c) The experimental probability is lower than the theoretical probability and seems to be about 0.1.

Combined events and tree diagrams

1. (a)

Outcome on coin								
H	(1, H)	(2, H)	(3, H)	(4, H)	(5, H)	(6, H)	(7, H)	(8, H)
T	(1, T)	(2, T)	(3, T)	(4, T)	(5, T)	(6, T)	(7, T)	(8, T)
Score on die	1	2	3	4	5	6	7	8

   (b) $\frac{1}{16}$
2. (a)

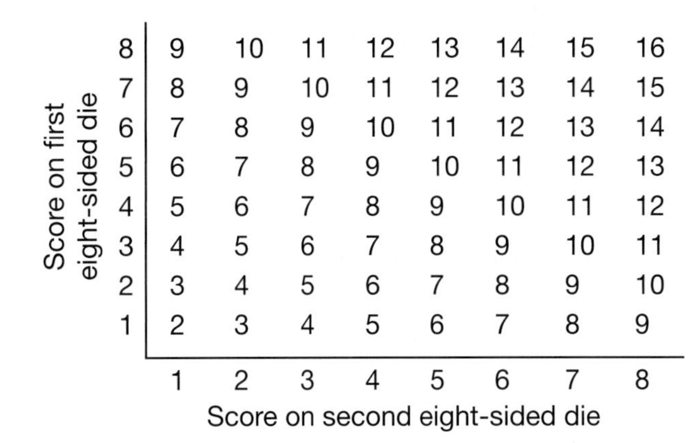

Score on first eight-sided die								
8	9	10	11	12	13	14	15	16
7	8	9	10	11	12	13	14	15
6	7	8	9	10	11	12	13	14
5	6	7	8	9	10	11	12	13
4	5	6	7	8	9	10	11	12
3	4	5	6	7	8	9	10	11
2	3	4	5	6	7	8	9	10
1	2	3	4	5	6	7	8	9
Score on second eight-sided die	1	2	3	4	5	6	7	8

   (b) 9, $\frac{1}{8}$ (c) 2 and 26, $\frac{1}{32}$ (d) $\frac{7}{64}$
3. (a)

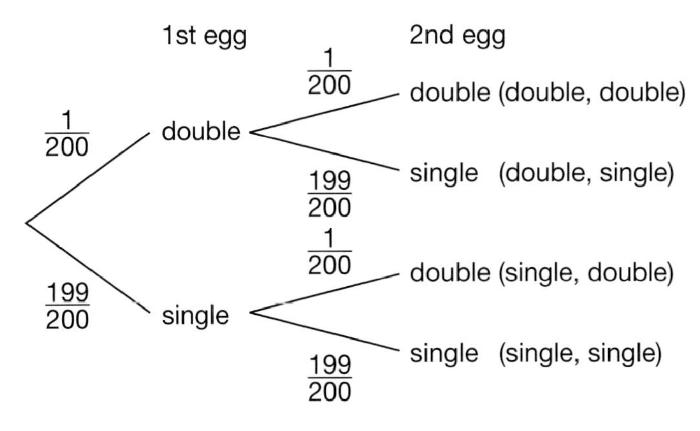

   (b) (i) $\frac{1}{40000}$ (ii) $\frac{199}{20000}$

4. (a)

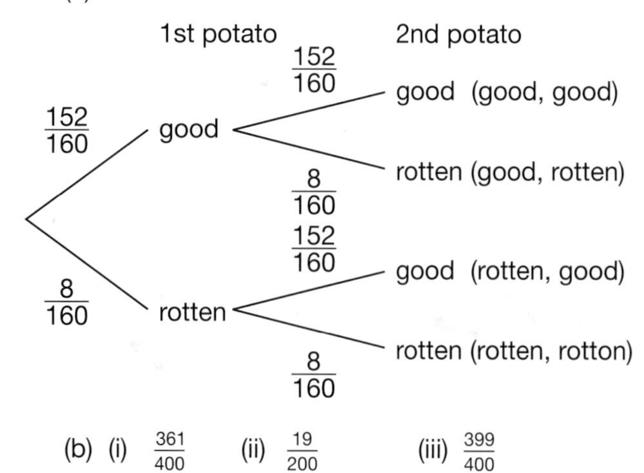

(b) (i) $\frac{361}{400}$ (ii) $\frac{19}{200}$ (iii) $\frac{399}{400}$

Conditional probability

1. (a)

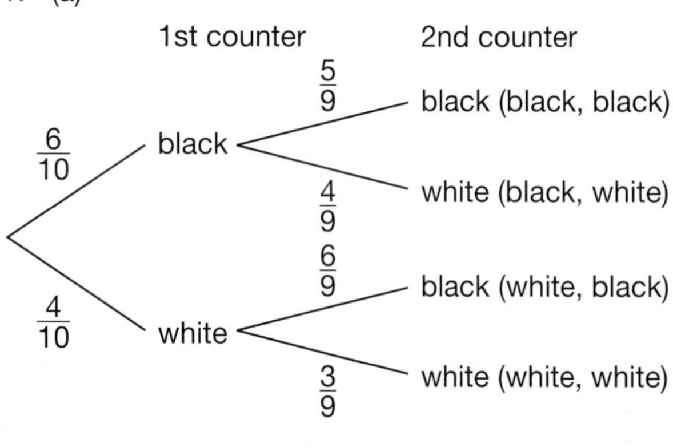

(b) (i) $\frac{8}{15}$ (ii) $\frac{1}{3}$

2. (a)

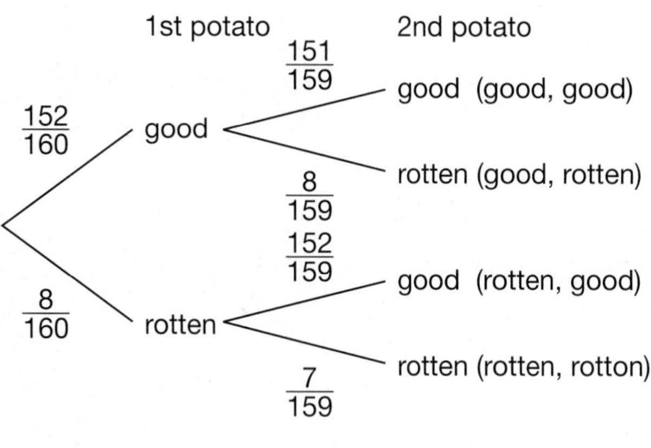

(b) (i) $\frac{2869}{3180}$ (ii) $\frac{76}{795}$ (iii) $\frac{3173}{3180}$

Practice questions

1. (a) $6 < t \leqslant 7$ **(1)**

   (b) midpoints: 2.5, 5.5, 6.5, 8.5 **(1)**
   $2.5 \times 18 + 5.5 \times 64 + 6.5 \times 76 + 8.5 \times 42 = 1248$ **(1)** $\div 200$ **(1)** $= 6.24$ **(1)**

   (c)

Time, t (minutes)	$0 < t \leqslant 5$	$5 < t \leqslant 6$	$6 < t \leqslant 7$	$7 < t \leqslant 10$
Cumulative frequency	18	82 **(1)**	158 **(1)**	200

   (d) Points plotted correctly **(2)**, smooth curve through the 4 points **(1)**

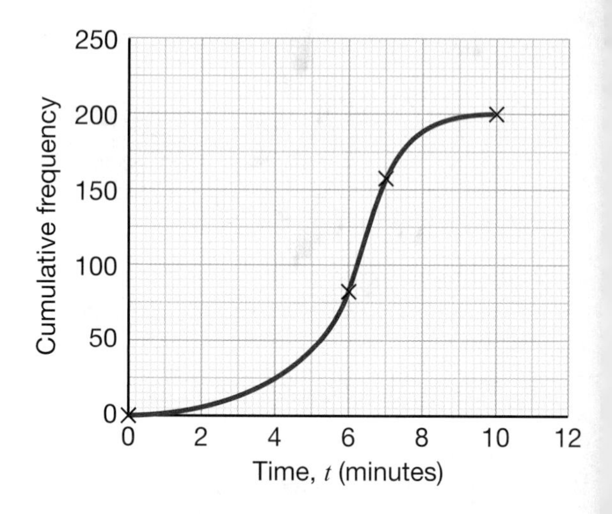

   (e) median $= 6.2$ minutes **(1)**, upper quartile $= 6.7$ minutes **(1)** interquartile range $= 6.7 - 5.6 = 1.1$ minutes **(1)**

2. (a) (i) $\frac{1}{4}$ or 0.25 **(1)** (ii) 125 **(1)**

   (b) $\frac{2}{8} \times \frac{3}{8}$ **(1)** $= \frac{3}{32}$ **(1)** (c) $\frac{3}{8} \times \frac{2}{7}$ **(1)** $= \frac{3}{28}$ **(1)**

3. (a) 6 °C **(1)** (b) $-11 \div 7$ **(1)** $= -1.57$ °C **(1)**

   (c) -3 **(1)**

4. (a) brand B **(1)**

   (b) $360 \times (42 \div 90)$ **(1)** $= 168°$ **(1)**

   (c) $\frac{36}{90}$ **(1)** $= \frac{2}{5}$ **(1)**

5. (a) midpoints: 2, 7, 12, 17 **(1)**
   $2 \times 8 + 7 \times 19 + 12 \times 23 + 17 \times 10 = 595$ **(1)** $\div 60$ **(1)**
   $= 9.9$ text messages **(1)**

   (b) midpoints being used or actual data unknown **(1)**

6. (a)

Time, t (minutes)	$0 < t \leqslant 10$	$10 < t \leqslant 20$	$20 < t \leqslant 25$	$25 < t \leqslant 30$	$30 < t \leqslant 40$
Frequency	2 **(1)**	16 **(1)**	12 **(1)**	10 **(1)**	14

   (b) $(10 + 14)$ **(1)** $\div 54$ **(1)** $= 44.4\%$ **(1)**

   (c) $0.5 \times 16 + 12 + 10$ **(1)** $= 30$ **(1)**

7. (a) 0.7×0.9 **(1)** $= 0.63$ **(1)**

   (b) 0.7×0.1 **(1)** $+ 0.3 \times 0.9$ **(1)** $= 0.07 + 0.27 = 0.34$ **(1)**

8. $8 \times 9 = 72$; $6 + 8 + 12 + 9 + 11 + 7 + 6 = 59$ **(1)**
   $x = 72 - 59$ **(1)** $= 13$ **(1)**

Appendix

Formulae

Compound interest

Total amount $= P\left(1+\frac{r}{100}\right)^n$

Speed

Speed $= \frac{\text{distance}}{\text{time}}$

Solving quadratic equations

$$x = \frac{-b \pm \sqrt{b^2 - 4ac}}{2a}$$

Pythogoras's theorem

$a^2 + b^2 = c^2$

Trigonometry

$\sin\theta = \frac{\text{opposite}}{\text{hypotenuse}}$

$\cos\theta = \frac{\text{adjacent}}{\text{hypotenuse}}$

$\tan\theta = \frac{\text{opposite}}{\text{adjacent}}$

Sine rule: $\frac{a}{\text{Sin}A} = \frac{b}{\text{Sin}B} = \frac{c}{\text{Sin}C}$

Cosine rule: $a^2 = b^2 + c^2 - 2bc\cos A$

Area of triangle $= \frac{1}{2}ab\sin C$

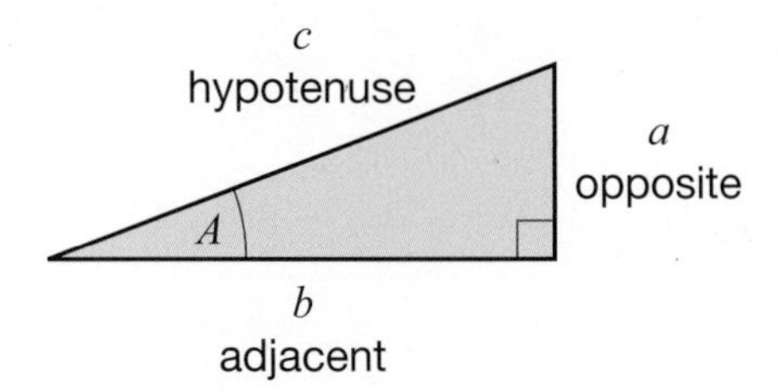

Circles

Circumference $= \pi d$ or $2\pi r$

Area $= \pi r^2$

Areas

Rectangle = length × width

Triangle $= \frac{1}{2} \times$ base × height

Parallelogram = base × height

Trapezium $= \frac{1}{2}(a+b)h$

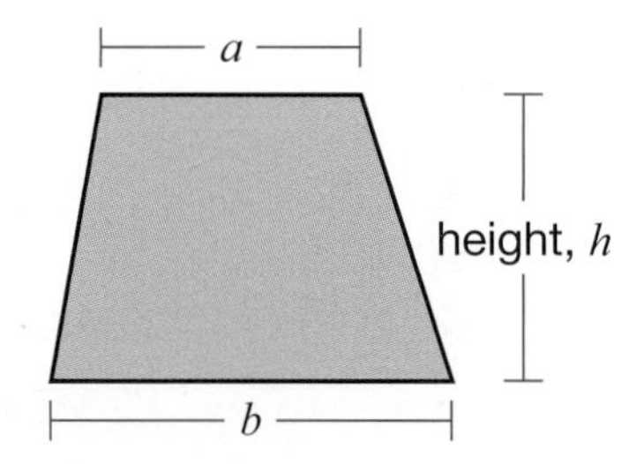

Volumes

Prism = area of cross-section × length

Sphere $= \frac{4}{3}\pi r^3$

Cone $= \frac{1}{3}\pi r^2 h$

Cylinder $= \pi r^2 h$

Surface area

Sphere $= 4\pi r^2$

Cone $= \pi r l + \pi r^2$

Cylinder $= 2\pi r h + 2\pi r^2$